KU-208-411

BRITISH HYDROLOGICAL SOCIETY

THIRD
NATIONAL
HYDROLOGY
SYMPOSIUM

THIRD NATIONAL HYDROLOGY SYMPOSIUM

UNIVERSITY OF SOUTHAMPTON
16-18th
SEPTEMBER
1991

Principal Sponsor: the National Rivers Authority

This volume is dedicated to the memory of John Pirt.

© Copyright
Institute of Hydrology 1991

ISBN 0 948540 30 3

Third National Hydrology Symposium

produced by the Institute of Hydrology
on behalf of the British Hydrological Society

August 1991

British Library Cataloguing-in-publication data

A catalogue record for this book is
available from the British Library

+
DRH
5
B

LN0897

CONTENTS

Session 4 *Unusual hydrological events* *Page*

Session 5 *Snow and ice* *Page*

Session 6 *Large data bases for hydrology* *Page*

Session 1

Demand Management and Forecasting

Demand forecasting: the new challenge to the water industry

P. Herbertson

The Water Act of 1989 has brought about new roles and responsibilities in the water industry, not least in the field of water demand forecasting. Water companies have an obligation to develop new water resources, whilst the National Rivers Authority, as environmental regulator, has a duty to conserve water resources and to publish demand forecasts. OFWAT, the economic regulator, has received a variety of water company forecasts in evidence for their appraisal of long-term investment programmes in water resources and water supply systems.

Whereas regional water authorities were once seen by NIMBY environmentalists as the last defence against major new developments, as a result of water service infrastructure deficiencies, the greens are eager to recast this role to the NRA. In practice water companies are now clearly in the business of selling more water, whilst the NRA's regulatory powers are limited to securing the proper use of water resources and ensuring environmental enhancement. This underlies new attitudes to forecasting by water companies and the NRA.

The purpose of demand forecasting remains threefold: strategic (up to 30 years) for long-term planning; medium term (5 to 15 years) for investment appraisal; and short term (weekly, seasonal) for operational planning. Strategic forecasts are important to the NRA in reviewing national water resource requirements. Water companies and OFWAT have a particular interest in medium term forecasting and investment planning. Water companies and the NRA both have an interest in short-term forecasts in connection with meeting peak demands and managing water resources, particularly in time of drought.

Forecasting methodology can conveniently be summarised under three heads: the subjective approach (i.e. the engineer's judgement of old – aided by steel rule or flexi-curve); component analysis much utilised by some Regional Water Authorities in the 1980s; and statistical extrapolation or trend analysis, favoured by economists.

1991 is a year of some significance for demand forecasters. It is a census year so that OPCS can give of their best for a decade. The National Metering Trials reach a milestone with the publication of their second report and completion of the Isle of Wight metering. OFWAT discover that two-thirds of the population actually prefer meters. Many water companies achieved profits even greater than forecast. The NRA published their first national demand forecasts, following tentatively in the footsteps of the late National Water Council (1975) and the Water Resources Board (1973). But 1991 is also the third year of drought in England and those with long memories will recall the indelible 'blip' that the 1976 drought made on annual consumption and current forecasts.

The challenges facing the demand forecaster in 1991 are numerous. It is hoped that comprehensive National Metering Trials data will be published by the water companies and made available for a variety of analyses; there is a particular need to review the derivation and variation of minimum night flows as an all important demand component; also the relationship between per capita consumption and property type needs to be analysed in the wetter parts of the country. Of particular interest in the longer term will be the possible change of metered per capita consumption as the novelty effect wears off.

The challenge facing OFWAT lies in achieving consistent definitions and targets for unaccounted for water and levels of service so that they can be incorporated in company component forecasts, allowing investment programmes to be on a consistent basis.

The NRA also needs to meet the challenge of ensuring that water company forecasts are derived in a consistent manner. They also have a particular interest in monitoring the long-term demand management effect of domestic metering, particularly in the drier South East. There is also much work to be done on the likely effects of climate change on domestic and agricultural consumption.

The papers that follow provide some valuable insights to these problems. Fenn and Gurnell demonstrate a method for separating out minimum night flows from continuous zonal consumption data and then derive short-term ARIMA forecasts of water demand over a week and month for operational purposes. Shaw looks at the *per capita* consumption from over 70 continuous zonal metering areas and derives a relationship with ACORN property types, which is the basis for component forecasting in the NRA Southern Region. Lambert analyses regional variations in demand growth since 1975 and presents an important new methodology for deriving compatible rural/urban leakage targets for inclusion in component forecasts.

Bircumshaw and Fenn give a specific example of a single line component based forecast, with allowance for an increasing peak week factor as unaccounted for water is reduced to targets.

Hall introduces fuzzy linear regression analysis to derive upper and lower limits to a preferred best fit line, using the example of the relationship of water consumption to price in arid climate. It will be interesting to see if the data from the National Metering Trials will yield up their secrets to fuzzy logic.

The authors are to be congratulated on the way they are addressing some of the challenges facing demand forecasters in the 1990s. For those that are not authors, take note that there still remains much interesting and important work to be done. Go to it!

Estimation of net domestic per capita water consumption for demand forecasting in NRA Southern Region

P.J. Shaw

Abstract

Forecasts of anticipated maximum water demands are prepared by the National Rivers Authority for water company supply areas in Southern Region using a component-based method where total demand is subdivided into metered, unmetered and unaccounted elements. A special feature of Southern Region is the use of control areas for the estimation of the domestic unmetered component. These are metered groups of domestic properties, flow logged on a continuous 15-minute basis. In total, the control area population is about 1% of the regional population and the number of properties monitored in this way is believed to be the largest in the United Kingdom.

The control areas are operated and maintained by the water companies who send logger data to the NRA for quality control and archiving. This is done using software (WASIR) developed in-house by the former Southern Water Authority. The control areas were set up to measure the link between property types and water consumption. The property types within control areas and company supply areas have been categorised using the ACORN socio-economic groups derived by CACI Market Analysis Ltd. These groupings are used with daily net water consumption results to estimate domestic consumption by each ACORN group. A range of 128 to 180 litres per person per day net domestic use by ACORN group was found in 1988.

Introduction

Under section 125 of the 1989 Water Act, the National Rivers Authority has a duty to conserve, redistribute and secure the proper use of water resources and to take the necessary action for this purpose. As part of these duties NRA Southern Region now produces bi-annual forecasts of potable water demand for the region as a whole and for the seven water companies within the region including, separately, the seven divisions of Southern Water Services.

Prior to the establishment of the NRA, similar forecasts were produced by Southern Water Authority as part of its duties under Section 24 of the 1973 Water Act. Much of the format and methodology from these forecasts was retained in the first forecast produced by the NRA in 1990 which used 1988 as its base year. The forecasting follows a component-based method in which the unmetered domestic per capita water consumption is estimated using data obtained from a network of control areas across the region. These are groups of domestic properties which are metered as discrete units and for which detailed flow records are obtained on data loggers.

Demand forecast components

The methodology used in the NRA 1990 water demand forecast followed the established component method which has been in use in Southern Region since 1984. At that time the DoE required all water authorities to adopt forecasts based on components of demand rather than trend analysis. The principal components of supply identified in the NRA 1990 forecast were:

unmetered domestic and commercial use;
metered commercial and industrial use;
unaccounted-for water;
metered domestic use.

Here, unaccounted-for water includes leakage from the distribution system and other items such as mains flushing, fire fighting and some legitimate domestic night use. The metered domestic component was added to the list of components for the first time in 1990 in recognition of possible expansion in this sector.

The position for the forecast base year (1988) was established by reference to water company information on total and metered consumption, leakage levels and, where relevant, large individual consumers. Unmetered domestic consumption levels were established from the control area network. In contrast to previous forecasts, only two forecast lines were constructed, both corresponding to high growth, but relating to existing and reduced leakage. This was because in managing catchments the NRA is concerned to establish the maximum reasonable demand that could arise for public supply, and is not concerned with the infrastructure investment decisions to the same extent as the water undertakers. On the other hand, the difference between forecast lines representing existing and target levels of leakage are of particular concern because this indicates the potential saving in new demand on the environment even with high growth.

Establishment of control areas

To provide an estimate for the unmetered domestic component of demand and to gain a better understanding of domestic water consumption, control areas began to be established across the region in 1985. Initially control areas were set up in Southern Water Authority divisions and in 1987 they were established in the supply areas of the statutory water companies. At the present time there are over 70 control areas in operation. Their distribution is shown in Figure 1.

The criteria for the selection of control areas were that they should be domestic properties and that ideally the residents in each area should fall into a single socio-economic class. Also the total number of properties within the control areas should be about 1% of the regional total. In practice each metered control area varies in size and most do not contain a single socio-economic class but as a group they can still be analysed to provide average water consumption estimates for the socio-economic groups represented. The population in control areas ranges from less than 100 to over 2000 but typically is about 500.

The control areas chosen were known to have low levels of leakage. Many difficulties were encountered in setting up the areas. Some required two meters, other areas with large diurnal variations in flow required dual flow meters and some types of data logger suffered from condensation problems. These difficulties were overcome by the water companies and Southern Water Services (SWS) who continue to run the control areas as part of a long-term regional monitoring network.

Having established a representative set of control areas it was important to be able to distinguish between daytime flows and night flows within each area and thereby attempt to separate net domestic consumption from leakage. This could only be achieved with frequent flow measurements and data loggers were attached to the control area flow meters to record flows continuously at 15-minute intervals.

Control area data processing

Software was produced in-house by Southern Water Authority to handle the large volume of logger flow data from the control areas. The package for Water Supply Information Retrieval (WASIR) runs on IBM PC-AT compatible microcomputers and can be used

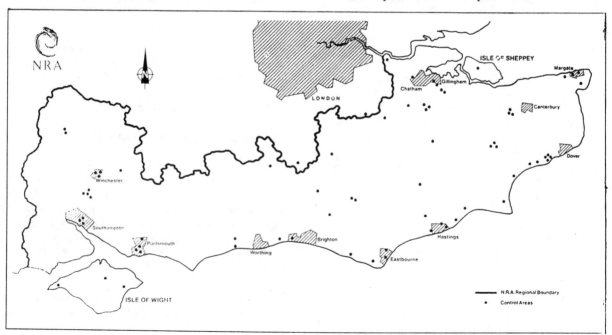

Figure 1   Location of divisional and water company control areas

for a variety of applications including district waste control metering, waste district step testing, flow and pressure logging for network analysis, source meter logging, consumer meter logging and of course domestic consumption monitoring for demand forecasting. WASIR is now marketed by Information Technology Southern and only a brief description of the main features of the software relating to control area data is given here.

Data from a choice of loggers can be downloaded to WASIR. These include DTS Celia, Spectrascan, Golden River, Wessex and Sarasota Sherpa. The basic data unit for domestic consumption monitoring in the control areas is 15-minute flow although WASIR can process data at intervals from 1 minute to 24 hours. The raw data from the control area loggers is downloaded to floppy disk and quality controlled by the participating SWS divisions and water companies and is then forwarded to the NRA together with a report on any problems associated with the period logged. Data is thus received by the NRA in the form of intermediate data files containing 15-minute flows for each logger. This is loaded on the NRA copy of WASIR and edited using screen plots and the logger reports to remove any further incorrect data. Corrected intermediate files are returned to the water companies and then the data is archived. The archiving process combines the results from multiple loggers if necessary and stores information to disk in the form of 15-minute flows for each complete control area. Archived files are

stored in a compressed data format which can be interrogated to produce a variety of screen plots and reports. An example of the 15-minute flow data collected during one week in a control area is shown in Figure 2.

For the production of the biannual NRA demand forecasts, it is important to estimate the net domestic water consumption in the control areas having allowed for leakage. The method adopted with WASIR is to subtract the minimum night flow from each daily total flow using the two lowest consecutive night flows between the hours of midnight and 6 am. When the control areas were established it was thought that this would produce night flows which were relatively independent of any regular legitimate night use of water. The concept was that there must be some time during the night when no water is being used. However, it is assumed that the deducted night flow may still contain an element of legitimate night use which will then appear in the unaccounted-for component where equivalent night flow rates may be higher than leakage rates reported by the water undertakers. According to NWC/DoE STC Report 26, legitimate night use can be expected to be up to 2 litres/property/hour, although in the view of some companies this figure is too high. The principle adopted in dealing with the control area data was that the deduction of arbitrary and unmeasured quantities would undermine the validity of the measurements actually made.

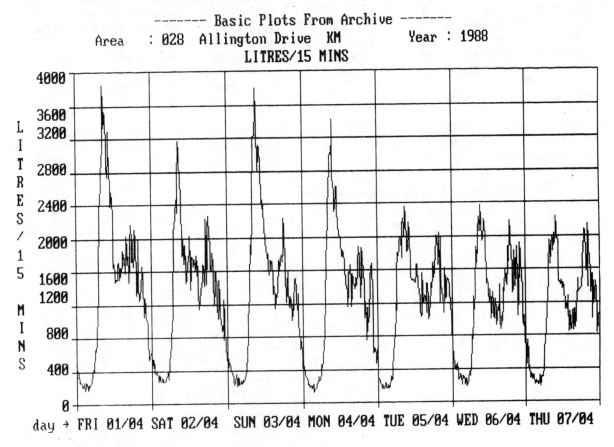

Figure 2 One week's 15-minute flow data from a control area

Relating control area results to water supply areas

Control area results were related to water company supply areas using the ACORN (A Classification Of Residential Neighbourhoods) socio-economic classification of property types. The ACORN groupings were established by CACI Market Research Ltd from a cluster analysis of the 1981 census information and comprise the following main categories.

A profile of the number of properties within each of the above ACORN groups has been established for each of the control areas and for the water company supply areas. CACI Ltd provided reports for each water supply area giving the ACORN profiles by population and by household numbers by relating post codes within the supply areas to the enumeration district data from the 1981 census. Updated profiles were subsequently produced by CACI using demographic modelling. A combination of CACI Ltd analysis and doorstep survey was used to produce ACORN profiles of each control area.

Analysis of control area results

Statistical analysis of control area results is performed on annual summaries of net water consumption in the control areas obtained from the WASIR archive. Table 2 shows part of the summary table for 1988 which was used as the base year in the regional NRA demand forecast. Although the original intention was to establish control areas containing single ACORN types, in practice this could not be achieved. However, there are sufficient single type areas to provide an initial assessment of net domestic per capita consumption by ACORN type and these estimates can then be refined using all data for a particular year.

The stages involved in the control area data analysis are:
  (a) the calculation of initial estimates of net PCC from the results for control areas of a single ACORN type;

(b) refinement of the initial estimates using the full amount of control area data for the year;
(c) calculation of confidence limits on the final estimates;
(d) scaling up of control area data to water supply areas.

a. Initial net PCC estimates for each ACORN group

Initial estimates of net domestic per capita consumption (PCC) were obtained using the results from the single ACORN type control areas. The weighted mean estimate of the initial PCC for each ACORN type is given by the total measured consumption (vm) divided by the total population (p) for those control areas:

$$\text{- initial PCC' = vm / p}$$

where ' denotes by ACORN type.

Measured water consumption for single ACORN type control areas in 1988 is shown in Table 3. It can be seen that not all the ACORN groups described in Table 1 are represented by the control areas but this is a reflection of the general composition of the population in Southern Region and these groups do account for about 90% of the population.

b. Refinement of initial net PCC estimates

Since the ACORN population profile is known for each control area, the initial estimates of net PCC can be used to calculate a theoretical annual volume of water consumption for each area which can then be compared to the measured volume:
    calculated volume by ACORN type (vc')
        = initial PCC'. p'
    calculated volume for each control area (vc)
        = sum of vc'

The differences between the calculated and measured control area consumptions can then apportioned on a volumetric basis and adjusted estimates of PCC by

Table 1. ACORN socio-economic groups

```
---------------------------------------------------------------
  ACORN group          Property description
---------------------------------------------------------------
      A                Agricultural areas
      B                Modern family housing, higher incomes
      C                Older housing of intermediate status
      D                Poor quality older terraced housing
      E                Better-off council estates
      F                Less well-off council estates
      G                Poorest council estates
      H                Multi-racial areas
      I                High status non-family areas
      J                Affluent suburban housing
      K                Better-off retirement areas
---------------------------------------------------------------
```

Table 2. Annual summary of control area results.

control area	population in each ACORN group B	C	E	F	J	K	total popn.	measured volume (1/d)
1	0	1021	69	1114	0	0	2204	288724
2	0	0	0	0	0	346	346	62899
3	0	0	0	0	0	493	493	91698
4	0	239	18	0	605	0	862	118043
.								
.								
66	1496	0	0	0	0	0	1496	188496

Table 3. Initial estimates of net PCC

				ACORN group							
B		C		E		F		J		K	
p'	vm	p'	vm	p'	vm	p'	vm	p'	vm	p'	vm
107	12519	734	112239	82	13202	32	4480	619	79232	346	6289
306	41310	47	8648	785	94985	26	2990	81	12717	493	91698
837	105512	69	9384	622	67176	564	75576	65	10010	141	14946
321	54570	164	23124	266	35378			177	36816	936	192816
196	37436	62	6882					290	39730	99	20295
250	35500	334	46760							160	23200
269	36853	162	24138							339	53562
520	64480	268	31624								
159	18921										
267	42987										
1496	188496										
PCC'	135.1		142.9		120.1		133.5		144.9		182.8

p'= population, vm = measured water consumption (1/d)

ACORN type within each control area can then be derived:

> volume adjustment by ACORN group (va')
> = (vm - vc).(vc'/ vc)
> new vc' = old vc'±va'
> adjusted PCC' = vc'/p'

The required final estimates of net domestic PCC by ACORN type are then obtained by dividing the sum of the adjusted volumes in each ACORN group by the population within each group:

> weighted average PCC' = sum of vc'/sum of p'

c. Calculation of confidence limits on net PCC estimates

Confidence limits were calculated for the weighted average estimates of net domestic PCC as follows. The proportion of the control area population represented by each ACORN group is:

$$pr' = p'/sum\ of\ p'$$

The weighted sample variance (sv) is the mean weighted square deviation about the weighted arithmetic mean:

$$sv = sum\ of\ (pr'.(adjusted\ PCC' -$$
$$weighted\ average\ PCC')^2)$$

The estimated population weighted variance (pv) is:

$$pv = sv . n/(n-1)$$

where n is the number of PCC estimates within each ACORN group.

The standard error is then the square root of the population weighted variance divided by n.

Finally, the confidence range is given by the standard error multiplied by Student's t-value at the 95% level with n-1 degrees of freedom.

Table 4 summarises the statistical results obtained for the 1988 control area results.

d. Scaling up ACORN net domestic PCC to water supply areas

ACORN population profiles are also available for the water supply areas of each of the water undertakings in Southern Region. The estimates of net domestic PCC obtained from the analysis of control area results can be used with these profiles to estimate the average net domestic PCC for a water supply area. The estimates for the water supply areas are then used with data for unmetered population in the demand forecasts for the region. For reasons of confidentiality, it is not possible to describe the results for individual water companies in detail. However, the range of water supply area net domestic PCC obtained in 1988 was found to be 139

Table 4 Summary of control area results by ACORN group in 1988

```
--------------------------------------------------------------
                                  ACORN group
                   B        C        E        F        J        K
--------------------------------------------------------------
consumption (l/d) 1344645 1118899 1228498  520676 1182394 1113797
population           9565    7971    9626    4048    7476    6178
n                      22      28      16      12      13      16
weighted mean PCC   140.6   140.4   127.6   128.6   158.2   180.3
sample variance     500.8   320.6   305.3    90.6   405.7   558.2
popn. variance      524.6   332.5   325.7    98.8   439.5   595.5
standard error        4.9     3.4     4.5     2.9     5.8     6.1
Student's t         2.080   2.052   2.131   2.201   2.179   2.131
confidence interval  10.2     7.0     9.6     6.4    12.6    13.0
--------------------------------------------------------------
PCC in l/person/d, t at 95% level with n-1 degrees of freedom
```

to 160 l/person/day with confidence intervals of ±5 l/person/day.

Concluding remarks

About 70 control areas are now in operation in NRA Southern region and these continue to provide valuable detailed information on domestic consumption. The full set of control area results became available for analysis in 1988 which was taken as the base year in the first demand forecast review produced by NRA Southern in 1990. During this time SWS have started work on the national metering trials and properties in the Isle of Wight control areas are now metered. In future it will be possible to compare control area results with those from metered areas.

Analysis for control area results in 1989 and 1990 is nearing completion and as further data become available it will be possible to consider the reproducibility of the results and the effects of factors such as drought restrictions. It will also become possible to examine the significance of the differences between the estimates of net domestic PCC by ACORN group taken over several years. The analysis described above could equally well be applied on the basis of the numbers of properties .

References

NWC/DoE Standing Technical Committee 1980. Report 26: Leakage control policy and practice.

Regional variations in demands for water, and realistic leakage targets

A. Lambert

Abstract

Analyses of growth in monthly public water supply from 1975 to 1987, grouped by Water Authority areas, show significant regional variations. Simple conclusions based on grouped data for England and Wales are shown to be unrepresentative and potentially misleading. Increases in annual supplies have been greatest along the South coast, and in Thames and Anglia, but less than 10% elsewhere. Maximum monthly demands occur in winter in northern areas, and in summer in the south. The potential for significant savings in consumption from summer demand management is therefore likely to be significant only in southern areas. The urban area leakage targets of DOE/NWC Report 26 (1980) can now be extended to rural distribution systems using a methodology developed by Welsh Water. Examples are given for the 'Passive' and 'District Metering' methods of leakage control.

Supply statistics for England & Wales

The Water Services Association (formerly Water Authorities Association) hold statistics of monthly public water supply from 1975 up to the time of privatisation (1.9.89). These show the monthly average supply of potable and non-potable water for each of the ten Water Authorities in England and Wales, including the supply statistics of Statutory Water Companies within these areas.

For England and Wales overall, these statistics show a 13% increase in annual supply from 1975 to 1987 (14,491 to 16,329 Megalitres per day), with the highest monthly demand in the year occuring 8 times in July, 3 times in June, once in May and once in January. These grouped statistics reinforce the general public perception of inexorably rising demands throughout England and Wales, associated with the use of hosepipes for garden watering every summer.

The paper will show that this 'model' only applies to 50% of Water Authority areas in England and Wales at most, because of the wide regional variations which exist within England and Wales in terms of rates of growth of supply and times of seasonal peak demands.

Hydrologists have a good understanding of the regional variations of topography, climate, rainfall, evapotranspiration, streamflow, hydrogeology, irrigation need etc. within the UK. The purpose of this brief paper is to provide some complementary information on regional variations in demands, and recent trends in leakage control. This should highlight some important features of relevance to demand forecasting.

Regional variations in supply statistics, 1975 to 1987

Magnitude and occurence of seasonal peak demands

Simple analysis of the basic data shows there are fundamental regional differences in the seasonal peak supply requirement and the time of year when it occurs. Table 1A shows the monthly peaks expressed as the % by which the highest individual monthly supply within a calendar year exceeds the annual average supply for that calendar year. The highest % values for each region during the 13-year period are marked with an asterisk. Table 1B shows the months in which the supply peak occurred in each year. The two tables can be used together to show, for example, that in 1975 the Thames monthly peak occurred in June and was 10% above the annual average for 1975.

Table 1B shows that the peak monthly supply requirement occurs in summer virtually every year in South-West, Wessex, Southern, Thames and Anglian, i.e. the same incidence as the grouped England & Wales data shows. The asterisked data in Table 1A shows that, for these five regions, the highest monthly peaks (expressed as % of annual average) in

Table 1A Excess of peak month over annual average supply for year
(Figures are in % related to each particular year)

	S'West	Wessex	S'thern	Thames	Anglia	Wales	SevTr	NW	Yorks	N'rian
1975	14	10	13	10	10	4	7	4	3	2
1976	13	9	15	15*	9	7	8	5	9	3
1977	14	10	12	11	9	4	4	1	2	2
1978	9	6	9	5	3	3	2	3	3	3
1979	19*	15	17	12	13*	6	8	5	5	3
1980	7	6	11	9	8	8	6	4	4	6
1981	15	7	8	7	5	4	4	5	6	6
1982	8	5	8	5	7	8	6	9*	10*	8*
1983	15	16*	19*	14	13*	9*	8*	2	6	2
1984	8	13	14	9	9	4	6	6	5	6
1985	10	5	9	5	2	3	4	5	5	2
1986	8	8	12	7	10	2	5	3	4	4
1987	8	6	10	5	5	3	3	6	5	6
AVE	11.2	8.9	12.0	8.7	7.7	4.9	5.5	4.4	5.1	4.0

Table 1B Months when peak monthly supply occurred (Jan=1, Dec=12)

	South -west	Wessx	South -ern	Tham -es	Angl -ian	Wales	Sevrn Trent	North West	Yorks	North brian	Englnd & Wales
1975	8	7	6	6	8	6	6	6	6	11	6
1976	7	7	6	6	2	2	2	2	2	6	6
1977	8	7	7	7	7	7	7	11	7	2	7
1978	6	6	6	6	9	6	6	2	2	11	6
1979	7	7	7	7	7	7	7	2	2	7	7
1980	8	5	5	5	5	5	5	5	1	2	5
1981	8	8	8	7	7	12	12	12	12	12	7
1982	8	6	7	7	7	1	1	1	1	1	1
1983	7	7	7	7	7	7	7	3	7	12	7
1984	6	7	7	7	7	5/6	7	6	2	2	7
1985	7	7	7	7	9	7	2	2	2	6	7
1986	7	6	7	7	7	6	6	3	7	1	7
1987	7	8	7	7	7	7	1/3	2	1	2	7
Summer	13	13	13	13	12	10	8	3	4	3	12
Winter	0	0	0	0	1	3	5	10	9	10	1

the 13-year period were between 13% and 19% above the annual mean, and occurred in either June 1976, July 1979 or July 1983.

The other five regions exhibit different characteristics. In North-West, Yorkshire and Northumbrian, the monthly peak occurs in winter in three years out of every four, and the asterisked data from Table 1A shows the highest monthly peak (8% to 10% above annual average) occurred in Janury 1982. In Severn-Trent and Wales, the highest monthly peak was July 1983 (8% to 9% above annual average), but there were several years where the monthly peak occurred in winter.

Water supply and distribution systems must be sized to meet peak supply requirements, whenever they occur, and it is informative to compare the extreme summer and winter monthly peaks recorded over the 13-year period for each region (Figure 1).

Although monthly data are not ideal for this type of analysis, some broad conclusions can be drawn from Figure 1. In the South-West, Southern, Wessex and Thames regions, the summer peak month generally exceeds the winter peak month by 12% to 16%. In these areas, management of consumer demand (e.g. by compulsory metering with rising block tariffs)

could be expected to lead to significant reductions in capital investment in water resources and distribution systems.

The other six regions all have winter peak month supplies of 8% to 10% above the annual average, and for the three northernmost regions (North-West, Yorkshire and Northumbrian) the winter situation is likely to be the worst case for distribution system design and investment. The summer peak months in these three regions are only 5% or less above the annual average, and it is difficult to envisage much saving in water resources investment arising from summer demand management.

In Wales and Severn-Trent, the differences between summer and winter monthly peaks are negligible, and for Anglian the summer peak is only 5% above the winter peak. Distribution systems will need to be sized to meet winter peaks, and any savings in water resources investment arising from summer demand management are likely to be localised and to require careful evaluation.

The existence of large supply peaks in winter, related to severe freezing periods, (Dec 1981/Jan 1982, Jan 1987, and more recently Feb 1991) may come as a surprise to many hydrologists, but such events are an

1.10

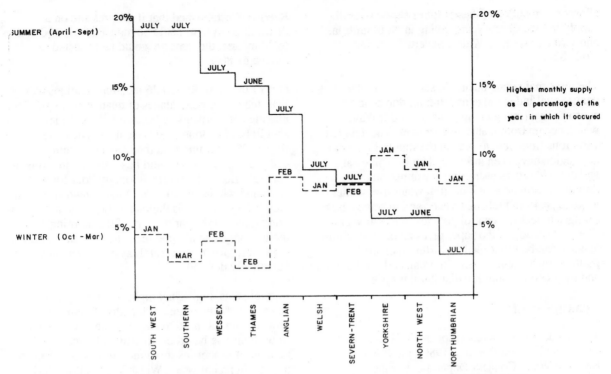

Figure 1 Difference between summer and winter highest monthly supplies recorded 1975-1987

unfortunate fact of life for distribution engineers in all but the most southerly parts of England. These supply peaks arise from a marked incidence in burst mains and services when a thaw occurs after freezing of the ground surface layers (see IWES Water Practice Manual No 4 (1980) pp 85/86, for a more detailed description of the 1981/82 winter event in Severn-Trent region).

Winter supply peaks take weeks or months to rectify, as every burst and leak (many on private premises) must be located and repaired before supply requirements are reduced back to normal. Such events cannot be managed by techniques of consumer demand restriction such as hosepipe bans which are used to rapidly curb summer supply peaks.

Rates of growth of demand

For comparative purposes, Water Services Association expresses the supply data for the ten

Water Authority areas in relation to a base of 100 units of supply in winter 1975. The annual average supply for each area can then be expressed as percentages of this winter 1975 base (see Table 2).

The 'England and Wales' grouped figure referred to earlier is shown in the last column for comparison.

Simple inspection of this data shows wide variations in the rate of increase of demands. The 'grouped data' increase of 15% by 1987 is seen to be atypical of any of the ten areas, which split broadly into two groups:

Group A: South-West, Wessex, Southern, Thames and Anglian, showing increases of between 20% and 36% over the 13-year period;

Group B: Severn-Trent, Yorkshire, Northumbria, North-West and Wales, showing increases of between 5% and 11% over the 13-year period.

Table 2   Annual average supply by Water Authority area, 1978-87, expressed as % of winter 1975 supply

	South -west	Wessx	South -ern	Tham -es	Angl -ian	Severn -Trent	Wales	North West	Yorks	North brian	Eng & Wales
1975	106	104	105	104	104	101	101	101	100	99	102
1976	99	96	99	101	96	94	95	98	94	100	97
1977	103	97	101	102	100	97	98	99	98	103	100
1978	110	103	107	106	104	102	102	101	102	106	104
1979	114	107	111	109	113	107	108	104	109	115	109
1980	115	107	112	110	112	106	107	102	107	108	108
1981	117	108	112	108	112	105	106	101	107	108	107
1982	121	112	118	112	116	108	107	103	111	111	110
1983	125	113	119	113	117	108	107	104	110	107	111
1984	124	115	121	116	118	109	102	106	110	106	112
1985	131	116	120	116	121	109	104	111	110	105	113
1986	136	118	121	119	125	110	104	111	111	106	114
1987	136	120	124	121	126	110	108	109	111	105	115

Closer examination of these figures shows overall supply in the last few years falling in Northumbria, and virtually static in Wales, Severn Trent and Yorkshire.

The three main components of supply are metered commercial/industrial consumption, domestic consumption (mainly unmeasured), and leakage which occurs from mains and services. The detailed variations from year to year in the supply figures in any region have been influenced by hosepipe bans and drought orders restricting consumption in droughts, reductions in industrial water use, winter leakage peaks in particular years, and in some cases, changes in leakage control policies in recent years. The next section of the paper gives an outline of how leakage can be influenced by different control policies, by housing density in urban and rural areas, and by pressure control in distribution systems.

Leakage control

The standard UK reference document is Leakage Control Policy and Practice (1980), published as National Water Council/ Department of the Environment Standing Technical Committee Report Number 26. It was based on the largest programme of field measurements ever undertaken in the UK Water Industry, over a seven-year period, and provided a firm economic and factual foundation upon which leakage control policies could be based.

Prior to Report 26, 'passive' leakage control was exercised in many areas; bursts and leaks which were self-evident at ground level, or which were causing low pressure/no water problems for customers, were repaired, but active policies of searching for more difficult leaks were manpower-intensive and thought to be uneconomic in many cases.

Using Report 26, it could be shown that District Metering - installing weekly-read meters to cover defined areas of the distribution systems - was an active leakage control policy which could be economically justified in most areas, and since the early 1980s most UK water undertakers have been progressively installing district meters. In recent years, there have been remarkable developments in new technology for recording flows and pressures, and locating leaks.

Data in the prospectuses of the privatised Water Companies indicate that leakage constituted approximately 25% of total water supply in England and Wales in 1989, with wide regional variations. The implementation of district metering programmes means that in most regions leakage is being progressively reduced, and interpretation of trends in supply statistics needs to recognise this. So what could be considered 'realistic' leakage control performance?

Local factors such as condition of mains and pressure within distribution system (higher in hilly areas) can have marked local influence on what is achievable.

Report 26 established that if the pressure on a distribution system could be reduced from 100 metres to 30 metres, the leakage would be expected to reduce by 80%.

One of the main Report 26 recommendations was that 'the use of percentages of quantities supplied for making comparisons of leakage in leakage levels should be abandoned' because it is misleading. Report 26 recommended that leakage within distribution systems should be expressed in terms of net night flow rate in litres/property/hour for urban areas and whole systems, or l/km-of-mains/h for rural areas. 'Night Flow' is the rate of flow into a distribution system in the early hours of the morning, when there is only a small amount of actual consumption. However, 'urban' and 'rural' systems were not objectively defined.

In rural areas, higher net night flows per property can be expected due to greater lengths of mains per property, and Report 26 suggests that the net night flow should be based on an artificially increased number of properties for comparison with urban area targets. In recent years, Welsh Water (1990) has developed a realistic methodology for this, using the concepts of 'Equivalent Connections', 'Connections to Mains Factor' and two-part formulae based on both length of mains and number of connections for different types of leakage control.

Consider a typical distribution system in an urban area under a passive leakage control policy. Report 26 shows that a net night flow of the order of 18 l/property/h might be expected. Perhaps 1 l/prop/h would be genuine consumption, leaving 17 l/prop/h as estimated leakage.

Because leakage varies with pressure, and distribution system pressures vary diurnally, the daily leakage is derived by multiplying the night leakage by 20 hours (not 24), i.e.

$$17 \times 20 \text{ h} = 340 \text{ l/property/d, or about 125 m}^3/\text{y}.$$

This is approximately 2.5 times the amount assumed for normal domestic per capita use, so in an urban area, with typically 100 connections per km of mains, 'passive' leakage could be expected to be equivalent to an extra 2.5 persons (an 'average' family) in each property.

With district metering, it can be shown that the leakage in the same urban area might be reduced to about 140 l/property/day (50 m³ per year) to the equivalent of 1 person per property, i.e. a leakage saving equivalent to 1.5 persons per property.

The techniques for target-setting in rural areas are outside the scope of this short paper, but can be used to show that district metering leakage targets for medium intrinsic leakage will vary inversely with the number of connections per km of mains, as shown in Figure 2.

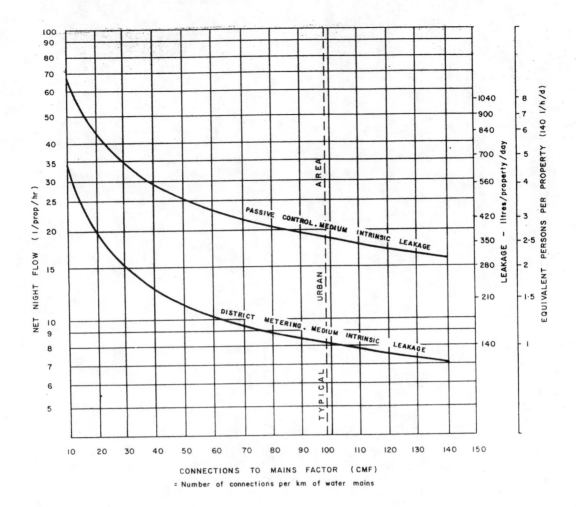

Figure 2

A more elegant method of comparing leakage levels between different urban and rural areas is to express net night flows in terms of litres per equivalent connection per hour. They can then be compared directly with the targets for urban areas in Figure 9 of Report 26.

Equivalent Connections (N') can be calculated from the equation:

$$N' = 37.5 \times L + 0.625 \times N$$

where L is length of mains in km, and N is number of connected properties.

Acknowledgements

To Philip Turton and the Water Authorities Association for the basic supply statistics obtained in 1988, and to Welsh Water for permission to publish this paper.

References

IWES, 1984. Water Practice Manual No 4, Water Distribution Systems. Published by Institution of Water Engineers & Scientists (now Institute of Water & Environmental Management).

NWC/DOE, 1980. Standing Technical Committee Report No 26. Republished 1985 by Water Authorities Association.

Welsh Water, 1990. Towards a More Rational Method of Comparing Leakage Control Performance. Note to OFWAT and NRA.

Identification, modelling and forecasting of domestic water consumption in thirteen control areas in Hampshire

C.R. Fenn & A.M. Gurnell

Abstract

Five years of water into supply data from 13 control areas in Hampshire are used to model short-term (1 day to 1 month) variations in water use in households in different types of domestic neighbourhood. A 7-term moving average of minimum night flows (MNF) is used to separate the true use and leakage components in the supply data. Exponential smoothing (ES), ARIMA and TFN techniques are used to model and forecast the true use series over one month ahead horizons. ARIMA-derived forecasts are far superior to ES-derived forecasts. TFN models using air temperature and precipitation as input variables have non-significant forcing parameters, and reduce to ARIMA models. An ARIMA (1,0,0)(0,1,1) model provides high quality forecasts (MAPE 6%) of water consumption in all control areas. A regional (lumped parameter) ARIMA (1,0,0)(0,1,1) model provides a similar quality of forecast of consumption in any given control area. The structural form of the ARIMA model indicates that the demand for water in domestic neighbourhoods in Hampshire has a simple form, with a strong 7-day cyclical component, a 1-day persistency and a 7-day unsteadiness.

Introduction

In the absence of widespread household metering, measurements of water fed into supply in control areas form the best available database for investigating spatial and temporal variations in water consumption in domestic neighbourhoods. The sum of true (or legitimate) consumption in all households in an area is invariably less than the corresponding total water fed into supply figure measured at the area meter; leakage in the distribution network constitutes the primary loss component, with leakage on consumer's premises and water taken from hydrants for fire-firefighting being other losses.

Minimising leakage is one of the design principles of the control area programme, and so supply data from control areas are especially valuable for analyses of patterns in the demand for water from domestic households. Herein, a simple leakage filter is used to derive time series of true water use from water into supply data from 13 control areas in Hampshire. Various time series techniques are then used to model the demand for water from domestic neighbourhoods, with the intention of developing a robust tool for short-term (1 day to 1 month ahead) forecasting applications.

The database

Time series containing daily entries of total water fed into supply, maximum 15-minute flow, minimum 15-minute flow and the number of missing 15-minute interval data points for 13 control areas in Hampshire were derived from 15-minute interval archive data supplied by Southern Water Services (Hampshire Division) Ltd. The database covers the years from 1984 to 1989, as indicated in Table 1. The data were standardised to per household units (e.g. l/h/d: litres per household per day) using the PAF property count index given in the CACI Acorn Index database of each control area. Data enabling standardisation to a per capita basis were not available.

The data were carefully quality-appraised with respect to the frequency and length of periods of missing data (a maximum span for interpolation of 7 days was applied) and the presence of data measurement, logging or downloading errors (as identified, following leakage separation, by step, ramp or pulse shifts unrelated to leakage events). Only error-free series of over 60 days duration were selected for further analysis (so as to enable the identification of seasonal patterns in water use). Figure 1 illustrates the full sequence of quality

Table 1 *Summary of the data drawn from the Hampshire Water into Supply Archive. The PAF values are taken from the CACI Acorn Index*

Area code	Area name	PAF	Archive data obtained for 1985	1986	1987	1988	1989
HAMPSHIRE SOUTH							
004	OSTERLEY ROAD	363	*	*	*	*	
005	SURREY HOUSE	29	*	*	*	*	
006	VELMORE HOUSE	25			*	*	
008	LYDGATE ROAD	350	*	*	*	*	
009	WHYTEWAYS	340	*	*	*	*	
010	IVY ROAD	285	*	*	*	*	
A13	HOCOMBE ROAD	587		*	*	*	*
A14	HURSLEY ROAD	280					*
HAMPSHIRE NORTH							
011	MAKINS COURT	88	*	*	*	*	*
012	BRACHER CLOSE	37	*	*	*	*	*
013	TEG DOWN	232	*	*	*	*	*
014	WEEKE	415	*	*	*	*	*
015	HIGHCLIFFE	282	*	*	*	*	*
016	KING GEORGE ROAD	32	*	*	*	*	*

control (and subsequent analysis) procedures applied. Summary details on the final ensemble of time series used for analysis (32 in total) are given in Table 2. It can be seen that at least one series covering two seasons was available for each control area.

Leakage separation

A leakage filter based on the 15-minute minimum night flow (MNF) was developed to meet the following criteria: (i) the filter should yield a leakage series which provides a smooth but robust trace through actual MNF's (i.e it should not be unduly influenced by occasional high and low values arising from (say) legitimate consumer use or faulty logging; (ii) it should be weighted to compensate for high night-time water pressures; (iii) it should be easy to apply, with a minimum need for operator intervention or decision-making. Data from control areas with particularly high quality records were used to trial various possible estimators. For each trial, the 15-minute MNF was weighted by the accepted 20/24 night-time pressure compensation factor.

Five different smoothing procedures were investigated: polynomial smoothing, Holt's linear exponential smooothing, Winter's seasonal smoothing, resistant nonlinear smoothing and moving average smoothers. Different orders for the parameters of each smoothing routine were examined. The resistant smoothing and moving average smoothing approaches gave the best results (as judged against both qualitative and quantitative goodness-of-fit criteria). The moving average approach was chosen above the resistant smoother approach, because it is conceptually simpler, is less restrictive in its data requirements and requires no decisions (other than the averaging length) to be made by the user. A 7-day moving average model (MA7) was ultimately selected as the leakage filter, following investigations with 3, 5, 7, 9, 11 and 13-day moving average modelling trials, and ARIMA modelling of true use as separated by 5, 7 and 15-day MA filters; the results from these trials showed the 7-day MA filter to be optimal in terms of removing leakage without introducing spurious pattern into the estimated true use series.

Figure 2 (Makins Court, 06.08.85 to 22.11.87) illustrates the performance of the leakage filter in purging leakage events of various types from the total supply record; it can be seen that the MA7 method successfully removes (in sequence) a short duration ramp event, a short duration pulse event and a long duration ramp event to leave a relatively 'clean' true use series.

Patterns in true water consumption

The time series of true water use shown in Figure 2 displays a strong 7-day cycle and a damped seasonal fluctuation around a relatively stationary mean. Time series of water consumption in other control areas behave similarly. There are, however, considerable differences in the base level consumption and the amplitude of the weekly cycle in the different control areas. The nature and possible socio-economic causes of areal variations in the demand for water are dealt with elsewhere (Gurnell *et al.*, 1990).

The data for the 1984-88 period show there to be little difference between summer and winter consumption (with summer use being less than 6% more than winter use in most control areas). The data for the hot summer of 1989 suggest otherwise, but there were insufficient data at the time of the present study to draw reliable conclusions on any trends in the peakiness of demand. All control areas

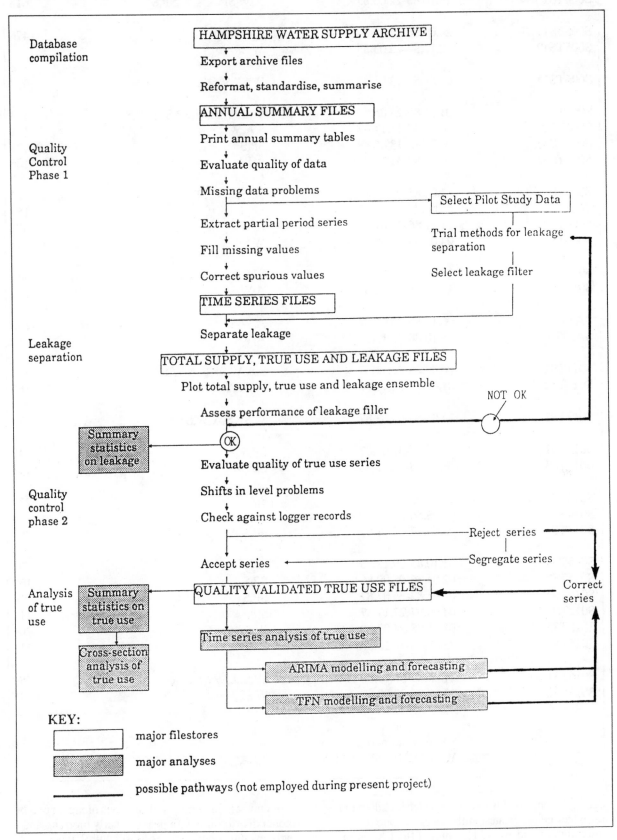

Figure 1 Quality control and analysis framework

Table 2 *The final time series datbase, consisting of those blocks of data passing both the high-pass (missing values) and the low-pass (shifts in level) quality control filters (1985 to 1988 data only)*

Series	Dates	Seasons Included	N
S004TS1	10.10.85-22.06.87	A,W,SP,S,A,W,SP,S	613
S005TS11	24.07.86-11.11.87	S,A,W,SP	476
S005TS12	12.12.87-22.03.88	W,SP	
S006TS1	01.01.87-13.01.88	W,SP,S,A,W	378
S008TS1	01.01.85-23.05.87	W,SP,S,A,W,SP,S,A,W,SP	873
S008TS21	24.07.87-11.11.87	S,A,W	111
S008TS31	04.02.88-13.06.88	SP,S	131
S008TS32	16.09.88-31.12.88	A,W	106
S009TS1	11.04.85-03.03.86	SP,S,A,W,SP	327
S009TS2	04.04.86-09.09.86	SP,S	159
S009TS3	01.11.86-26.01.87	A,W	87
S009TS4	04.02.88-18.05.88	W,SP	105
S010TS1	19.01.85-01.04.86	W,SP,S,A,W,SP	438
S010TS21	16.10.86-23.05.87	A,W,SP	220
SA13TS1	06.11.86-26.05.87	A,W,SP	202
SA13TS2	14.10.88-31.12.88	A,W	79
S011TS1	06.08.85-22.11.87	S,A,W,SP,S,A,W,SP,S,A	839
S011TS2	01.01.88-31.12.88	W,SP,S,A,W	366
S012TS1	14.01.86-09.08.87	W,SP,S,A,W,SP,S	573
S013TS1	07.04.87-31.08.87	SP,S	147
S013TS3	23.08.88-18.12.88	S,A,W	118
S014TS1	29.05.85-26.12.85	S,A,W	212
S014TS2	04.03.86-05.02.87	SP,S,A,W	339
S014TS3	03.03.87-22.11.87	SP,S,A	265
S015TS1	01.10.85-09.12.85	A	70
S015TS2	02.04.86-08.09.86	SP,S	160
S015TS3	07.05.87-26.07.87	SP,S	81
S015TS4	04.08.87-22.11.87	S,A	111
S015TS5	01.01.88-24.07.88	W,SP,S	206
S015TS6	23.08.88-18.12.88	S,A,W	118
S016TS1	21.05.85-30.11.86	SP,S,A,W,SP,S,A	559
S016TS21	23.12.86-27.09.87	W,SP,S,A	335

Notes: Seasons defined as follows:
W = D,J,F; SP = M,A,M; S = J,J,A; A = S,O,N

display strong weekly cycles in water use, demand for water being greatest at the weekend and at a minimum in mid-week. The diurnal fluctuation in demand differs according to the size and socio-economic characteristics of the control area, but a bi-modal distribution with peaks in early morning and early evening characterises most control areas reasonably well.

1.18

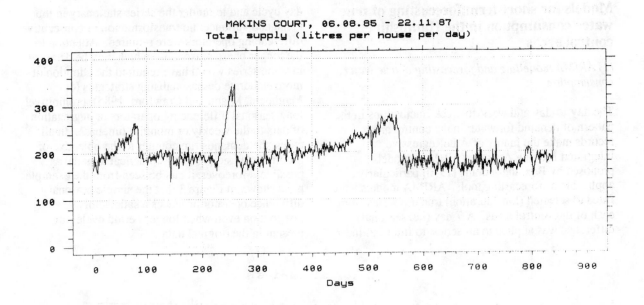
MAKINS COURT, 06.08.85 - 22.11.87
Total supply (litres per house per day)

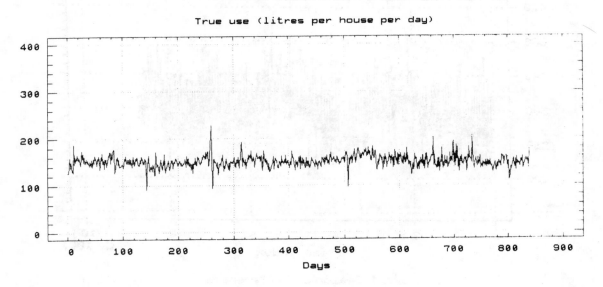
True use (litres per house per day)

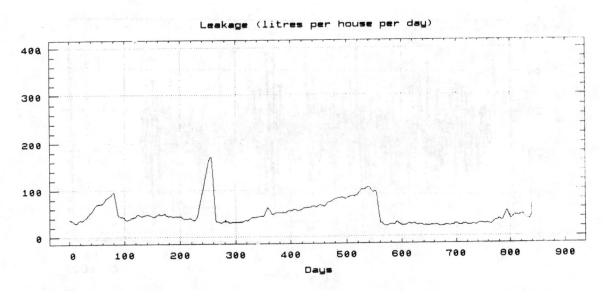
Leakage (litres per house per day)

Figure 2   Time series plots for total water supply (top plot), true water use (pp. consumption, centre) and leakage (bottom) from Makins Court, 6 July 1985 to 22 November 1987

1.19

Models for short-term forecasting of true water consumption in the Hampshire control areas

(1) ARIMA modelling and forecasting of true water consumption

The day-to-day and week-to-week fluctuations in the pattern of demand for water in the control area records make the family of AutoRegressive Integrated Moving Average (ARIMA) models proposed by Box and Jenkins (1976) particularly applicable as forecasting tools. ARIMA models were fitted to selected (long duration) true use series from each of the control areas. A 7-day (i.e. seasonal) difference was applied to all series, to filter out the 7-

day cycle and to render the series stationary in the mean and variance; no transformation or consecutive differencing operators were required. Attention to the longer phase seasonality which may be detected in some series would have required the adoption of more elaborate deseasonalising strategies (cf. Maidment, Miaou and Crawford, 1985), prohibitively long seasonal differencing operators or aggregation of data to the weekly or monthly timebase. In all cases, the demands run counter to the objective of producing as simple and as practical a model as possible. Moreover, it can be seen from the example plots shown in Figure 3 that the simple seasonal difference operator produces a satisfactory distribution even when longer period cycles are present in the original data.

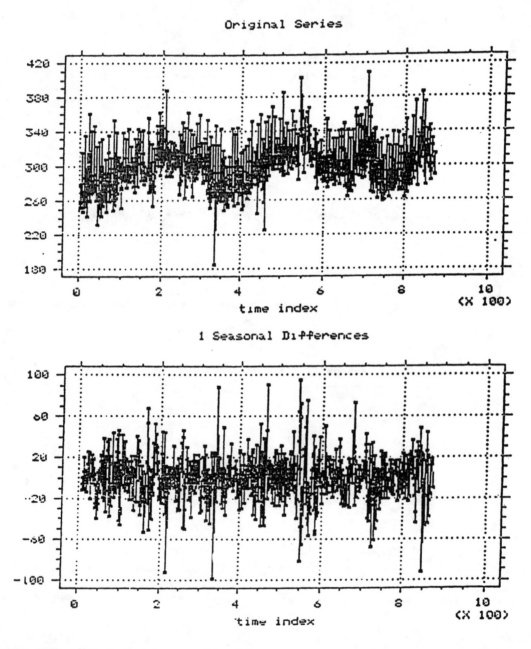

Figure 2   Time series plots of the water into supply data of series S008TS1 (Lydgate Road, 1 January 1985 to 23 May 1987). The upper plot shows the original (unfiltered) data; the lower plot shows data filtered by a seven-day 'seasonal' difference operator. The 'time index' is in days (x100). The seven-day difference removes weekly and annual cycles from the original series.

1.20

Table 3 ARIMA models fitted to selected time series for each of the 13 control areas

Series modelled	n	Model fitted	ESS	Coefficients OK?	Residuals OK?	Model selected
004 OSTERLEY ROAD						
S004TS1	613	(100)(110)	281232	Yes	No	
		(100)(210)	253768	Yes	No	
		(100)(111)	225256	No (SAR1)	No	
		(100)(011)	225799	Yes	Yes	
		(101)(011)	224221	? (MA1)	Yes	
		(100)(012)	225348	No (SMA2)	No	
		(001)(011)	236388	Yes	No	(100)(011)
005 SURREY HOUSE						
S005TS11	476	(100)(110)	292978	Yes	No	
		(100)(111)	218638	No (SAR1)	No	
		(100)(011)	218645	Yes	Yes	(100)(011)
006 VELMORE HOUSE						
S006TS1	378	(101)(110)	156357	No (MA1)	No	
		(100)(110)	157485	Yes	No	
		(100)(011)	120572	Yes	Yes	
		(300)(011)	114189	Yes	Yes	(100)(011)
008 LYDGATE ROAD						
S008TS1	873	(100)(011)	304012	Yes	No	
		(100)(210)	282626	Yes	No	
		(100)(310)	272475	Yes	Yes	
		(100)(011)	258869	No (SAR1)	Yes	
		(100)(111)	258363		Yes	(100)(011)
009 WHYTEWAYS						
S009TS4A	81	(100)(110)	20842	No (AR1 SAR1)	No	
		(100)(011)	15181	No (AR1)	Yes	
		(011)(011)	15091	No (MA1,SMA1)	No	
		(000)(011)	15470	Yes	Yes	
		(000)(111)	15045	No (SAR1)	Yes	
		(000)(012)	14530	Yes	Yes	(000)(012)
010 IVY ROAD						
S010TS1A	414	(100)(110)	358207	Yes	Yes	
		(100)(011)	301461	Yes	Yes	
		(101)(111)	287405	No (SAR1)	Yes	
		(101)(011)	287678	Yes	Yes	(101)(011)

Series modelled	n	Model fitted	ESS	Coefficients OK?	Residuals OK?	Model selected
A13 HOCOMBE ROAD						
SA13TS2	79	(200)	450391	No (AR2)	No	
		(100)(010)	187862	Yes	Yes	
		(100)(011)	176328	Yes	Yes	(100)(011)
SA13TS21	72	(100)(110)	75445	Yes	Yes	
		(100)(011)	70120	Yes	Yes	(100)(011)
011 MAKINS COURT						
S011TS1	839	(100)(110)	129728	Yes	No	
		(100)(111)	101988	? SAR1	Yes	
		(100)(011)	102530	Yes	No	
		(100)(210)	119369	Yes	Yes	
		(100)(310)	113288			(100)(011)
012 BRACHER CLOSE						
3012TS1A	549	(100)(110)	206514	Yes	No	
		(100)(011)	169142	Yes	Yes	
		(200)(011)	158597	Yes	Yes	
		(200)(012)	158594	No (SMA2)	Yes	(200)(011)
013 TEG DOWN						
3013TS1A	123	(100)(100)	478429	Yes	No	
		(100)(011)	326766	Yes	Yes	
		(100)(111)	325457	No (SAR1)	Yes	(100)(011)
014 WEEKE						
S014TS2A	315	(100)(110)	374162	Yes	No	
		(100)(011)	291971	Yes	Yes	(100)(011)
015 HIGHCLIFF						
S015TS6A	94	(101)(011)	31379	No (MA1)	Yes	
		(100)(011)	31393	Yes	Yes	(100)(011)
016 KING GEORGE RD						
S016TS1	559	(101)(100)	2.24 E6	Yes	No	
		(101)(110)	2.13 E6	Yes	No	
		(200)(110)	2.16 E6	Yes	No	
		(101)(111)	1.61 E6	Yes	No	
		(101)(011)	1.76 E6	Yes	No	
		(101)(011)	1.64 E6	Yes	No	(101)(111) or (101)(012)
		(101)(012)	1.61 E6	Yes	Yes	

1.21

Table 4 Forecast stastistics of ARIMA models fitted to seven trial control areas

Control Area	Series Modelled	Forecast Period	Model Fitted	Min%	Max%	MAPE
009	S009TS4A	15.04 - 18.05.88	(100)(011)	0.24	10.45	4.54
			(000)(012)	0.50	10.53	5.02
010	S010TS1A	09.03 - 01.04.86	(100)(011)	0.16	21.38	4.85
			(100)(110)	0.52	19.77	5.77
			(101)(011)	0.24	21.51	4.80
A13	SA13TS21	01.01 - 24.01.89	(100)(011)	0.65	12.17	5.95
			(100)(110)	1.92	24.38	14.08
012	S012TS1A	17.07 - 09.08.87	(100)(011)	0.26	35.78	6.25
			(200)(100)	0.45	35.87	6.29
013	S013TS1A	08.08 - 31.08.87	(100)(011)	1.06	33.92	13.31
014	S014TS2A	13.01 - 05.02.87	(100)(011)	0.27	11.46	4.31
015	S015TS6A	15.11 - 18.12.88	(100)(011)	0.68	7.57	3.36
			MEAN			6.08

Note: MIN% = the smallest absolute percentage error in the set of 24
MAX% = the largest absolute percentage error in the set of 24
MAPE = the average absolute percentage error of the set of 24

(Absolute percentage errors calculated as [100.(($|$Actual-Forecast$|$)/Actual)]

Tentatively identified ARIMA models for each series were selected by inspecting time series, autocorrelation (acf) and partial autocorrelation (pacf) plots. Estimation and diagnostic checking of the parameter values and statistics of each model led to the selection of the best model for each series. The constant proved to be statistically insignificant in all models, indicating that the 7-day difference successfully produced series of zero mean. Table 3 summarises the results obtained. The ARIMA $(1,0,0)(0,1,1)$ model emerges as the best model in most cases, and as a good model, judged in terms of both adequacy and parsimony, in all cases. This apparent commonality of model form across control areas implies a consistency in the factors influencing the demand for water, and offers scope for the development of a general model at the regional scale. The form of the model indicates that the demand for water in a household has a 1-day persistency (i.e. the volume of water used on a given day is reasonably similar to that used on the previous day; the AR(1) term); a strong 7-day cycle (the 7-day (seasonal) difference operator); and a week to week unsteadiness (i.e. the water used on a given day of the week varies from one week to the next in a random-like fashion - perhaps reflecting the

influence of unpredictable events like changes in weather: the SMA(1) term).

The quality of forecasts from the ARIMA models developed was tested against 'virgin data' (i.e. data which were not used to estimate the models). Data from seven different control areas, covering different times of year, were used. A forecast horizon of 24 days was used for all trials. Table 4 gives details of the trials conducted. The forecasts are evidently of high quality; on average, the ARIMA models provide short-term forecasts of the demand for water with a mean absolute percentage error (MAPE) of only 6%. Plots of actual versus forecast series produced for each test period indicated that forecast series track actual series closely; Figure 4 illustrates the quality of fit achieved. It can be seen that the forecasts essentially amount to a fairly simple repeating trace of 7-day period. This points to a simplicity in structure of the domestic demand for water. Under such circumstances, the success of the ARIMA model may be mainly due to the differencing procedure used to deseasonalise the data rather than to the stochastic model implied by the AR and MA terms of the fitted model (c.f. Chatfield, 1989). It is thus

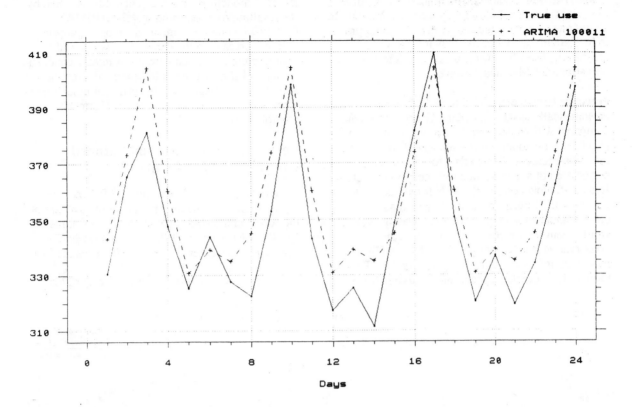

Figure 4 Actual and forecast true water consumption in the Highcliff control area, 25 November to 18 December 1988. The forecast is obtained with an ARIMA (1,0,0)(0,1,1) model.

appropriate to assess whether simpler seasonal smoothing methods are able to provide forecasts of equivalent quality.

(2) ES modelling and forecasting of true water consumption

The exponential smoothing (ES) methods due to Brown, Holt and Winter, plus an exponential time trend method were used to produce forecasts of water demand in each of the seven test periods referred to above. Forecasts from all three methods are generated as weighted extrapolations of a smoothing model fitted to the historic series. Trial and error modelling with different weights for the different ES models examined showed that optimal ES forecasts are obtained with Winter's method using weights of 0.2, 0.1 and 0.1 for alpha (level estimator), beta (trend estimator) and gamma (seasonal estimator). Figure 5 plots forecasts from the ARIMA (1,0,0) (0,1,1) and the Winter ES (0.2,0.1,0.1) models against observed data (series SA13TS2, Hocombe Road, 1 to 24 Jan 1989). The ARIMA forecasts are significantly better than the Winter ES forecasts; the MAPE of the ARIMA model is 6%, that of the ES model 27%. The lower plot in Figure 5 shows how the ES forecast diverges from the general level of the historic data as the forecast horizon lengthens, reflecting the influence of the strong trend in the set of data immediately before the forecast point (the Christmas/ New Year period, in this case). The ARIMA model is more robust to non-repeating influences of this type.

It is concluded that forecasts from ARIMA models are better than those from ES models in quality to cost terms as well as in quality terms alone.

(3) TFN modelling and forecasting of true water consumption

Given that the demand for water in domestic households may be expected to vary according to weather conditions, transfer function-noise (TFN) models using air temperature and precipitation as input variables were also examined. TFN models - which are inherently superior to regression models in representing and forecasting the dynamics of the response of an output time series variable to the forcing influence of one or more input variables - have been successfully applied to a number of water resources problems (e.g. Gurnell and Fenn, 1984; Maidment, Miaou and Crawford, 1985).

Precipitation, being a non-continuous variable, was modelled as an intervention variable in all cases. The preparatory procedures applied were: an AR(1) model (i.e. ARIMA (0,1,0)) for the air temperature series; an ARIMA (1,0,0)(0,1,1) for the water consumption (output) series. The prepared output series was then prewhitened by the input series' AR(1) model, and the transfer function model identified from the impulse response function. Table 5 summarises the transfer function and noise models identified for the five series modelled with the TFN approach. The TF model takes the (0,1,0) form in all cases. The noise model differs from one control area to another, but the (1,0,0)(0,1,1) form is common. In all but one case, the input lag of the TF model proved to be insignificant when the TFN models were estimated. The TFN model thus reduces to the univariate ARIMA model used earlier.

Forecasts from the one TFN model which proved to be statistically sustainable (King George Road) are compared with those from the equivalent ARIMA (1,0,0)(0,1,1) model and the Winter ES (0.2,0.1,0.1) model in Figure 6. Actual data for the forecast period are not available, due to a meter malfunction. It is clear, however, that the TFN forecasts 'flatten out' over the forecast horizon. Since data for this control area display high amplitude weekly cycles, it would seem reasonable to conclude that the more conservative fluctuations predicted by the TFN model are inferior to those predicted by the ARIMA model. It would thus appear that the extra costs of

the TFN modelling approach cannot be justified by the resulting forecasts, and that the ARIMA (1,0,0)(0,1,1) model remains the most appropriate tool for forecasting the demand for water in the control areas examined herein. A related conclusion is that at the daily timescale examined, climatic data are not of significance for the efficient modelling and forecasting of true water use in the Hampshire control areas.

Forecasts with a regional (lumped parameter) ARIMA model

A 'lumped parameter' or regional ARIMA (1,0,0)(0,1,1) model was formed by taking the average of the AR(1) and SMA(1) parameter values of the specific area ARIMA (1,0,0)(0,1,1) models. The resulting regional forecasting model takes the form:

$$Y_t = 0.481Y_{t-1} + Y_{t-7} - 0.481Y_{t-8} + e_t - 0.8276e_{t-7}$$

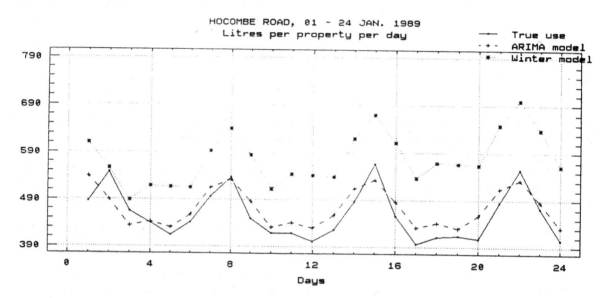

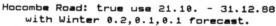

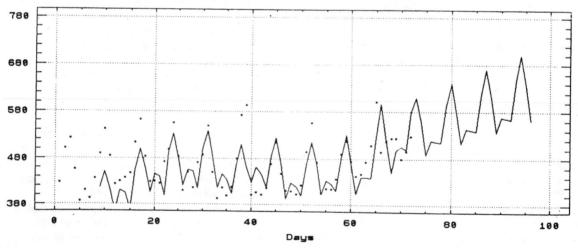

Figure 5 *Actual and forecast true water consumption in the Hocombe Road control area. The upper plot shows the superiority of the ARIMA (1,0,0)(0,1,1) model over the Winter (0.2,0.1,0.1) ES model. The lower plot shows the recent trend bias in the Winter ES forecast.*

1.24

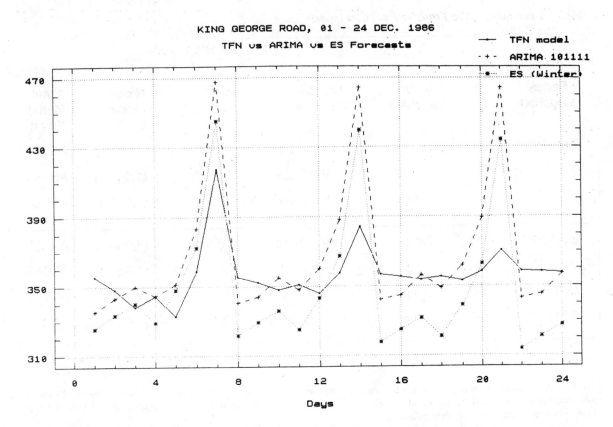

Figure 6 TFN, ARIMA and ES forecasts of true water consumption in the King George Road control area, 1 to 24 December 1986. Note the decay in amplitude of the TFN forecast and the difference in level of the ES forecast compared to the others.

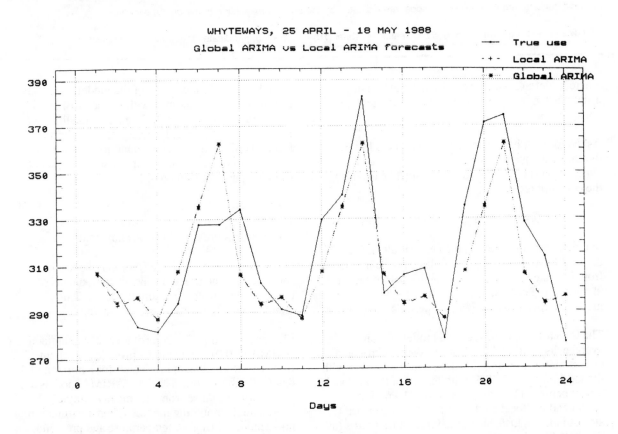

Figure 7 Actual and forecast true water consumption in the Whyteways control area, 25 April to 18 May 1988. Forecasts from the global ARIMA (1,0,0)(0,1,1) model are indistinguishable from those of the ARIMA (1,0,0,)(0,1,1,) model of the Whyteways control area.

Table 5 *A summary of the Transfer Function models fitted*

			Identification Stage			
Series Modelled	n	Input Variables	Output Variables	Transfer Function	Noise Model	Final Model Fitted
SA13TS21	72	Temp	V7 Trueh	(0,1,0)	μ,(1,0)(0,1)	ARIMA
		Ppt	V7 Trueh	(0,1,0)	μ,(1,0)(0,1)	ARIMA
		Temp Ppt	V7 Trueh	(0,1,0) (0,1,0)	μ,(1,0)(0,1)	ARIMA
SOO8TS1	873	Temp	VV7 Trueh	(0,1,0)	(3,0)(0,1)	ARIMA
SO11TS1	839	Temp	Trueh	(0,1,0)	μ,(1,0)(1,1)	ARIMA
SO11TS2	366	Temp	Trueh	(0,1,0)	μ,(1,0)(1,2)	ARIMA
SO16TS1	559	Temp	Trueh	(0,1,0)	μ,(1,0)(1,0)	TFN

Notes: Trueh denotes true water consumption per household per day.

The transfer function model is given in (r,s,b) notation; r indicates the time span over which past values of the input variable X_t influence the output variable Y_t; s indicates the time span over which new values of X_t have influence over Y_t; b indicates the lag time before new values of X_t start to influence Y_t.

The noise model is given in (p,q)(P,Q) notation; p denotes a consecutive autoregressive operator; P denotes a seasonal autoregressive operator; q denotes a consecutive moving average operator; Q denotes a seasonal moving average operator.

The differencing terms for the noise model are indicated by the operations applied to the output variable.

∇ indicates first order differencing; $\nabla 7$ indicates seasonal (7d) differencing; μ indicates that a constant was fitted

where Y_t defines water use per household on day t; e_t defines the residual (actual minus estimated consumption) on day t.

As the forecast horizon extends beyond the lags in the forecast equation, forecast values of Y_t and expectation (i.e. zero) values of e_t must be used, so the equation reduces to:

$$Y_t = 0.481Y_{t-1} + Y_{t-7} - 0.481Y_{t-8}$$

In either case, the model indicates that the household demand for water on any given day may be predicted from its water use on days 1, 7 and 8 before the day in question. Forecasts were made with the regional model for each of the seven trial periods used earlier.

The forecasts from the regional model are, on average, as good as those from a given control area's own model; the average MAPE from forecasting with the local model is 6.08%, with that from the regional model being 6.11%. Forecasts from the regional model and the local model for any given area are almost indistinguishable in the forecast trial plots (as illustrated in Figure 7). The technical implication of this result is that the overall form of the model appears to govern its performance to a greater extent

than the numerical weights of the model; the 7-day differencing operator may well be the most crucial aspect of the fitted model. The operational implication is that highly successful short-term forecasts of the domestic demand for water in any chosen control area may be made with a regional (lumped parameter) model.

Conclusions

The analyses presented herein show that:

(1) A simple MA7 leakage filter may be used to separate the true use and leakage components of a control area's water into supply record. This conclusion is likely to be generalisable.

(2) For the Hampshire control area data examined, an ARIMA (1,0,0)(0,1,1) model provides excellent forecasts of the demand for water for a horizon of 1 day to 1 month. Forecasts from ARIMA models are far superior to those from technically-simpler exponential smoothing models. Transfer-function noise models using air temperature and precipitation series as forcing variables either reduce to simple ARIMA models or yield poorer forecasts than their univariate ARIMA counterparts. The results imply

that the ARIMA $(1,0,0)(0,1,1)$ model captures the serial pattern in the demand for water in Hampshire's control areas particularly well. This conclusion is reinforced by the results of forecasting with a regional (lumped parameter) model, which gives forecasts of 6% MAPE, as good as those which may be obtained with site- specific models of the same form. The operational benefits of such consistency and transferability are considerable.

Acknowledgements

The work reported in this paper was undertaken by the GeoData Institute, University of Southampton, acting under contract to Southern Water Services (Hampshire Divison) Ltd. Dr. C.R. Fenn was seconded to work on the project from Worcester College of Higher Education. Southern Water Services' permission to publish results from the project is gratefully acknowledged.

References

Box, G.E.P. & Jenkins, G.M. 1976. *Time Series Analysis, Forecasting and Control* (revised edition). Holden Day, San Francisco.

Chatfield, C. 1989. *The Analysis of Time Series: An Introduction* (4th edition). Chapman and Hall, London.

Gurnell, A. M. & Fenn, C.R. 1984. Box-Jenkins transfer-function models applied to suspended sediment concentration - discharge relationships in a proglacial stream. *Arctic and Alpine Research*, 16, 1, 93-106.

Gurnell, A.M., Clark, M.J. & Fenn, C.R. 1990. Time series and cross-sectional summary statistics and analyses. Control Area Consumption Analysis Report 4, The GeoData Institute, Southampton.

Maidment, D.R., Miaou, S. & Crawford, M.M. 1985. Transfer function models of urban daily water use. *Wat. Resour. Res.* 21, 425-432.

A study of residential water demand using fuzzy linear regression analysis

M. J. Hall

Abstract

The relationship between residential per capita water demand and the unit price of water is fundamental to the framing of charging policy, and has therefore attracted considerable attention where domestic water consumption has been metered. Many investigators have continued to rely upon ordinary least squares regression techniques to derive such relationships. However, where data are inherently limited in scope and prone to measurement error, fuzzy linear regression analysis presents a viable alternative. Application of this approach to cross-sectional data from five cities and towns in the USA and Australia has illustrated the sensitivity of results to the measure of vagueness to be optimised and the choice of a suitable reference point. The ability of fuzzy regression analysis to provide upper and lower limits to an estimate as well as a preferred value is seen to have wider applications in demand forecasting.

Introduction

The problems of demand estimation and forecasting in the United Kingdom are exacerbated by the limited amount of metering that has been performed, particularly on residential properties, as a matter of routine. Apart from the well-known exceptions, such as Malvern and the Fylde area (see Males, 1975), such information as has been made available has been collected as the result of special surveys, of which those initiated by the then Central Water Planning Unit in the Midlands (Thackray et al., 1978) and the South West of England (Hooper, 1986) are particularly significant. Such data and their regular updating (see Hall et al., 1988, for example) are essential to the estimation of the 'unmeasured' component of total water demand. These analyses have tended to be more complex, if not speculative, than those for conurbations where metering was the norm rather than the exception. For example, the Johns Hopkins University Residential Water Use Project (Howe and Linaweaver, 1967) was more concerned with the choice of explanatory variables than with estimating the vagaries of domestic water demand.

This predominance, or absence, of metered consumption figures has helped to determine the directions in which studies on both sides of the Atlantic have progressed. A survey of the American literature shows a prevailing interest in econometric models of water demand, with particular attention being paid to price elasticity. Indeed, the representation of block-rate schedules in such models is the subject of continuing debate (see, for example, Billings and Agthe, 1980; Jones and Morris, 1984; Agthe et al., 1986; and further references therein). However, Martin and Thomas (1986) have expressed the rather agnostic view that precise estimates of price elasticities for a given area may not be necessary if the aim is policy formulation. Those authors concentrated on the interpretation of well-defined price and consumption data from five cities and towns in Australia and the United States, covering a wide range of locations having a strongly seasonal rainfall pattern. Those authors contend that such data provide a more reliable basis for future policy than estimates for individual urban areas. Nevertheless, their identification of a model relating price per cubic metre and average per capita water use is strongly influenced by the Ordinary Least Squares (OLS) approach.

OLS regression analysis focuses upon the relationship between a dependent and an independent variable, and concentrates upon the minimisation of measurement error. However, water resources planners seldom have the luxury of comparatively large data sets that are capable of yielding statistically significant relationships. In these circumstances, fuzzy linear regression may provide an alternative interpretation. In particular, small data sets, such as those employed by Martin and Thomas (1986), may be used to evaluate the goodness of the relationship between the dependent and independent variables.

Fuzzy sets, numbers and operations

By definition, a Fuzzy Set is a collection of objects without clear boundaries. More formally, if A is a fuzzy set on the set X, then an element x of X can belong to A. The grade of membership can be described by the membership function, m(x), which is limited to values within the interval zero to one, i.e. if m(x)=1, then x clearly belongs to A, otherwise if m(x)=0, the inverse holds. The value of the membership function therefore reflects the level of belief, or vagueness, that x fulfills the condition of belonging to the set. Sets which assume membership levels of zero or one are known as 'crisp' sets. The membership level assigned usually depends upon the context of the problem. The H-level set, 0<H<1, of the fuzzy set A is the crisp set, {x, m(x) > H}.

In practice, particular attention is focussed upon a special class of fuzzy numbers called L-R fuzzy numbers for which

L(x)=R(x)=1 if x<0, and L(x)=R(x)=0 if x>1

and L(x), R(x) are strictly decreasing functions on the interval [0,1]. More specifically, a fuzzy number, M, is an L-R fuzzy number if:

$$m(x) = L\{(m - x)/b\} \text{ for } x \leq m, b>0$$
$$= R\{(x - m)/c\} \text{ for } x>m, c>0 \quad (1)$$

M may therefore be denoted by $(m, b, c)_{LR}$. L-R fuzzy numbers may have different L and R functions.

Figure 1 shows the membership function of an L-R fuzzy number for which L(x) = 1-x and R(x) = $1-x^3$.

Fuzzy linear regression

Fuzzy linear regression differs from Ordinary Least Squares (OLS) linear regression in having the parameters of the linear function as fuzzy numbers. However, in fuzzy linear regression, there is no simple measure of the degree of fitness, such as the minimum sum of squares, but only a level of belief in the fitting of the postulated function to the data.

In a fuzzy regression, the y^*_i for each measured x_i are fuzzy numbers with a specified membership function, and the degree of belief, H, is chosen to reflect the quality of the data and the existence of the regression relationship. The parameters, a^* and b^*, of the regression

$$y^*_i = f(x_i) = a^* + b^*.x_i \quad (2)$$

are then fuzzy numbers which should be estimated such that the H-level subset of the regression, $f_H(x)$, contains the H-level subset of the measurement, y_{iH}. In other words, for each data point, y_i, corresponding to x_i, H indicates the degree of belief that the point approaches the line of regression. Since many fuzzy functions may satisfy this requirement, that chosen should be the 'crispest' among them. Identification of the parameters of the fuzzy regression may therefore be considered as a constrained optimisation problem in which the crispness of the fuzzy linear function is maximised, or alternatively, its vagueness is minimised, subject to the constraints that each measurement point must fit a linear function with a membership level equalling or exceeding H. Solutions differ according to the measure of crispness (or vagueness) that is adopted.

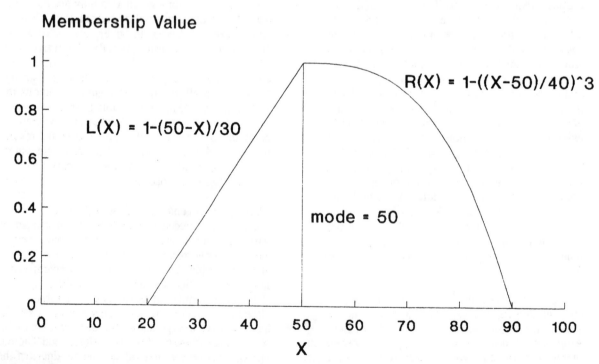

Figure 1 Typical membership functions with a mode of 50, and left and right scaling factors of 30 and 40 respectively

1.30

Suppose that n data points, (x_i, y_i), are available, and that the y_i are crisp. A fuzzy function is defined such that

$$f^*(x_i) = a^* + b^*.(x_i - x_r) \qquad (3)$$

where $a^* = (A, b_1, c_1)_{LR}$ and $b^* = (B, b_2, c_2)_{LR}$ are the L-R representations of the unknown parameters of equation (3), and x_r is a reference point for the x_i. The condition that the H-level sets of y^* are contained within the H-level sets of $f^*(x_i)$ have been derived by Bardossy (1990) as:

$$y_i - A + B(x_i - x_r) > R^{-1}(H).\{c_1 + c_2(x_r - x_i)\}; \quad x_i \le x_r \qquad (4)$$

$$y_i - A + B(x_i - x_r) > R^{-1}(H).c_1 + L^{-1}(H).b_2(x_i - x_r); \; x_i > xr \qquad (5)$$

$$A - B(x_i - x_r) - y_i > L^{-1}(H).b_1 + R^{-1}(H).c_2(x_i - x_r); \; x_i > x_r \qquad (6)$$

$$A - B(x_r - x_i) - y_i > L^{-1}(H).\{b_1 + b_2(x_r - x_i)\}; \quad x_i \le x_r \qquad (7)$$

Equations (4) to (7) are linear with respect to the unknown parameters A, B, b_1, c_1, b_2, and c_2, and for any given L, R, x and y, form the constraints for the optimal estimation of the parameters, which is also dependent upon the adopted measure of crispness (or vagueness). Typical choices of the latter include the 'average vagueness' of the parameters,

$$b_1 + c_1 + b_2 + c_2 \qquad (8)$$

as proposed by Tanaka et al. (1982), or the 'prediction vagueness' introduced by Bardossy (1990), which represents the vagueness of the fuzzy regression function defined on the domain of the independent variables. The latter approach leads to the objective function

$$c_1.R^* + b_1.L^* + \{0.5(d^2 + e^2)/(d + e)\}.(c_2.R^* + b_2.L^*) \qquad (9)$$

where $d = x_r - x^-$; $e = x^+ - x_r$, and R^*, L^* are the integrals of the chosen R and L membership functions between the limits of zero and one. Using either measure of vagueness, the functions to be minimised are both linear with respect to the unknown parameters, and the constrained optimisation problem may be solved with the aid of linear programming.

Residential water consumption in arid regions

The problems of deriving reliable estimates of domestic per capita water consumptions in developing countries with an arid climate are manifold. In these circumstances, cross-sectional comparisons of reasonably reliable data for cities of similar climate in other parts of the world may provide a better basis on which to formulate a water supply and distribution policy than local records that are either incomplete or of dubious quality, or both.

The data compiled by Martin and Thomas (1986) provide a ready example of the latter approach in

which figures from five locations, each for a single year between 1978-79 and 1981-82, were combined in order to examine the long-run price elasticities for residential water in an arid climate. The data on average daily per capita consumption and unit prices are summarised in Table 1. Further discussion of the comparability of the data may be found in the paper by Martin and Thomas (1986).

Table 1: Household water consumption data in five arid cities (from Martin & Thomas, 1986)

Location & date	Per Capita Consumption, $l\,cap^{-1}d^{-1}$	Price per cubic metre, \$ US
Coober Pedy, S. Australia, 1980-84	50	14.04
Kuwait, 1973-1981	184	0.67
Perth, Western Australia, 1981-82	288	0.31
Tucson, Arizona, 1978-79	371	0.27
Phoenix, Arizona, 1979	595	0.09

Relating water consumption to price

The data on residential per capita water consumption and unit price of water shown in Table 1 were initially subjected to an OLS regression analysis in which the logarithm of the consumption was taken as the dependent variable, Y, and the logarithm of the unit cost as the independent variable, X. The relationship obtained was:

$$Y = 5.133 - 0.479\,X \qquad (10)$$

which had an explained variance of 99 per cent and a standard error of estimate of 0.104 log units. When the disparate nature of the data represented by this equation is considered, the result is surprisingly good for such a low number of degrees of freedom. More importantly, from the practical viewpoint, all error is assumed to be concentrated in the consumption data and the associated costs are supposedly error free. The continuing debate on the representation of cost in econometric models of water consumption already referred to in the Introduction is more than sufficient to throw doubt upon the latter supposition. A viable set of alternative assumptions is provided by fuzzy linear regression.

In applying this technique to represent the data of Table 1, a number of prior assumptions are necessary, each of which is based upon the conceptions of the analyst about the worth of the data and the applicability of the chosen relationship. The latter are reflected in the level of credibility, H, which is usually chosen to lie within the range $0.5 < H < 0.8$. At the lower end of this range, predicted Y-values will be imprecise, but at the upper end they become increasingly crisp. Following Bardossy *et al.* (1990), a credibility level of 0.7 was chosen for this study, applicable uniformly to all (X,Y) pairs.

The form of the membership functions for the fuzzy regression parameters, a^* and b^*, must also be selected. In general, these functions are assumed to take the general form

$$L(x) = R(x) = 1 - x^k \qquad (11)$$

where the k increases with the degree of belief in the modal value (or the degree of suspicion about values away from the mode). Here a k-value of one was adopted, giving symmetrical triangular membership functions.

The remaining assumptions involve the choice of the criterion of vagueness to be minimised, and the selection of the reference point for the independent variable. Both average and prediction vagueness were employed in this exercise, and the sensitivity of the models to the choice of reference point was also explored. The reference point should be chosen to coincide with the region in which the regression is at its most accurate. Either the average or the mid-range are typically adopted, but the maximum or the minimum may also be appropriate, depending upon the context of the problem.

Once the parameters of the selected model have been estimated, its performance may be examined visually by plotting the derived relationship along with the uncertainty band represented by zero levels of the left- and right-hand membership functions. Bardossy *et al.* (1990) have suggested that the preferred model is that for which the bandwidth is as small as possible, and the variation of that bandwidth along the abscissa reflects the degree of belief in the relationship. Those authors have also suggested that where there is no prior basis for selecting a reference point, the prediction vagueness is preferred to the average vagueness.

These recommendations were partly supported by the results of this study. For example, Figure 2 shows the log linear model obtained by minimising average vagueness, using the mid-range as the reference point. The uncertainty band is narrowest at the reference point, but the limits fan out sharply for both lower and higher values of the independent variable. In contrast, when the prediction vagueness is minimised, the bandwidth at the reference point is wider but the upper and lower limits hardly diverge, as shown in Figure 3. In the latter case, the relationship obtained was:

$$Y = 5.109 - 0.485 (X - x_r) \qquad (12)$$

The above computations were repeated using the average as the reference point. With the average vagueness, the divergence of the membership limits was found to be less marked, with the values of A and b_1 increasing and b_2 notably lower. With the prediction vagueness, b_1 and b_2 were comparable in

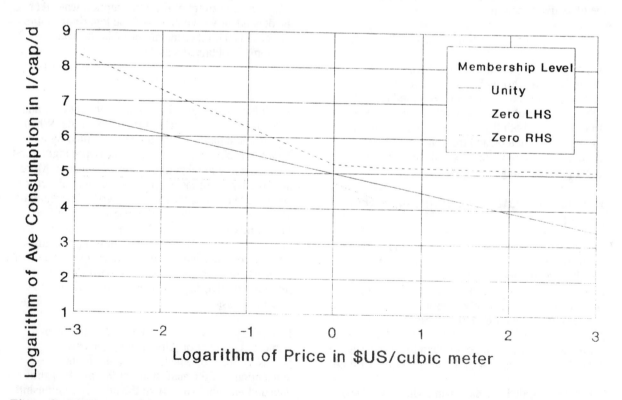

Figure 2   Model minimising the average vagueness with the mid-range as the reference point

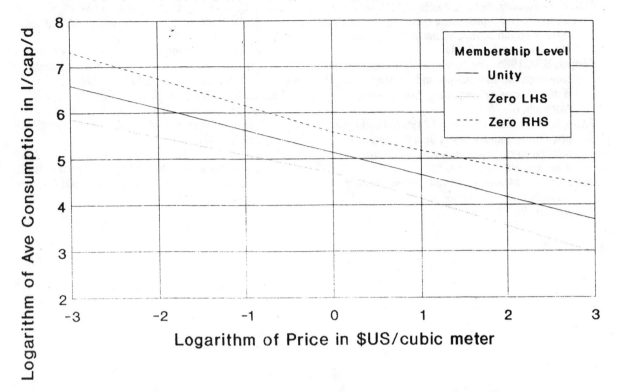

Figure 3   Model minimising prediction vagueness with the mid-range as the reference point

value to the mid-range reference point model, but the regression equation changed to

$$Y = 5.431 - 0.439 \, (X - x_r) \qquad (13)$$

Using the criteria of Bardossy *et al.* (1990), the preferred model is that which minimises the prediction vagueness with the mid-range as the reference point, illustrated in Figure 3.

Concluding remarks

There are many variables that must be considered in compiling a forecast of the demand for water which are inherently imprecise. Nevertheless, the analyst generally has at least a subjective notion of the range within which their values could be expected to fall, if not an informed opinion about the most likely figures. These are precisely the circumstances in which fuzzy numbers can provide the most appropriate representation. When the relationships between such variables form an integral part of the forecast procedure, then fuzzy regression analysis is an effective substitute for the conventional OLS variety, particularly where data sets are small. The familiar least squares criterion is replaced by that of the minimum vagueness, which provides a measure of the goodness of the fuzzy regression.

When fuzzy regression analysis was applied to the data of Table 1 in order to derive a relationship between the average daily per capita residential water consumption and the unit cost of water in arid zone cities, the preferred model was obtained by using the mid-range as the reference point and minimising the

prediction vagueness. The bandwidth about the regression line so obtained was found to be the smallest among several candidate models, and the limits of zero membership diverged relatively slowly for values of the independent variable both above and below the reference point. The model indicates that, for water selling at 1 $US per cubic metre, a per capita consumption of 170 l d^{-1} can be anticipated. However, this figure would not be expected to fall below 110 l d^{-1} nor exceed 264 l d^{-1}. This feature of the methodology whereby upper and lower limits can be obtained directly as well as a best estimate is seen as having wider applications in water demand forecasting.

Acknowledgement

The helpful discussion of the problems of implementing fuzzy regression analysis by A. Bardossy, Universität Karlsruhe, during the preparation of this paper is gratefully acknowledged.

References

Agthe, D.E., Billings, R.B., Dobra, J.L. & Raffiee, K. 1986. A simultaneous equation demand model for block rates. *Wat. Resour. Res.* 22, 1-4.

Bardossy, A. 1990. Note on fuzzy regression. *Fuzzy Sets and Systems* 37, 65-75.

Bardossy, A., Bogardi, I. & Duckstein, L. 1990. Fuzzy regression in hydrology. *Wat. Resour. Res.* 26, 1497-1508.

Billings, R.B. & Agthe, D.E. 1980. Price elasticities of water: a case of increasing block rates. *Land Economics* 56, 73-84.

Hall, M.J., Hooper, B.D. & Postle, S.M. 1988. Domestic per capita water consumption in South West England. *J. Inst. Water and Environ. Management* 2, 626-631.

Hooper, B.D. 1986. The survey of domestic water consumption. In Gardiner and Herrington (eds) *Water Demand Forecasting*, Geo Books, Norwich, 69-76.

Howe, C.W. & Linaweaver, F.P. 1967. The impact of price on residential water demand and its relation to system design and price structure. *Wat. Resour. Res.* 3, 13-32.

Jones, C.V. & Morris, J.R. 1984. Instrumental price estimates and residential water demand. *Wat. Resour. Res.* 20, 197-202.

Males, D.B. 1975. Household use of water. Central Water Planning Unit, Reading, Technical Note No 7.

Martin, W.E. & Thomas, J.F. 1986. Policy relevance in studies of urban residential water demand. *Wat. Resour. Res.* 22, 1735-1741.

Tanaka, H., Uejima, S. & Asai, K. 1982. Linear regression analysis with fuzzy model. IEEE Trans on Systems, Man and Cybernetics SMC-12, 903-907.

Thackray, J.E., Cocker, V. & Archibald, G.G. 1978. The Malvern and Mansfield studies of domestic water usage. *Proc. Institution of Civil Engineers Part I* 64, 37-61.

The Testwood Lakes Scheme

J. Bircumshaw & C.R. Fenn

Abstract

The Testwood Lakes Scheme is being promoted by Southern Water Services to secure water supplies for a major part of South Hampshire into the early part of the next century. The scheme involves the construction of bankside storage reservoirs on the floodplain of the River Blackwater immediately upstream of its confluence with the River Test. This paper describes the various studies which have taken place to assess the feasibility of the scheme, and the factors which have influenced the design of the scheme. Particular attention is given to the hydrological studies which were undertaken to assess the need for, the reliability of, and the flood flow and level consequences of the scheme.

Introduction

The need for a number of reservoirs to augment water supplies in South Hampshire was first identified in the mid-1960s. In 1965 Herbert Lapworth and Partners were commissioned by the water undertakings to carry out a study which identified a number of reservoir sites, and further work by Manders, Raikes and Marshall between 1975 and 1980 identified 17 possible locations for reservoirs in South Hampshire. It is from this report that the concept of the Testwood Lakes scheme has developed. The 58 ha. site of the proposed reservoirs is located to the north of Totton and to the north-west of the Testwood Water Supply Works (Figure 1).

The Testwood Water Supply Works is operated by the Hampshire Division of Southern Water Services Ltd. It provides water to parts of the City of Southampton, the area to the west of Southampton Water and also the Isle of Wight. The river intake is situated approximately 1 km downstream of the point where the River Test passes under the M27 motorway. The current abstraction licence is 136 Ml d^{-1}. The Testwood Lakes scheme is intended to support the Testwood intake in three distinct ways:
(a) as a strategic reserve supply to safeguard public water supply (PWS) against pollution incidents in the River Test (e.g. arising from spillages on M27 motorway, or from turbid overflows from River Blackwater floods);
(b) as a means of balancing seasonal variations in supply, and thus safeguarding PWS against low flows in the River Test;
(c) as a means of enhancing the overall resources available in the South Hampshire region.

The scheme is thus intended to give security of supply to Southern Water's customers, and to maximise the use of the existing licence. Purchase of the site for the reservoirs was completed in January 1990, and in March of that year, consulting engineers Rofe, Kennard & Lapworth were appointed to undertake a feasibility study into the proposals. The rest of this paper outlines the studies which have been undertaken. Particular attention is given to the hydrological work conducted, but outlines of the engineering and environmental studies undertaken are also presented.

Hydrological studies

A series of hydrological studies examining the need for, the reliability of, and the flood flow and level consequences of the Testwood Lakes Scheme were undertaken by Southern Science Ltd.

(i) Demand forecasting: assessing the need for the Testwood Lakes Scheme

Component-based single line demand forecasts for the Hampshire Division (Southern Resource Area) were used to determine the point at which demand is likely to exceed currently available or planned resources. The latest demand forecast (due to D.M. Bates, Southern Water Services (Hampshire Division) Ltd.) is shown as Table 1. The data for 1988 to 1990 are actual figures. Forecasts for all components are based on factors and premises accepted by Southern Region NRA (e.g. 1% p.a. growth in domestic unmetered demand, all new domestic population entered into the metered domestic category, leakage targets met by 1996). The reduction in unaccounted-for water (UFW), reflecting the expected attainment of leakage targets by 1996, is an important feature of the forecast, given the NRA's insistence that resource savings be made via leakage control before they would wish to sanction the development of new resources. To reflect the effect of the reduction in UFW, the peak to average factor is increased by 0.25% per year to the target year of 1995/6, and by 0.04% p.a. thereafter.

The demand forecast as presented may ultimately prove to be conservative, under the influence of two 'lurking variables'. Climate change is one grey influence. The high peak to average factors recorded

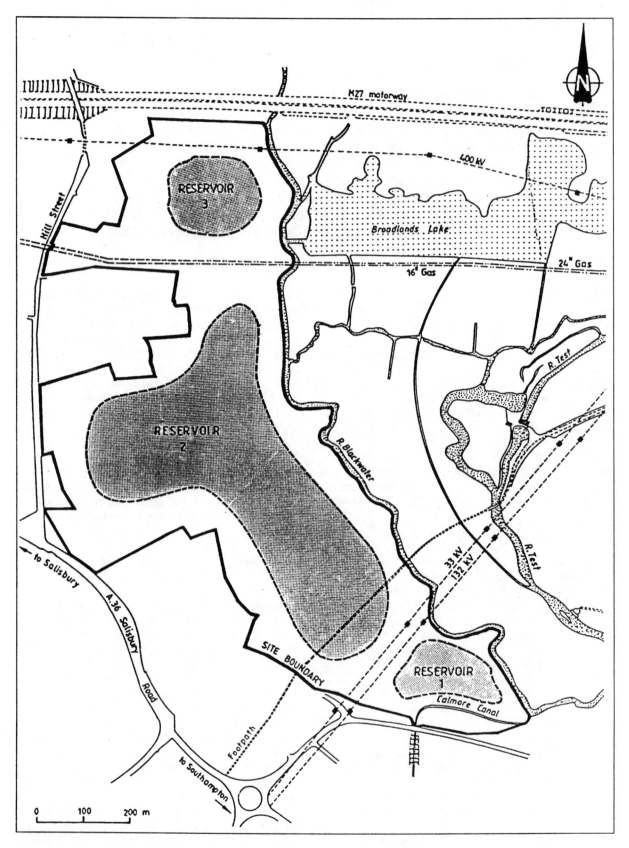

Figure 1   Location map showing preliminary layout of the Testwood Lakes

Table 1   Component-based single line demand forecast table for the Hampshire South Water Supply Area, excluding the Testwood Lakes

HAMPSHIRE SOUTH SINGLE LINE DEMAND FORECAST (EXCLUDING TESTWOOD LAKES)

Component:	1.1	1.2	1.3	2.1	2.2	2.3	2.4	3.1	3.2	3.3	3.4	3.5	4.1	4.2	5.1	5.2	5.3	6.1	6.2	7.1	7.2
	POPULATION			UNMETERED ACCOUNTED FOR				METERED ACCOUNTED FOR					UNACCOUNTED FOR		TOTAL DEMANDS			RESOURCES		RELIABILITY FACTOR	
YEAR	TOTAL POP 000s	UM POP 000s	METERED POP 000s	Domestic pcc l/h/d	DOMESTIC TOTAL Ml/d	COMM TOTAL Ml/d	TOTAL UM Ml/d	Metered pre-88 Ml/d	Metered post-88 l/h/d	DOMESTIC TOTAL Ml/d	COMM/IND TOTAL Ml/d	TOTAL METERED Ml/d	Per-cap UFW l/h/d	TOTAL UFW Ml/d	AVERAGE PWS Ml/d	Peak/Av Factor	PEAK PWS Ml/d	PDO Ml/d	ADO Ml/d	AVERAGE DEMAND	PEAK DEMAND
1988	454.500	442.100	12.400	136.300	60.258	2.200	62.458	4.800	0.000	4.800	38.000	42.800	111.100	50.495	155.753	1.210	188.461	211.100	196.200	1.260	1.120
1989	454.500	442.100	12.400	156.400	69.144	2.200	71.344	5.508	0.000	5.508	38.380	43.888	94.400	42.905	158.137	1.300	205.578	211.100	196.200	1.241	1.027
1990	463.700	451.200	12.500	157.800	71.199	2.300	73.499	5.557	0.015	5.572	38.664	44.236	84.500	39.183	156.918	1.280	200.855	211.100	196.200	1.250	1.051
1991	473.000	451.200	21.800	137.300	61.950	2.300	64.250	4.835	1.226	6.061	39.050	45.112	81.400	38.502	147.864	1.230	181.872	231.100	216.200	1.462	1.271
1992	478.000	451.200	26.800	138.673	62.569	2.300	64.869	4.884	1.897	6.781	39.441	46.222	78.880	37.705	148.795	1.230	183.018	231.100	216.200	1.453	1.263
1993	483.000	451.200	31.800	140.060	63.195	2.300	65.495	4.932	2.581	7.514	39.835	47.349	76.360	36.882	149.726	1.230	184.163	231.100	216.200	1.444	1.255
1994	488.000	451.200	36.800	141.460	63.827	2.300	66.127	4.982	3.279	8.261	40.234	48.494	73.840	36.034	150.655	1.230	185.306	231.100	216.200	1.435	1.247
1995	493.000	451.200	41.800	142.875	64.465	2.300	66.765	5.032	3.990	9.022	40.636	49.658	71.320	35.161	151.584	1.230	186.448	226.100	211.200	1.393	1.213
1996	498.000	451.200	46.800	144.304	65.110	2.300	67.410	5.082	4.716	9.798	41.042	50.840	68.800	34.262	152.512	1.230	187.590	222.700	207.800	1.363	1.187
1997	498.480	451.200	47.280	145.747	65.761	2.300	68.061	5.133	4.829	9.962	41.453	51.415	68.800	34.295	153.771	1.230	189.139	222.700	207.800	1.351	1.177
1998	498.960	451.200	47.760	147.204	66.419	2.300	68.719	5.184	4.945	10.129	41.867	51.996	68.800	34.328	155.043	1.230	190.703	222.700	207.800	1.340	1.168
1999	499.440	451.200	48.240	148.676	67.083	2.300	69.383	5.236	5.062	10.298	42.286	52.584	68.800	34.361	156.328	1.230	192.284	222.700	207.800	1.329	1.158
2000	499.920	451.200	48.720	150.163	67.754	2.300	70.054	5.288	5.181	10.469	42.709	53.178	68.800	34.394	157.626	1.230	193.880	213.600	198.700	1.261	1.102
2001	500.400	451.200	49.200	151.665	68.431	2.300	70.731	5.341	5.302	10.643	43.136	53.779	68.800	34.428	158.938	1.230	195.494	213.600	198.700	1.250	1.093
2002	501.520	451.200	50.320	153.181	69.115	2.300	71.415	5.394	5.518	10.913	43.567	54.480	68.800	34.505	160.400	1.230	197.292	213.600	198.700	1.239	1.083
2003	502.640	451.200	51.440	154.713	69.807	2.300	72.107	5.448	5.738	11.186	44.003	55.189	68.800	34.582	161.878	1.230	199.109	213.600	198.700	1.227	1.073
2004	503.760	451.200	52.560	156.260	70.505	2.300	72.805	5.503	5.962	11.465	44.443	55.908	68.800	34.659	163.371	1.230	200.946	213.600	198.700	1.216	1.063
2005	504.880	451.200	53.680	157.823	71.210	2.300	73.510	5.558	6.189	11.747	44.887	56.635	68.800	34.736	164.880	1.230	202.802	213.600	198.700	1.205	1.053
2006	506.000	451.200	54.800	159.401	71.922	2.300	74.222	5.614	6.421	12.034	45.336	57.371	68.800	34.813	166.405	1.230	204.678	213.600	198.700	1.194	1.044
2007	507.120	451.200	55.920	160.995	72.641	2.300	74.941	5.670	6.656	12.326	45.790	58.116	68.800	34.890	167.946	1.230	206.574	213.600	198.700	1.183	1.034
2008	508.240	451.200	57.040	162.605	73.367	2.300	75.667	5.726	6.896	12.622	46.248	58.870	68.800	34.967	169.504	1.230	208.490	213.600	198.700	1.172	1.025
2009	509.360	451.200	58.160	164.231	74.101	2.300	76.401	5.784	7.139	12.923	46.710	59.633	68.800	35.044	171.078	1.230	210.426	213.600	198.700	1.161	1.015
2010	510.480	451.200	59.280	165.873	74.842	2.300	77.142	5.841	7.387	13.229	47.177	60.406	68.800	35.121	172.669	1.230	212.383	213.600	198.700	1.151	1.006
2011	511.600	451.200	60.400	167.532	75.590	2.300	77.890	5.900	7.639	13.539	47.649	61.188	68.800	35.198	174.277	1.230	214.361	213.600	198.700	1.140	0.996

NEW RESOURCES	PDO	ADO
Present	248.800	233.900
ESSO	-22.700	-22.700
IOW Ind	-15.000	-15.000
New HL Pump	25.000	25.000
Ott > Winch link	-5.000	-5.000
Winch > And link	-5.000	-5.000
Industrial increase	-9.100	-9.100

POTABLE TOTALS PDO	ADO	YEAR
211.100	196.200	1990
236.100	221.200	1990
221.100	206.200	1990
231.100	216.200	1991
226.100	211.200	1995
222.700	207.800	1996

during 1989 and 1990 may auger the need for a higher ratio than that currently assumed, to reflect a possible growth in the summer season peakiness of demand associated with the warmer, drier summer scenarios of IPCC and other climate change predictions. The imminent replacement of the rating-based system of water charging is the other significant looming effect. The adoption of household metering with differential tariff structures may be expected to affect the demand for water in a more complex manner than the '10% drop followed by gradual recovery to the old equilibrium' response identified in the initial results from the national metering trials currently being conducted. The demand forecast is thus best seen as a current 'best bet' which needs frequent revision.

The adequacy of existing and planned resources is built into the demand forecast in terms of assessed Peak Drought Output (PDO) and Annual Drought Output (ADO) calculations based on all available sources. The PDO defines output from sources in a 2% drought year at the time of peak demand (typically July), whilst the ADO defines the output of the source at a time of average demand and minimum resources (typically September); the PDO is thus always greater than the ADO. The final two columns of the forecast table indicate the reliability of resources in meeting demands. A reliability factor of 1.0 defines the threshold of resource inadequacy. It can be seen that South Hampshire's resources are able to meet average demand throughout the planning horizon (to 2011); but that they are likely to be unable, as they stand, to meet anticipated peak demand from 2009 onwards. The Testwood Lakes Scheme is seen as a means of rectifying this shortfall.

(ii) Simulation modelling: the reliable yield of the Testwood Lakes

Analysis of the (extended) flow records of the Blackwater and Test indicates that even in a 2% design drought year, there are few days when flows are so low that the downstream MRF restricts abstraction at the Testwood PWS intake to less than the 136 Ml/d licence figure. The PDO of the source is thus 136 Ml/d. The ADO of the source was assessed in relation to the pattern of demand from its main users: PWS demand to the Isle of Wight, the industrial supply to ESSO at Fawley, and the PWS demand of the Hampshire South area. Various plausible profiles of demand from these end-users were explored. The most realistic combined profile of demand upon the source is shown in Figure 2 (upper diagram); the corresponding ADO of the source is 108 Ml d⁻¹.

Given development of reservoirs with sufficient storage, the ADO may evidently be increased to 136 Ml d⁻¹. Simulations of the yield which may be obtained with reservoir storage available suggest that the yield of the source would be increased by 12.3 Ml d⁻¹ ADO and 14.7 Ml d⁻¹ PDO with a reservoir of 1000 Ml usable storage (Table 2); the

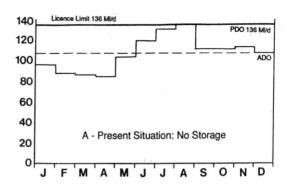

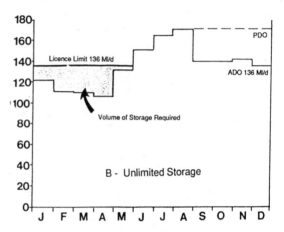

Figure 2 Present and potential yields from Testwood: the top diagram illustrates how the present PDO is licence-restricted and the present ADO is demand-controlled; the lower diagram shows how storage could raise ADO to the licence limit and increase PDO to a level controlled by the seasonal demand profile.

potential yield benefit of the scheme is thus restricted by a reservoir of this limited capacity. Further simulations using unlimited storage volumes suggest that the optimum usable storage for the scheme lies in the range 2000 Ml to 2500 Ml. This would provide an increase in yield of about 21 Ml d⁻¹ in the ADO (i.e to the 136 Ml d⁻¹ licence limit) and 25 Ml d⁻¹ in the PDO (Figure 2, lower diagram).

(iii) River modelling: implications for flood flows and levels in the Blackwater-Test valley

The micro-FLUCOMP river modelling package (Hydraulics Research Ltd.) was used to assess the likely flood flow and level consequences of the loss of floodplain associated with the development of the Testwood Lakes. FLUCOMP is a one-dimensional model for single channel systems, so certain simplifying assumptions were required. The River Blackwater was treated as a main channel receiving the Calmore Canal and the River Test as tributaries. Overbank flows from the Blackwater are allowed to pass over the Test as dictated by flood stage by assuming bankfull flow in the Test. These assumptions are considered to be reasonable in the light of

Table 2 Results from yield simulations with zero storage, 1000 Ml storage and unlimited storage available

Run No	IOW Supply	Ind Supply	Hants Supply	W'out Storage ADO	PDO	1000 Ml Storage ADO	PDO	Net Increase ADO	PDO	Res Storage	Unlim Storage ADO	PDO	Net Increase ADO	PDO
111	L	L	L	104.5	115.9	116.7	129.6	12.2	13.7	1465	119.7	132.8	15.2	16.9
112	L	L	M	99.0	117.8	112.2	133.5	13.2	15.7	2173	119.7	132.8	15.2	16.9
113	L	L	H	93.0	117.1	106.5	134.2	13.5	17.1	2638	119.6	150.6	26.6	33.5
121	L	M	L	94.9	105.3	106.3	117.9	11.4	12.6	1704	110.6	122.8	15.7	17.5
122	L	M	M	90.7	107.9	102.2	121.7	11.5	13.8	2364	110.4	131.3	19.7	23.4
123	L	M	H	83.3	105.0	97.5	122.8	14.2	17.8	2701	110.5	139.2	27.2	34.2
131	L	H	L	87.8	97.4	98.5	109.3	10.7	11.9	1888	103.9	115.3	16.1	17.9
132	L	H	M	84.6	100.6	94.7	112.8	10.1	12.2	2506	103.6	123.3	19.0	22.7
133	L	H	H	76.3	96.1	90.7	114.3	14.4	18.2	2767	103.8	130.8	27.5	34.7
211	H	L	L	100.8	111.9	113.3	125.8	12.5	13.9	1510	116.4	129.2	15.6	17.3
212	H	L	M	95.9	114.1	108.9	129.6	13.0	15.5	2206	116.2	138.3	20.3	24.2
213	H	L	H	90.5	114.0	103.5	130.4	13.0	16.4	2584	116.3	146.6	25.8	32.6
221	H	M	L	91.2	101.2	103.0	114.3	11.8	13.1	1758	107.3	119.2	16.1	18.0
222	H	M	M	87.6	104.3	99.1	118.9	11.5	13.6	2398	107.1	127.5	19.5	23.2
223	H	M	H	80.9	101.9	94.4	119.0	13.5	17.1	2672	107.3	135.1	26.4	33.2
231	H	H	L	84.1	93.3	95.2	105.7	11.1	12.4	1942	100.6	111.7	16.5	18.4
232	H	H	M	81.2	96.6	91.6	109.0	10.4	12.4	2539	100.4	119.5	19.2	22.9
233	H	H	H	73.7	92.9	87.7	110.5	14.0	17.6	2737	100.5	126.7	26.8	33.8
	AVERAGE			88.9	105.2			12.3	14.7				20.8	24.9

the flood flow behaviour of the main rivers. The River Blackwater has a flashy regime (Base Flow Index (BFI)=0.41), and floods its east and west floodplains in most years. The Test, by contrast, is dominantly groundwater-driven (BFI= 0.94) and has a relatively stable flow regime, with a seasonal range of only a metre or so and a damped response to storm events; some rapid runoff derives from the tertiaries of the River Dun basin, but overbank flows from the Test at Testwood are uncommon. The assumption that flooding of the Blackwater-Test valley is largely a River Blackwater phenomenon is thus considered to be realistic, and taking bankfull flows in the Test during peak flows in the Blackwater may be regarded as a defining a 'worst case situation' (examination of flow records suggest that the Dun quickflows lag behind the Blackwater flows by 2 to 6h, but that the Test remains in bank at times of Blackwater flooding).

A FLUCOMP model of the Blackwater-Test valley incorporating 16 floodplain/channel cross sections in the reach downstream of the M27 motorway (chainage 3113m) to immediately upstream of the tidal limit at Testwood Mill (chainage 1m) was constructed. The absence of out-of-bank stage readings for locations upstream and downstream of the two footbridges crossing the Blackwater and the single span service road bridge crossing the Test meant that the bridges could not be incorporated into the model; afflux imparted by all three structures is likely to be negligible, so this limitation is not considered to be significant. Roughness values for the channel (n=0.045) and floodplain (n=0.099) elements were derived from out-of-bank measurements previously made by Hydraulics Research Ltd (Ramsbottom, 1989). Stage-discharge readings from the Blackwater at Nutsey Bridge (chainage 1520m) were used to verify the model; measured and simulated water levels matched to within 5%.

Floodwater levels were computed for flood discharge events with return periods of 2.33, 5, 10, 20, 50 and 100 years. An initial set of simulations determined the existing (pre-works) flood level conditions for the reach. Post-works simulations were thereafter computed by excluding the right floodplain of the Blackwater in the reach between chainages 1520m to 3113m, save for an 8m corridor alongside the river. Measured peak flow data (Blackwater at Ower, Test at Broadlands, Testwood) were judged to be insufficient for flood modelling purposes, so flood hydrographs for each of the nominated design events were generated with FSSR16 UH methods (using the micro-FSR package) for both the Blackwater (taking a 75% winter profile) and the Calmore Canal (taking a 50% summer profile, since 35% of the catchment is urbanised). The results (Figure 3) show that Calmore floods are not superimposed on Blackwater floods. The attenuation rate parameter of all Blackwater design floods was calculated to be small (<< 2.0×10^{-6}), so steady flow modelling could be used to calculate maximum flood levels (using FLUCOMP's backwater analysis mode) for each design flood. Table 3 summarises the combinations of discharges used in the modelling. The standard design flows combine peak flows in the Blackwater, post-peak baseflows in the Calmore Canal and bankfull flows in the Test.

Variants based on peak flows in the Calmore Canal and mean and peak flows in the Test are also examined (the mean, bankfull and peak flows for the Test at Testwood were calculated from Broadlands flows adjusted to account for downstream abstractions and diversions). A design stage of 2.8 m AOD at Testwood Mill was taken as a fixed downstream control for all simulations (as agreed with Southern Region NRA).

Results from the pre-works and post-works steady flow simulations are summarised in Table 4. It can be seen that the exclusion of the designated area of Blackwater floodplain is predicted to lead to a maximum increase in flood levels elsewhere in the Test valley of 0.05m. An areal illustration of present-day flood levels is shown in Figure 4; flood limits to the west of the Test above the Test-Blackwater confluence are based on accurate EDM surveys of the area, but those beyond this area are based on large scale OS maps and must thus be regarded as approximate. It would appear that the right floodplain of the Blackwater acts as a dead storage element in the system, conveying little overbank flow. The development of the Testwood Lakes may thus be regarded as having no significant flood level implications.

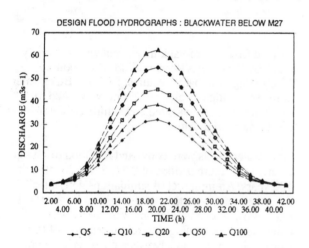

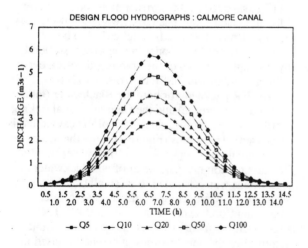

Figure 3   Design flood hydrographs for the River Blackwater and the Calmore Canal

Engineering studies

(i) Geological studies

A ground investigation contract was carried out to gain information on soil types, to assess the quantities and extent of gravel and peat deposits and to obtain soil parameters to permit outline design of excavation slopes and embankment cross sections. The typical geology of the site along the flood plain is as follows:

Depth to base (m)	Geology
0.1 - 0.7	Topsoil
0.7 - 4.4	Soft-firm brown CLAY and brown/black clayey PEAT and brown PEAT-ALLUVIUM
4.0 - 6.8	Medium dense-dense grey brown fine to coarse subrounded to subangular flint GRAVEL with occasional cobbles - ALLUVIUM
>15	Firm-stiff grey silty CLAY and dense grey fine-medium SAND - BRACKLESHAM BEDS

(ii) Layout of the reservoirs

The flexibility for different layouts for a series of reservoirs was severely constrained by two factors: one, that parts of the site were extremely narrow; two, that major services crossed the site and would be very costly to divert. The range of raw water storage capacity for each reservoir was assessed based on varying depth of excavation and height of embankment above original ground level. The preliminary calculations showed that the maximum water storage which could be achieved on the site was approximately 3000 Ml. The bottom 1m depth of water was excluded from the usable storage calculation on the basis that to extract it would be impracticable and undesirable. The final proposal excluded reservoir development on areas of important ecological interest, avoided felling of high quality trees around the site periphery, took account of the ground investigation results and used flatter outer embankment sideslopes to create a more acceptable land form. These factors reduced the maximum usable storage to around 2000 Ml.

(iii) Outline engineering design

The outline engineering design of the scheme considered the following aspects:

1. Construction of water-retaining embankments and/or cut-offs to control seepage from the reservoirs and to restrict inflow from groundwater. The typical embankment would use fill material from excavated alluvial deposits and from bedrock below the gravels. A bentonite cut-off trench could be constructed prior to gravel extraction which would minimise drawdown of

Table 3 Steady flow discharges used for backwater analysis in FLUCOMP1

Design Event	Blackwater m^3s^{-1}		Calmore m^3s^{-1}		Test m^3s^{-1}		Total m^3s^{-1}
Q2.33-	Q_p	24.8	Q	0.08	Q	11.3	36.22
Q2.33	Q_p	24.8	Q	0.08	Q_b	22.0	46.89
Q5	Q_p	32.16	Q	0.08	Q_b	22.0	54.24
Q5+	Q_p	32.16	Q_p	2.81	Q_b	22.0	56.97
Q10	Q_p	38.80	Q	0.08	Q_b	22.0	60.88
Q20	Q_p	45.36	Q	0.08	Q_b	22.0	67.44
Q50	Q_p	54.90	Q	0.08	Q_b	22.0	76.98
Q100	Q_p	62.54	Q	0.08	Q_b	22.0	84.62
Q100+	Q_p	62.54	Q_p	5.76	Q_p	40.0	108.26

Q_p denotes a peak flow
Q_b denotes a bankfull flow
Q   denotes a mean flow

the surrounding groundwater table. Alternatively a recharge trench would be excavated to return water pumped from the pits to the aquifer.

2. Transfer of raw water from the River Test to the lakes. Data on the existing pumping plant have indicated that flows up to the abstraction licence of 136 Ml d⁻¹ can be transferred to the lakes with a suitably-sized delivery main.

3. Transfer of raw water from the lakes to the water supply works. This will be achieved by gravity and/or pumping and could be to a number of locations within the treatment works.

4. Inlet, draw-off and overflow structures from each lake. The draw-off arrangements from the lakes could either use a draw-off tower or pipelines at different levels to permit selection of the best quality water. However, with the prime purpose of the lakes being to provide an emergency storage facility, it was considered more appropriate to provide mixing facilities.

5. Access roads, accommodation works and other ancillaries for gravel extraction, recreational activities and nature conservation. The access road for construction activities is proposed to be off Brunel Road to the Industrial Estate, although a secondary access to the main A36 is being discussed with the Highway Authority.

The design aspects of the scheme are now being pursued in greater detail as the post-feasibility stage proceeds.

Environmental assessment

The aims of the environmental appraisal were to study the existing site, establish its value and the range of species present and then to assess the impact of development proposals. A broad range of botanical species was identified together with invertebrates and birds. The site is recorded on the Agricultural Land Classification map 1971 as almost exclusively Grade 4 with a small patch of Grade 3. Loss of this land to agriculture is, therefore, not regarded as being of concern. The County Sites and Monuments Record showed no finds on the site itself. A full archaeological evaluation is however proposed. The information provided by the NRA confirmed that the River Blackwater contained mixed coarse fish and was used by sea trout but not salmon. The River Test is an important trout fishery.

Environmental assessment of the Testwood Lakes Scheme has identified the following positive impacts:
   a) The proposals would offer a more assured future for the area in conservation terms.
   b) The scheme proposed retention and management of the most important meadows on the site, most of the existing woodland, the Blackwater corridor and the majority of hedgerows.
   c) A conservation corridor would be established across the site from west to east including new woodland which would permit a wildlife link from the Test Valley to the Hill Street area.

The negative impacts identifed are:
   a) loss of the grassland which covers most of the existing site;
   b) loss of ditches and associated vegetation;
   c) loss of some alder woodland and hedgerows.

Table 4   Results from backwater analysis of flood flow levels. The tables show the predicted maximum water level along the River Blackwater upstream from Testwood Mill (chainage 1m) to the M27 motorway (above chainage 3113m).

TESTWOOD LAKES FLUCOMP MODEL RESULTS

MAXIMUM FLOODWATER LEVEL FOR DESIGN FLOOD OF STATED RETURN PERIOD (years):

CHAINAGE m	BANK HT mAOD	Q2.33- mAOD	Q2.33 mAOD	Q5 mAOD	Q5+ mAOD	Q10 mAOD	Q20 mAOD	Q50 mAOD	Q100 mAOD	Q100+ mAOD
(A) CURRENT (PRE-WORKS) SITUATION										
1	2.8	2.8	2.8	2.8	2.8	2.8	2.8	2.8	2.8	2.8
100	2.87	2.87	2.917	2.955	2.971	2.995	3.039	3.109	3.171	3.379
300	3.03	2.991	3.098	3.179	3.21	3.254	3.316	3.412	3.492	3.683
400	3.11	3.044	3.17	3.264	3.299	3.342	3.408	3.513	3.585	3.774
650	3.26	3.162	3.328	3.438	3.475	3.526	3.613	3.71	3.79	3.974
900	3.27	3.265	3.456	3.578	3.615	3.666	3.76	3.852	3.93	4.107
1100	3.43	3.338	3.542	3.666	3.707	3.757	3.849	3.944	4.02	4.197
1200	3.47	3.373	3.584	3.711	3.751	3.802	3.894	3.989	4.066	4.244
1325	3.12	3.491	3.677	3.8	3.841	3.89	3.978	4.075	4.149	4.325
1520	2.86	3.71	3.766	3.878	3.914	3.963	4.043	4.136	4.207	4.36
1603	3.37	3.735	3.785	3.894	3.93	3.979	4.057	4.15	4.22	4.369
2005	3.7	3.929	3.945	4.029	4.047	4.102	4.164	4.246	4.309	4.418
2333	4.1	4.124	4.123	4.195	4.2	4.252	4.301	4.372	4.423	4.489
2611	4.232	4.287	4.287	4.364	4.365	4.413	4.459	4.525	4.57	4.602
2853	4.74	4.467	4.467	4.538	4.538	4.589	4.634	4.694	4.737	4.75
3113	5.02	4.586	4.586	4.647	4.647	4.701	4.745	4.799	4.84	4.846
(B) AFTER RESERVOIR DEVELOPMENT (POST-WORKS SITUATION)										
1	2.8	2.8	2.8	2.8	2.8	2.8	2.8	2.8	2.8	2.8
100	2.87	2.87	2.917	2.955	2.971	2.995	3.039	3.109	3.171	3.379
300	3.03	2.991	3.098	3.179	3.21	3.254	3.316	3.412	3.492	3.683
400	3.11	3.044	3.17	3.264	3.299	3.342	3.408	3.513	3.585	3.774
650	3.26	3.162	3.328	3.438	3.475	3.526	3.613	3.71	3.79	3.974
900	3.27	3.265	3.456	3.578	3.615	3.666	3.76	3.852	3.93	4.107
1100	3.43	3.338	3.542	3.666	3.707	3.757	3.849	3.944	4.02	4.197
1200	3.47	3.373	3.584	3.711	3.751	3.802	3.894	3.989	4.066	4.244
1325	3.12	3.491	3.677	3.8	3.841	3.89	3.978	4.075	4.149	4.325
1520	2.86	3.71	3.766	3.877	3.914	3.963	4.042	4.136	4.207	4.36
1603	3.37	3.737	3.787	3.896	3.932	3.981	4.059	4.152	4.222	4.37
2005	3.7	3.958	3.973	4.064	4.08	4.136	4.2	4.283	4.345	4.442
2333	4.1	4.148	4.149	4.228	4.233	4.288	4.342	4.416	4.469	4.526
2611	4.232	4.297	4.298	4.374	4.376	4.429	4.48	4.548	4.597	4.629
2853	4.74	4.474	4.474	4.547	4.548	4.603	4.65	4.713	4.76	4.775
3113	5.02	4.597	4.597	4.664	4.664	4.722	4.765	4.825	4.87	4.877
(C) DIFFERENCES IN FLOODWATER LEVEL (m), POST-WORKS VS PRE-WORKS SITUATIONS										
1	2.8	0	0	0	0	0	0	0	0	0
100	2.87	0	0	0	0	0	0	0	0	0
300	3.03	0	0	0	0	0	0	0	0	0
400	3.11	0	0	0	0	0	0	0	0	0
650	3.26	0	0	0	0	0	0	0	0	0
900	3.27	0	0	0	0	0	0	0	0	0
1100	3.43	0	0	0	0	0	0	0	0	0
1200	3.47	0	0	0	0	0	0	0	0	0
1325	3.12	0	0	0	0	0	0	0	0	0
1520	2.86	0	0	-0.001	0	0	-0.001	0	0	0
1603	3.37	0.002	0.002	0.002	0.002	0.002	0.002	0.002	0.002	0.001
2005	3.7	0.029	0.028	0.035	0.033	0.034	0.036	0.037	0.036	0.024
2333	4.1	0.024	0.026	0.033	0.033	0.036	0.041	0.044	0.046	0.037
2611	4.232	0.01	0.011	0.01	0.011	0.016	0.021	0.023	0.027	0.027
2853	4.74	0.007	0.007	0.009	0.01	0.014	0.016	0.019	0.023	0.025
3113	5.02	0.011	0.011	0.017	0.017	0.021	0.02	0.026	0.03	0.031
MAX DIFF=		0.029	0.028	0.035	0.033	0.036	0.041	0.044	0.046	0.037

The cost of Scheme

The budget estimate for the scheme has indicated that a cost in excess of £15 million is likely for the total implementation of the lakes scheme over a ten-year period. However, this figure will be offset by the value of the gravel which will be sold for an estimated £4 to 5 million. Subject to permission

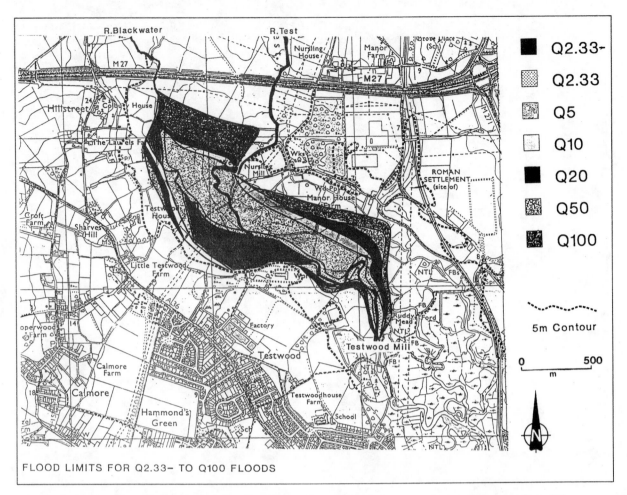

Figure 4 *Design flood limits across the Blackwater-Test valley in its present state. The removal of the western floodplain of the River Blackwater would raise flood levels by a maximum of 5 cm.*

being granted, it is intended that work on site will commence early in 1992.

Liaison with Interested Parties

A continuous dialogue has taken place with Local Planning Authorities, both at District and County level, with the NRA and conservation bodies such as the Nature Conservancy Council and the Hampshire and Isle of Wight Naturalists Trust, and also with local people who will be most closely affected by the proposals.

Conclusions

The Testwood Lakes scheme has brought together many professional disciplines. The different interests have combined to undertake a major study, and the post-feasibility work now taking place will culminate in the submission of Planning Applications in June 1991. Alongside the technical work, Southern Water Services has been anxious to keep the public informed, and has done this on a pro-active basis. Whilst the scheme itself is needed for water supply purposes, it is intended that a recreational facility will be created and enjoyed by local people.

Acknowledgements

The demand forecast presented here is by D.M. Bates (Southern Water Services (Hampshire Division) Ltd); earlier forecasts were developed by Southern Science Ltd. The yield simulation modelling was undertaken by D.M. Giles (Southern Science Ltd). Rofe, Kennard and Lapworth coordinated the feasibility study programme; information taken from the Feasibility Study Report which they submitted to Southern Water Services in October 1990 is gratefully acknowledged.

References

Herbert Lapworth and Partners, 1965. Preliminary report to Portsmouth Water Company and Southampton Corporation Waterworks on potential reservoir sites in South Hampshire.

Mander, Raikes & Marshall, 1980. Reservoir investigation - Hampshire. Report on engineering studies.

Ramsbottom, D.M. 1989. Flood discharge assessment - interim report. Hydraulics Research Report SR195, Hydraulics Research Ltd., Wallingford.

Session 2

Low Flow Management

Optimisation of system demand by Linear Programming and the assessment of subsequent reliability (based on the Umgeni system)

A.J.Tollow

Abstract

Linear Programming is applied to optimise the operation of reservoirs in series. Included is an iterative process which circumvents the difficulty associated with unexpected overflows. The "cost function" used is of the "*a priori*" type. One drawback is that it requires a check calibration. The value so derived may also be used to determine the severity of the reduction in consumption required during periods of prolonged low flows. An index of assessment, based on the principle of system reliability, is required to assist in the selection process. This takes the form of a "credibility" factor which is then used to calculate a "credibility index". The "index" determines the success or failure of any particular operating policy. The need for further applications of different forms of optimisation is reduced. The optimisation routine was tested out using 10 sets of 100 years of generated data for the Umgeni system. The results were compared with simulation, without optimisation, using the same data sets. A matrix of "credibility factors" were derived to calculate the "credibility index".

Introduction

The surface water reserves of the Durban-Pietermaritzburg region of sub-tropical Natal, located on the western fringe of the Indian Ocean have recently been enhanced by the construction of a new reservoir, the Inanda Dam. Inter-basin transfer of water is possible from the Mooi River to the Midmar reservoir on the Upper Umgeni River. Midmar is one of three major reservoirs in series, the other two being Albert Falls and Inanda. An assessment of the yields of the component parts of the system was made (Tollow, 1989) and a simulation model to test operating rules was written and tested. As a result further optimisation of the operation of the system was considered desirable and a Linear Programming option was inserted into the simulation model.

Linear Programming is usually used for the overall planning and scheduling of water resources projects to meet selected demand scenarios, such as that outlined in Loucks *et al.*(1981). Aspects of Linear Programming have been presented, in a general overview of reservoir management and operations, by Yeh (1985). Of those quoted, Windsor (1973) developed a methodology employing a recursive

Linear Programme as the method of optimisation of a multi-reservoir flood control system, and Dalgli and Miles (1980) proposed an alternative approach called "adaptive planning". The latter was a device used to exploit the advantages of a Linear Programme while modelling a complex system of reservoirs which had non-linear constraints. Neither approach could be applied directly to the Umgeni system. However, Fletcher (1981) presented Linear Programming in non-economic terminology. From this alternative approach a possible solution to the derivation of cost functions appeared feasible. The model used the National Algorithms Library (NAG).

The objectives and objective functions

The initial objectives were to:
    1) minimize the use of the transfer facility;
    2) minimize reductions in demand;
    3) minimize reservoir emptiness;
    4) minimize spills, and
    5) minimize water treatment costs.

Within the system there were additional objectives, such as to:
    i) maximize the use of the lowest reservoir;

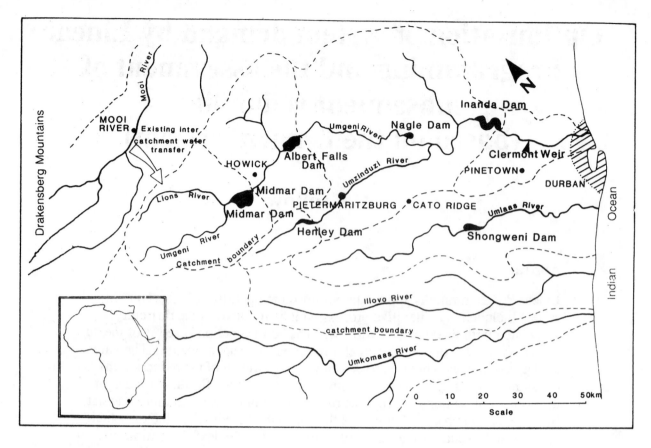

Figure 1 Location plan of the region

ii) minimize the use of the pumped abstraction from the Umgeni;
iii) maintain a minimum quantity in store to meet the demand during periods of reduced inflow;
iv) meet a minimum demand from each reservoir without exceeding the permissible maximum demand from any other reservoir.

The initial objective function is:

$$\text{Minimize}(cSp + cD + cR_D + cT_{RM}) =$$

$$(\sum_{i=1}^{n} c_i D_i + \sum_{i=1}^{n} c_i Sp_i + \sum_{i=1}^{n} c_i R_{Di} + \sum_{i=1}^{n} c_i T_{RMi}) \quad (1)$$

where: c = the "cost function"
Sp = the spills from the system of reservoirs
D = the demand from the resource
R_D = the reduction in demand (as a result of insufficient water in the system)
T_{RM} = is the transfer of water over the catchment boundary
n = the number of demand centres.

However, if "control band" concepts (Tollow, 1988) are used with the method, the transfer of water from one catchment to another, which would require pumping, can be limited. A need for the operation of the transfer scheme was determined by simulating demand patterns for 10 sets of 100 years of inflow data, generated from 55 years of original data.

The reduction in demand can be estimated in a similar manner but an additional step is needed in the simulation programme. This may either be based on a forecasting procedure, in which the demand is reduced in a series of steps according to the water remaining in store at any one time, or be based on a "semi-hindsight" approach in which the inflows are taken into account. Again the reliability of the system is assessed on the number of times any restriction is imposed and the severity of that restriction. The results from this concept of reliability are discussed in a later section.

Spills are intermittent and may be considered in two sections:
1) those lost from the system - spills from the lowest reservoir - and
2) within system spills - that is an upper reservoir filling a lower reservoir.

The latter is not a system loss but only a local reservoir loss. By considering the whole system and the individual parts to the system it is possible to reduce the impact of "spills".

Setting the constraints and boundaries

The boundaries and constraints of the system are now more readily defined in terms of one principal function, in this case the demand "D". Boundaries and constraints were derived. The system used to test the linear programming had three main demand centres. It is possible for an upper demand centre to supply a lower centre under gravity but only limited pumping capacity exists to permit a lower centre to supply an upper demand area. Each of the demand centres has a finite treatment capacity so that it is not possible for the uppermost demand centre to supply the whole region. Upper and lower bounds are needed for each demand centre and each reservoir.

The reservoirs are linked in both space and time by the continuity equation which also governs the whole system. At any one time "i" the change in storage may be stated as

$$Cs_i = I_i + T_{Ri} - D_i - R_i - E_i - Sp_i \qquad (2)$$

where

Cs = change in storage
I = uncontrolled inflow
T_R = regulated inflow or transfer to the reservoir
D = the demand from the reservoir
R = controlled reservoir release downstream
E = evaporative losses from the reservoir
Sp = uncontrolled spill from the reservoir.

By rearranging the equations in a suitable form it is possible to define limits and constraints for the demand "D". For example:

$$D_i = F_i + S_i + T_{Ri} - S_{i-1} - Sp_i \qquad (3)$$

where F = the net local inflow (inflow minus local losses, such as evaporation)

When no spills occur the upper limit for the demand may be set to the maximum reservoir capacity. When spills occur this may be modified accordingly.

The "cost functions"

In the system being studied tentative cost functions were derived and assigned numerical values which were expressed as integers. These were based on:
  1) the ratio of the reservoir capacity to catchment mean annual runoff;
  2) an assessment of water quality based on the location of the reservoir;
  3) the ability to supply the total area in relation to the overall capacity of the system; and
  4) maximizing the use of water from the lowest reservoir of the system to minimize the effect of spills from the system.

For large systems the selected functions could also be subject to optimisation procedures. For smaller systems a check using simulation is all that is required. The latter method using short runs of flow data was used and suitable values were derived.

Selecting the Linear Programming routine

The choice of routine was limited to those procedures available in the NAG Library (1988) in section E04 -

Minimizing or Maximizing a Function. These included non-linear and integer programming and routines which could be extended to encompass quadratic programming. Three Linear Programming routines were selected, E04MBF, E04NAF, and E04NCF. E04MBF was selected for the first stage to determine how a linear optimisation would perform. The results were checked by the second and third routines E04NAF and E04NCF using their linear forms. The results of the optimisation were compared with those of a simulation programme for the same system.

The optimisation programme

The optimisation programme was developed to test the feasibility of using Linear Programming. Although 10 sets of 100 years of monthly data were available only annual time steps were used in the optimisation process. The limited inter-basin transfer was taken into account when converting the monthly data to the annual values. The use of a "control band" approach (Tollow, 1988) would assist in countering any error due to an over- or under-estimation of the available water.

As part of an iteration process, the overall system demand may be reduced by up to 50% before optimising the demand from the individual reservoirs using Linear Programming. If there are spills from reservoirs further iterations may be introduced to obtain the best approximation. Once the demand is apportioned the result is tested in a simulation programme. As part of the simulation the effect of the interbasin transfer facility is incorporated. Provision is made to use an average of the monthly "control bands".

Results of the optimisation procedure

An example of the distribution of the demand between three reservoirs is shown in Figure 2. The comparison of the optimisation programme and the simulation programme showed some significant differences. The most noticeable was that even though, in the simulation, the lowest reservoir held more water in storage more often, it still emptied three times within the 10 x 100 years of analysis. The optimisation gave more effective utilization of the storage within the system (Table 1). The reason for this was wholly attributable to the ability to modify the demand within the system. Table 2 demonstrates the efficiency of the optimisation procedure as less water has to be transferred.

While in both the optimisation and the simulation Midmar never went below its lowest desirable storage, this could be accounted for by water from the transfer scheme meeting any deficit (Table 2). However, in the simulation, this resulted in less water being available to meet demands downstream at times of low natural inflow. In the most extreme 100 years Albert Falls reservoir is below its desirable level for almost half the time while the optimisation reduces this to 18% of the time.

Table 1 Comparison between optimisation and simulation of the percentage of time at the lowest desirable storage level

	Large Midmar[(i)]		Small Midmar[(i)]	
	Simulation	Optimisation	Simulation	Optimisation
Maximum	41	12	48	16
Average	27.1	5.3	34.0	8.5
Minimum	15	1	28	3
Standard Deviation	7.2	3.8	6.4	4.6

NOTE: (i)" Large Midmar" has a capacity of 266 MCM and "Small Midmar" 177 MCM. The capacities of the lower reservoirs remain the same. (Albert Falls 289 MCM and Inanda 225 MCM)

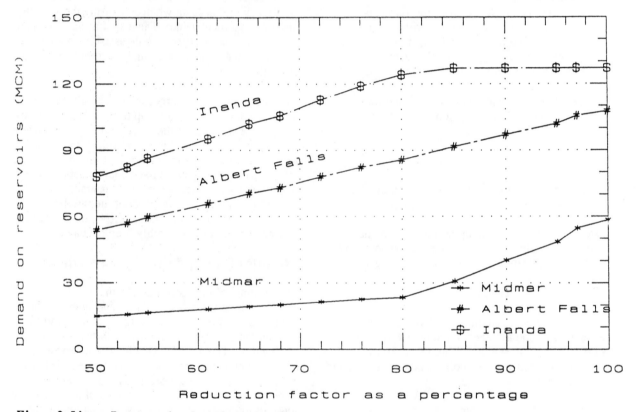

Figure 2 Linear Programming Optimisation - reduction factor versus annual demand

Using the optimisation routine

The optimisation routine can be used in forecasting the results of either setting the degree of restriction required for the period under review, or setting the demand to be met from each of the reservoirs during that period. This would be complementary to the monthly "control band". Under extreme circumstances when the demand is at the limit of the system it would permit the exploitation of water which would otherwise be lost. However, the concept of system reliability would need to be adopted.

Reliability, risk, resiliency and vulnerability

Various means have been employed in defining the reliability of a system and its susceptibility to becoming unstable. Yevjevich (1985) defined reliability as being (1 - risk) in probabilistic terms. He then went on to list twelve difficulties of the treatment of risk and uncertainty and drew the conclusion that that approach was flawed. Alternative measures of system performance were stated by Hashimoto et al.(1982) as:

    1) how often the system fails (reliability);

Table 2 *Comparison between optimisation and simulation of the required inter-basin transfers (expressed as a percentage of scheme operating time)*

| | Large Midmar | | Small Midmar | |
	Simulation	Optimisation	Simulation	Optimisation
Maximum	46	18	45	25
Average	26.2	10.3	31.9	13.8
Minimum	15	5	26	7
Standard Deviation	8.2	4.6	5.4	5.2

2) how quickly the system returns to a satisfactory state once a failure has occurred (resiliency); and 3) how significant the likely consequences of failure may be (vulnerability).

Duckstein (1987) defines the measures of system performance of Hashimoto *et al.* (1982) within a framework of performance indices. An alternative is the concept of "figures of merit" which are defined by Duckstein and Bernier (1986) as criterion functions defined over the components of the performance matrix. Shamir (1987) extends the definition as "functions which express the 'worth' of the performance indices" and includes some sources of uncertainty which affect reliability.

Hashimoto *et al.*(1982) also quote Kitson (1979) who emphasized the need in reservoir operating policy development to consider reductions in demand during drought periods and stated that this leads to the concept of expressing reliability in terms of frequency duration and intensity with which restrictions have to be placed on water consumption. A different definition of reliability was developed further by Clarke *et al.* (1980) in introducing the concept of "conservation measures".

Reliability and credibility

Table 3 sets out the conservation measures adopted in the Greater Durban region, which had a total population of about 3.5 million in 1985. The various measures listed were supplemented by publicity campaigns (McLeod 1983). These measures are used as a basis for determining the reliability of the Umgeni system.

Table 3 *Conservation measures introduced in Durban*

Degree of Severity	Range of Reduction in Demand as a %	Equivalent Action[i]	Remarks
E	50 - 60	Cut to 400 l/d per household[ii]	Very Severe
D	60 - 70	Strict enforcement of regulations[iii]	Severe
C	70 - 80	Request to industry for 10% cut in use	------------
B	80 - 90	Hosepipe ban	Inconvenient
A	90 - 100	Hosepipe Restrictions	Hardly Noticeable

NOTE: (i) Action taken by Durban Corporation (from McLeod 1983)
(ii) This was relaxed for very large households and a leak detection service for customers was introduced.
(iii) Extra inspectors employed but "wealthy" paid fines cheerfully (McLeod, 1983).

Using simulation alone, very little could be deduced about the reliability of the system, except that the lowest reservoir failed (became empty) three times; twice in one set and once in another. However, from the optimisation runs, with the same data, it was possible to obtain an indication of the "level of service" of the whole system, as indicated by the reduction in demand on the system as a whole. Because of differing legislation, including the requirement of universal water metering, it was possible to adopt policies that were not available to Clarke *et al.* (1980). Credibility has been associated with probability by Morris (1986) but this does not give a suitable approach in this instance. Another solution is to develop a "credibility index" to be able to assess the results of different operating policies.

The "credibility" of any action depends on the severity and duration. In this case it may be measured by a reduction in demand and the duration of that reduction, as shown in Table 4. However, additional factors need to be included to obtain an overall view. In order to differentiate between events of differing severity and duration and events of the same duration but differing severity, a "credibility factor" is introduced. Glantz (1982) documents a case of "customer reaction" to a policy of restrictions which in the event turned out to be too severe. Clarke *et al.* (1980) were also aware of the problem. Table 5 sets out an empirical "credibility factor" bi-diagonal matrix. It is based on the premise that a long duration minor restriction will be far less credible than one of a short duration and that short duration severe restrictions will cause a loss of credibility. A factor of five was chosen as the base unit as five years fitted well into the duration period for low flow events in this area. In other areas a value up to nine years (Tyson, 1986) may be more appropriate. The

Table 4 *Measure of the system reliability ranked by degree of severity*

Severity Equalled or Exceeded	Large Midmar Duration in Years						Small Midmar Duration in Years					
	1	2	3	4	5	6	1	2	3	4	5	6
$E^{(i)}$	2	2	3	1	1	–	1	8	2	–	1	1
D	4	5	3	1	1	–	5	11	3	–	1	1
C	6	5	3	1	1	–	11	12	3	–	1	1
B	8	6	4	1	1	–	17	12	3	–	1	1
A	13	7	4	1	1	–	25	12	3	–	1	1

NOTE: (i) *For numerical range of the cutback see Table 3.*

Table 5 *"The credibility factor"*

Duration of Restriction (years)	Severity of restriction				
	A	B	C	D	E
1	5	4	3	2	1
2	4	5	4	3	2
3	3	4	5	4	3
4	2	3	4	5	4
5	1	2	3	4	5
6	0	1	2	3	4

Table 6 Development of the "credibility index"

	Large Midmar	Small Midmar
Maximum	6.93	5.23
Average	4.75	3.85
Minimum	2.5	2.5
Standard Deviation	2.03	0.98
Percentage Credibility	95%	77%

credibility factor is used in the formulation of a credibility index. Applying the "credibility factor" to the results from the optimisation gave an overall 66% credibility for the Small Midmar and 60% for the Large Midmar. Further development of this approach is indicated.

The overall factor would require modification to take into account the duration of the events. This might be defined in probabilistic terms. In addition the number of events and their duration would need to be determined regionally. In an area of high rainfall, restrictions should be few and far between. In areas of lower and less predictable rainfall more frequent or longer duration restrictions would probably be acceptable.

Table 6 shows the effect of applying this correction factor. While the improvement in value for the small Midmar system is less marked, because so many of the events fall within the unadjusted area, there was an improvement for the large Midmar. The normal range chosen for this particular modification was an upper limit of 20% and a lower limit of 5% of the total set length.

Development of credibility

Table 5 listing the "credibility factors" was derived from:
  1) the duration of the event, and
  2) the severity of the event.
In a more general case a third factor affecting the "credibility" may be needed:
  3) the number of events in a given period.

The credibility factor may also need to be modified to account for the increasing difficulty found in meeting future reductions in demand once a severe event has taken place. This difficulty was highlighted by Hobbs (1985) when assessing the reductions in demand to be made by industry, which had in a previous low flow event installed water saving equipment and was unable to reduce demand to the extent requested.

Conclusions

While the "credibility index" is a measure of the performance of different operating policies, the credibility factor is comparable to the factors listed by Hashimoto et al. (1982) when defining reliability. Thus the empirical approach bears a relationship with the theoretical applications developed by Duckstein (1987). Alternatives using probability (Yevjevich, 1985; Morris, 1986) could result in the need to redefine the Linear Programme objective function in stochastic terms and although Yeh (1985) quotes some examples, it did not seem suitable in this particular application. A "Quadratic Programming" option forms part of two of the routines used (E04NAF, E04NCF) but the additional complexity seemed to outweigh any advantages, so that option has not been taken further. Instead the "credibility index" is used when determining the most favourable overall system demand, while the Linear Programme objective function serves to distribute the demand amongst the various reservoirs. The "credibility index" when used in conjunction with optimisation techniques is capable of being developed further to form a useful performance indicator.

Acknowledgements

The author wishes to acknowledge the assistance of the Computer Centre for Water Research (CCWR) for providing computer facilities and advice.

References

Clarke, K.F., Page, C. & Brew, J.S. 1980. Reliability of water resources. *J. Instn Wat. Engrs* 34, 61-73.

Dalgli, C.H. & Miles, J.F. 1980. Determining operating policies for a water resource system. *J. Hydrol.* 47, 297-306.

Duckstein, L. & Bernier, J. 1986. A system framework for engineering risk analysis. In Haimes & Stakiv (ed.) *Risk-Based Decision Making in Water Resources*. Proc. Engineering Foundation Conference, Santa Barbara California, 1985.

Amer. Soc. Civ. Engrs, New York, 90-110.

Fletcher, R. 1981. *Practical Methods of Optimisation - Volume 2 - Constrained Optimisation.* Wiley, Chichester.

Glantz, M.H. 1982. Consequences and responsibilities in drought forecasting: The case of Yakima, 1977. *Wat. Resour. Res.* 18, 3-13.

Hashimoto, T., Stedinger, J.R. & Loucks, D.P. 1982. Reliability, resiliency and vulnerability criteria for water resource system performance evaluation. *Wat. Resour. Res.* 18, 14-20.

Hobbs, L.D. 1985. The role of the Rand Water Board during the critical 1983/84 drought period. *The Civil Engineer in South Africa* 27, 7-12.

Kitson, T. 1979. The operation of reservoir systems in Britain. Workshop on Operation of Multi-Purpose Multiple Reservoir Systems, International Institute for Applied Systems Analysis / IMGW, Jodlowy Dwor, Poland.

Loucks, D.P., Stedinger, J.R. & Haith, D.A. 1981. *Water Resource System Planning & Analysis.* Prentice Hall, New Jersey.

Mcleod, N. 1983. Perspective of water consumption in Durban. *J. Faculty of Engineering, University of Durban-Westville* 1, 26-32.

Morris P.A. 1986. The credibility of probabilities: an application to water resources policy. In Haimes and Stakiv (ed) *Risk-Based Decision Making in Water Resources.* Proc. Engineering Foundation Conference, Santa Barbara California, 1985. Am. Soc. Civ. Engrs, New York, 65- 89.

NAG. 1988. NAG FORTRAN Library Manual Mark 13 - Volume 3 - E04. Numerical Algorithms Group, Oxford.

Shamir, U. 1987. Reliability of water supply systems. In: Duckstein and Plate (ed) *Engineering Reliability and Risk in Water Resources.* NATO ASI Series E: Applied Sciences - No. 124. Martinus Nijhoff Publishers, Dordrecht, 233-247.

Tollow, A.J. 1988. Some alternative approaches to mathematical modelling of reservoir systems. *Regulated Rivers: Research and Management* 2, 565-572.

Tollow, A.J. 1989. A further approach to the assessment of reservoir yield, *Proc. BHS Second National Hydrology Symposium* Sheffield, September 1989, 4.39-4.46.

Tyson, P.D. 1986. *Climate Change and its Variability in Southern Africa.* Oxford University Press, Capetown.

Windsor, J.S. 1973. Optimisation model for the operation of flood control systems. *Wat. Resour. Res.* 9, 1219-1226.

Yeh, W.W-G. 1985. Reservoir management and operations models: a state of the art review. *Wat. Resour. Res.* 21, 1797-1818.

Yevjevich, V. 1985. Risk and uncertainty in water resources planning and operation. In Plate and Buras (ed.) *Scientific Procedures Applied to the Planning, Design and Management of Water Resources Systems.* Proc. Hamburg Symposium 1983. IAHS Publication No. 147, Wallingford, 195-212.

Short and long term options for low flow alleviation

H. Goldsmith & E.L. Parry

Abstract

The reduction of baseflow is an inevitable consequence of developing groundwater resources. There has to be some trade-off between the level of groundwater exploitation and low flows. The problem is to decide how far low flows are allowed to fall. The National Rivers Authority (NRA) has identified 40 sites nationwide where real and urgent problems exist because of over-licensed resources, including six catchments on the heavily abstracted Sherwood Sandstones aquifer in the Severn Trent Region. This paper describes the findings of a study to identify and quantify the relative problems and potential benefits of low flow alleviation along the six watercourses.

In the short term, technical solutions have been proposed to combat problems in specific reaches, mainly by developing the groundwater resources still further. There are no easy long-term solutions. Simply revoking excessive Licences of Right which are for public water supply is an expensive option. Integrated resource management plans will have to be developed which include environmental low flow objectives as part of the demand on resources. The cost of developing the extra resources required to meet those demands will ultimately have to be paid by the consumer.

Introduction

When it is recognised that there has been a deterioration in the water environment due to overdevelopment of water resources, what can be done about it? This is the problem confronting the National Rivers Authority, who have the duty both to manage water resources efficiently and to protect the water environment (NRA, 1990), but who have also inherited a situation of over-licensed resources in some areas, examples of which are given in this paper.

Since its formation in 1989, the NRA has given low flow alleviation a high priority. Even before the formation of the NRA, there was growing public concern about the lack of flow in some rivers over the summer. But the old Water Authorities were both poacher and game-keeper of water resources and the dominant philosophy was to achieve water supply objectives rather than to preserve river flows. With the resource management and water supply functions now clearly separated, the NRA can act to protect and improve the water environment.

In 1990 the NRA Technical Director asked the Regional Resource Managers to draw up a list of locations where low flow problems were known to occur. In identifying the severity of the problems, the Regional Resource Managers were told to ask themselves the question: "would the current abstraction licences be issued by the NRA with hindsight of the effect on the catchment?". The survey revealed 40 catchments nationwide with serious low flow problems.

The NRA (Severn Trent Region) identified six catchments which were known to suffer from low flows. The selection of catchments was strongly influenced by complaints from the public, conservation groups, anglers and farmers. There was very little quantitative information on the causes and effects of low flows. As a first step towards low flow alleviation, the NRA appointed consultants to investigate low flows and to recommend possible solutions for each site. This paper summarises the findings of the study.

The catchments

The locations of the six catchments are shown in Figure 1 and summary descriptive parameters are listed in Table 1. The sizes of the catchments range

Table 1 Catchment parameters

WATERCOURSE	LOCATION	CATCHMENT AREA (sq km)	TOTAL LENGTH (km)	STATUTORY MAIN RIVER (km)	AVERAGE RAINFALL (mm)
Dover Beck	NE Nottingham	74	14	2	710
Rainworth Water	NE Nottingham	60	13	0	678
Leamonsley Brook	W Lichfield	3	4	0	702
Black Brook	S Lichfield	99	24	24	711
Battlefield Brook	NW Bromsgrove	34	11	0	731
River Worfe	E Telford	260	32	15	697

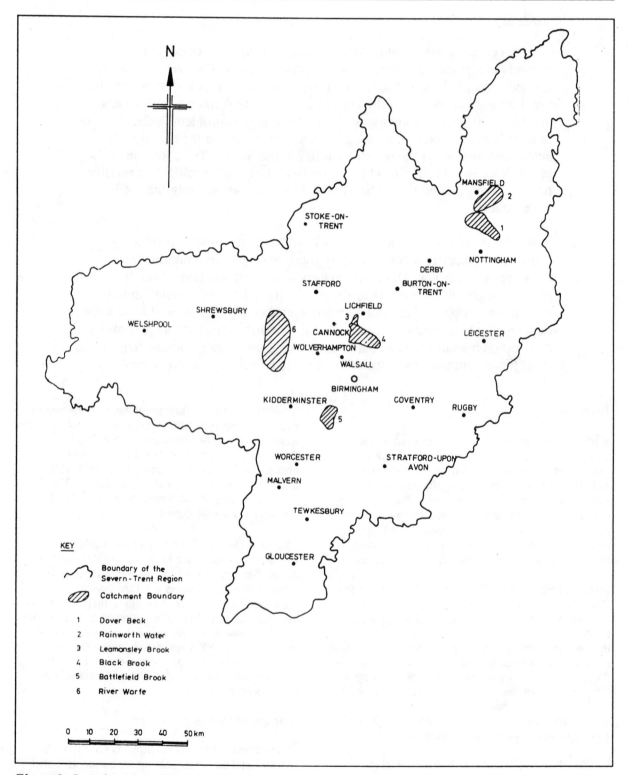

Figure 1 Location of study sites

from 3 km² up to 260 km². In the smallest catchment, Leamonsley Brook, there are two well-defined areas with low flow problems: Lichfield Pools, with a high amenity value in the centre of Lichfield; and Leamonsley Lower Pool, a graded nature reserve which dries out every summer. For the largest catchment, the River Worfe, the problems are less well focused. There are concerns about low river levels along the natural brown trout fishery and some farmers are unable to abstract their licensed quantity.

All six sites are rural catchments, with low rolling hills used mainly for agriculture. The headwaters of the watercourses are on the geological formation known as the Sherwood Sandstones. This is a very good aquifer which receives high recharge through sandy soils in the unconfined zone. Historically, the catchments abounded with springs which maintained a healthy baseflow even through dry summers. It is this underground resource which has been heavily exploited for public water supply and all six catchments contain several major abstraction boreholes, often sited only a few metres from the river bank. Most of the springs now exist only as place names. Present concerns about low flows need to be understood in the context of the historical development of these water resources.

Historical background to low flow problems

All six catchments have seen dramatic changes in both the quantity and quality of dry weather flows over the past century (Howard Humphreys, 1990). Table 3 shows the magnitude of the changes, the important ones being:
* human interference with "natural" conditions;
* groundwater development for public water supply;
* increased discharge of treated sewage effluent;
* increased surface abstraction for spray irrigation.

The catchments have a long history of human interference. Virtually every pool and lake was created artificially by damming naturally marshy areas or by the filling of excavated pits. The artificial pools were used for flood irrigation, fishing, ornamental lakes for Manor Houses, duck shoots, as mill ponds, and as storage reservoirs for water supply. The same is true of the watercourses, which have been diverted, straightened and culverted over centuries.

The development of groundwater began in about 1860 with Parliamentary Water Acts and the formation of the Statutory Water Companies to serve the domestic and industrial needs of the rapidly

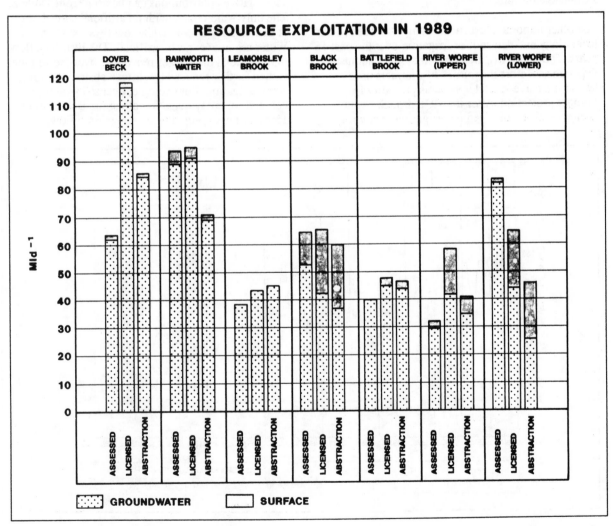

Figure 2 Resource exploitation in 1989

growing nearby towns. The real battles over low flows were fought when the second phase of the Waterworks Amendment Acts came before Parliament. Sheail (1982) quoted the Worfe as an example of the conflict between the countryside and city over water supply at the turn of the century. Every Bill was petitioned against by landowners and millowners who claimed that the Water Companies were drying up the catchment. Their objections were either ignored or overcome by various forms of compensation: compulsory purchase orders within the Bill; financial payments; or by connecting a mains supply.

The most recent growth in public water supply abstraction occurred with the post-war boom in the 1950s. These abstraction rights were then embodied in abstraction licences granted under the Water Resources Act 1963. All existing users were entitled to a "Licence of Right" for the quantity taken in the five years prior to the Act. Unfortunately, those quantities were not routinely measured and so in catchments like the Worfe, farmers applied for and were granted Licences of Right for surface abstraction well in excess of what they had ever taken. The Water Companies and River Authorities also applied for licences based on previous over-abstraction rather than with any reference to sustainable resources.

The other important historical change has been in the technology and demand for irrigation over the past 15 years. The major irrigated crop in the six catchments is potatoes. Before the mid 1970s, farmers used labour intensive sprinkler systems primarily for drought protection. After the 1976 drought, many farmers realised the need for irrigation to control both the uniformity and quality of the crop, and installed highly mobile spray guns and tractor mounted reels. Irrigation is now a prerequisite for getting a contract with a major food manufacturer or retailer. Surface abstraction for spray irrigation is now limited by availability of streamflow over the summer.

The balance of resources

The long term cause of diminishing low flows in all six catchments is reduced baseflow due to groundwater over-abstraction. Baseflow comes from the residual between recharge and abstraction. When long term abstraction exceeds long term recharge, then the water table declines, baseflow reduces and eventually ceases. Dry weather flows then rely upon support from minor aquifers, limited perched water tables and artificial discharges where these exist. The supply and demand for surface and groundwater resources in the six catchments is summarised in Table 2 and Figure 2. The consequence of over-abstraction on the water table is shown by Figure 3.

Along several watercourses, dry weather flows are already "alleviated" by artificial discharges of sewage effluent and mine drainage/tailings water. The relative contributions can be seen from Table 2. The only watercourse with no artificial contribution is Leamonsley Brook, while low flows in Rainworth Water are now entirely artificial. The little baseflow plus artificial discharges remaining over the summer is then further reduced by surface abstraction for spray irrigation. For example, licensed potential demand for spray irrigation along the Black Brook is 150% of the expected mean annual baseflow.

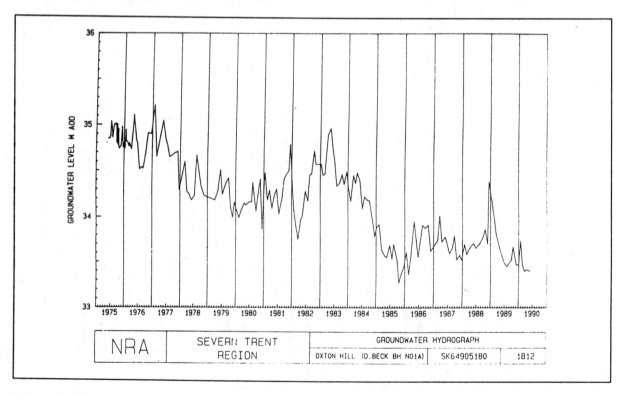

Figure 3 Groundwater hydrograph for Oxton Hill, D. Beck Borehole No. 1A (SK64905180)

Table 2 Resource supply, demand and outcome

ALL UNITS IN Ml d^{-1}

	Dover Beck	Rainworth Water	Leamonsley Brook	Black Brook	Battlefield Brook	River Worfe (Upper)(1)	River Worfe (Lower)(1)
GROUNDWATER							
Groundwater Unit	BLIDWORTH	CLIPSTONE	LICHFIELD	SHENSTONE	BROMSGROVE	COSFORD	WORFIELD
Assessed Resource	62.00	88.90	38.41	52.68	40.00	29.27	82.07
Licensed Resource(2)	116.25	91.02	43.51	42.22	44.83	41.69	43.77
1989 Abstraction(3)	84.43	68.85	45.18	36.75	43.72	34.54	25.47
SURFACE							
Consented Discharge(4)	2.30	5.95	0.00	13.21	0.02	3.53	2.96
Est. Artif. Discharge(5)	1.77	4.95	0.00	11.83	0.00	2.69	1.50
Licensed Abstraction	2.06	4.02	0.00	23.48	2.92	16.72	21.31
Est. Abstraction(6)	1.33	2.29	0.00	23.48	2.92	6.26	21.31
SUPPLY AND DEMAND							
Assessed Supply(7)	63.77	93.85	38.41	64.51	40.00	31.96	83.57
Licensed Demand(8)	118.31	95.04	43.51	65.70	47.75	58.41	65.08
Actual Abstraction(9)	85.76	71.14	45.18	60.23	46.64	40.80	45.78
OUTCOME							
Baseflow Residual(10)	0.00	0.00(11)	0.00	15.93	0.00	0.00	56.60
Est. Low Flow 1990(12)	3.00	1.00	0.70	20.00	0.00	0.00	20.00
Watertable trend(13)	Falling	Falling	Stable	Stable	Falling	Falling	Stable

Notes -

1. The upper reaches of the Worfe are on the COSFORD Groundwater Unit, but the lower reaches are on the WORFIELD Groundwater Unit.
2. 1990 licensed abstraction includes group licenses which may be linked to boreholes in another Groundwater Unit.
3. Includes both private and PWS boreholes. PWS abstraction is typically 95% of total abstraction.
4. Includes WRW discharges + mine drainage and tailings discharges.
5. Estimated actual artificial dry weather discharge based on Severn Trent Water Ltd estimates.
6. Total potential daily demand for spray irrigation + known dry weather abstractions.
7. Assessed groundwater resource + estimated artificial discharge.
8. 1990 licensed groundwater abstraction + licensed surface abstraction.
9. 1989 actual groundwater abstraction + potential surface abstraction for spray irrigation.
10. Mean annual daily residual between assessed groundwater resources and actual abstraction from the Sherwood Sandstones in 1989. Actual summer baseflow will be less than this figure, and will depend upon the baseflow curve.
11. Although the groundwater resource balance indicates a 20.05 Ml d^{-1} baseflow residual, actual baseflow is known to be zero.
12. Based on visual estimation or flow gaugings at the catchment outfall during summer 1990 field visits. May include springflow from minor aquifers.
13. Watertable trend for catchment, not necessarily for whole Groundwater Unit.

Reductions in flow can also be caused by induced extra leakage through the stream bed due to boreholes being sited next to watercourses. This may locally reduce levels along a particular reach or adversely affect a wetland area, but does not significantly affect overall resources.

The low flow regime of all six watercourses has changed over more than a century. The magnitude of the changes for the Dover Beck can be seen from Table 3. The most dramatic changes occurred at the start of groundwater resource development. How can we quantify and compare the adverse effects of reduced low flows in terms of contemporary user interests?

Present adverse effects

In the absence of low flow objectives, the study focused on reaches with perceived problems and assessed the impact in terms of: dry river bed, water quality objectives, fisheries, conservation, amenity and derogated surface abstraction rights (Table 4).

No flow is clearly the most extreme example of low flow. Some reaches of the watercourses are now permanently dry for several months in the summer. The only clearly defined objective for rivers is the River Quality Objective (RQO). The reaches which fail to meet their RQO are those where effluent discharges provide the majority of the low flow. Although baseflow dilution improves water quality, it is ultimately the quality of artificial discharges which is important. Reaches which are dry over the summer may nonetheless fail to meet their RQO. It is clearly unacceptable for low flows or poor water quality to

occur along rivers with designated fisheries. The length of reach affected is given in Table 4. There are also pools where fish rescues have been required, or where private fisheries have been destroyed.

Table 4 lists numbers of County Grade 1A conservative sites identified by the local Conservation Trust or NRA Conservation Officer as having suffered due to low flows. Unfortunately, the Conservation Trusts do not have the resources to do regular species surveys, and so the effects of reduced flows are rarely quantified.

The only aquatic ecology objective for river reaches is set indirectly by the RQO, which implies a corresponding biological water quality classification. The most recent biological score is given in Table 4 for the worst reach in each catchment. The biological classification generally mirrors the chemical classification, except for Rainworth Water which has a lower biological classification probably due to high chloride levels from mine tailings discharges.

Table 4 lists numbers of sites where low flows have an impact on amenity and recreational interests. These range from a dry stream bed through the centre of a town park, to a lake in a popular Country Park where the water quality is Class 3.

Licensed surface abstractors can be adversely affected by low flows and their statutory rights must be protected. Up to a third of surface abstractors on some watercourses are adversely affected by low flows. Many of these hold Licenses of Right. Surface abstractors are potentially both a cause of low flows for the reach downstream and victims of low flows if

Table 3   Dover Beck changes in low flows

YEAR	FLOW (Mld^{-1})	COMMENT
1868	29.0	Minimum flow recorded by Boro' Eng.
1894	18.0	Minimum gauged flow after 12 years of low winter rainfall
1973	6.9	MAM(7) at Lowdham weir
1976	1.6	Minimum gauged flow on record
1989	3.2	MAM(7) at Lowham weir
1990	2.0	Gauged flow 11/09/90

Note:
MAM(7) is a low flow duration statistic defined as the average of the year's lowest consecutive seven days flow.

Table 4 Adverse effects of low flows

	Dover Beck	Rainworth Water	Leamonsley Brook	Black Brook	Battlefield Brook	River Worfe (Upper)	River Worfe (Lower)
NO FLOW							
Dry channel (km) (1)	5.5	0.2	0.1	0	5.0	6.0	0
WATER QUALITY							
RQO not achieved (km)	5.3	6.6	0	0	5.0	0	0
Actual/RQO (2)	2/1B	3/2	Not Set	2/2	2/1B	1B/1B	1B/1B
FISHERIES							
Ec Fishery (km) (3)	8.8 C	0	0	0	0	0	27.1 S
Pools requiring fish rescue	2	0	2	0	0	1	0
CONSERVATION							
No. Grade 1A Wetland sites	2	1	1	0	0	0	0
Worst NWC score (4)	50	22	N/S	N/S	27	70	97
AMENITY							
No. sites affected	0	1	1	1	1	0	0
SURFACE ABSTRACTION							
Licence holders affected (5)	2	2	0	2	1	6	0
Total no. licence holders(6)	6	7	0	26	3	17	32

Notes -

1. Length of stream with zero flow or intermittent flow over the summer.
2. River Quality Objective (RQO) is for worst reach or for reach out of class. Actual measured quality is for 1989. See NRA (1989) for definitions of river quality classifications.
3. EC Designated Fisheries: S = Salmonid, C = Cyprinid.
4. National Water Council (NWC) score based on invertebrate count. 10-25 is poor. 26-50 is moderate. 51-100 is good. Greater than 150 is exellent. See Severn Trent Water Authority (1989) for details.
5. Only includes abstractors reportedly unable to abstract their licenced quantity.
6. Total number of surface abstraction licence holders along watercourse.

N/S = Not Sampled.

they cannot abstract their licensed quantity. This paradox serves to underline the need for integrated resource management to meet the demands of surface and groundwater abstractors as well as environmental low flow requirements.

Issues and objectives

The problems caused by over-abstraction raise three fundamental questions:

1. To what extent does society wish to restore the quantity and quality of the water environment?
2. Where will resources come from to restore low flows?
3. What policy instruments can the NRA use to achieve low flow objectives?

The important lesson from the history of the catchments is that human use of water resources has developed over centuries and has never been passive. One has to be careful when suggesting that "natural" conditions should be reinstated. The challenge is to define low flow objectives in terms of realistic present day requirements, rather than with reference to some idealised Victorian Picture Postcard Past.

The NRA is currently investigating a number of ways of defining low flow objectives. Although the principle of a minimum acceptable flow was introduced under the Water Resources Act 1963, it was not applied because of problems in relating flow and level to environmental parameters (Wood, 1981). A relatively simple method of using different weightings for fisheries, amenity and recreational interests was proposed by Drake & Sherriff (1987) to determine environmentally acceptable flows when granting new surface abstraction licences. The environmentally acceptable flow was defined as a proportion of a dry weather flow statistic and was really aimed at preserving existing conditions rather than restoring desirable low flows. Whether the methodology is formalised or not, the NRA has to use some form of weighting scheme to reflect the priority given to different environmental aspects, when deciding where to take action.

Short-term and long-term solutions

Immediate action may be desirable to protect the environment in the short term. Where there is potentially adequate flow, bed lining, resiting boreholes or resizing the channel may solve a local problem. But flow augmentation is usually necessary.

The obvious way to get a quick improvement in low flows is by sinking a borehole and developing the groundwater resources still further to provide a compensation flow. This form of active management has clear advantages for ensuring reliable flow at a particular reach, for instance, to provide flow through a park or to maintain flows at times of peak surface demand for spray irrigation. But this is not a sustainable long-term solution to problems caused by over-licensed and over-abstracted resources.

The NRA identified the present list of low flow problem sites by asking whether abstraction licences would have been granted with hindsight. If the answer is "no", then the problem can only be solved in the long term by reducing abstraction or increasing resources.

Present problems with resource licensing and consented discharges are largely historical in origin. The underlying problem for all six catchments is the lack of an integrated resource management plan. Until now, there has not been a quantitative link between the administration of surface licensing, groundwater licensing and consented discharges due to the absence of unique, catchment-based regulatory authorities. In their review of water resources management within member countries, the OECD Environment Committee came out strongly in favour of integrated management of surface water, groundwater and discharges at a regional level (OECD, 1989). They also recommended the use of economic policy instruments based on long-run marginal social cost pricing, which includes the environmental costs of resource development, to achieve management objectives.

Where present abstraction exceeds resources, it is in the Water Companies long-term interests to reduce abstraction because the safe yield reduces and pumping costs rise as the water table falls. There is also an incentive to relocate and increase abstraction from the confined zone where there are generally less groundwater quality problems. In two of the catchments in this study licences have recently been renegotiated, but only to reduce abstraction down to the level of assessed resources.

For abstraction reduction to be effective in restoring a specified level of baseflow, the licensed resource must be significantly less than the assessed resource. In catchments where this is considered desirable, licensable abstraction could be set at, say, 90% of assessed resources and seasonal pumping used to increase the proportion of baseflow over the summer. The exact level of acceptable resource exploitation will depend upon defined low flow objectives. In order to meet regional demands, other catchments may have to be considered as "sacrificial" with 100% of the assessed resource being licensed. The problem is how to reduce abstraction from over-exploited aquifers when the vast majority of those abstractions are under Licences of Right for public water supply.

Revocation of Licences of Right is very expensive and only a practical option where alternative resources exist. Financial compensation cannot compensate for a lack of water. If licences are revoked in a piecemeal way without considering the problem in a regional context, then the Water Companies will simply look to the next cheapest source, which is likely to be an under-used licence elsewhere. Thus licence revocation may simply move the problem around from one catchment to another. This problem can only be resolved in negotiation with the Water Companies and, if necessary, major new schemes for impoundment or transfer considered. The NRA has recently commissioned a national water resources study which will investigate the implications of environmental demands on resources.

The price of water and the value of the environment

The reason why Water Companies and Public Corporations developed the groundwater resources from these catchments was because they were close to urban demand centres and hence relatively cheap. The Water Services Association is suggesting that water charges to the consumer will treble by 1999, and a total of £28 billion will need to be spent on water infrastructure. This investment is primarily to meet EC water quality directives.

If extra water resources need to be developed or major water transfer schemes built in order to ensure that environmental needs can be met, then there may be an extra amount to add to that sum. If society is genuinely concerned about the value of the water environment, then the price of water must reflect that value ... and we must all be prepared to pay the bills.

Acknowledgements

The authors are grateful to the National Rivers Authority, Severn Trent Region, for permission to publish this paper. The study which forms the basis of this paper was undertaken by Howard Humphreys and Partners Ltd, consulting engineers, in association with BARNUS Ltd, environmental consultants. The views expressed in this paper are those of the authors and do not necessarily reflect those of their employers.

References.

Drake, P.J. & Sherriff, J.D.F. 1987. A Method for Managing River Abstractions and Protecting the Environment. *J. I.W.E.M.*, 1(1), 27-38.

Howard Humphreys & Partners 1990. Alleviation of Low Flows (ALF) Study: summary report. NRA Severn Trent Region internal report.

NRA, 1989. Objectives for Rivers and Canals.

NRA, 1990. Corporate plan 1990/91.

OECD, 1989. Water Resources Management. Integrated Policies. OECD, Paris

Salmon, S. & Rushton, K. 1988. The Bromsgrove aquifer study – Final report. University of Birmingham.

Severn Trent Water Authority. Water Quality 1988/89. Appendix 6. Water Quality - Biological.

Sheail, J. 1982. Underground Water Abstraction: Indirect Effects of Urbanisation on the countryside. *J. Hist. Geog.*, 8(4), 395-408.

Wood, T.R. 1981. River management. In: Lewin, J. (ed.), *British Rivers*. George Allen & Unwin, London.

Operational control in a major river regulation system

C. Dobson & R.C. Cross

Abstract

The droughts of 1989 and 1990 have tested the operation of the River Severn Regulation system, now operated by the National Rivers Authority on behalf of several separate water undertakings, as well as agricultural and industrial users. Traditional water resource planning has enabled derivation of control rules and operating guidelines for this complex conjunctive use scheme, based on statistical analysis of historic flow data to simulate operation during a design drought sequence.

This paper describes the operational experiences during two recent droughts, showing how tactical decisions are taken to optimise releases and minimise wastage. Data collection from hydrological monitors, from water users, and its use in a microcomputer system for release management is discussed. The computer package, based on standard spreadsheets, allows hydrologists to simulate various release strategies, based on known or predicted river responses. The results are available quickly and allow close liaison between NRA and river abstractors to make efficient use of water released. Experience in 1989 and 1990 has demonstrated improved operational practices which have increased regulation efficiency. This information is now being used to modify control rules by feeding back into the long term water resource planning activity.

Introduction

The Severn Regulation system was designed and constructed in the 1960s. Its major component is an impounding reservoir at Llyn Clywedog, with additional surface water available from a compensation water bank in Lake Vyrnwy, and groundwater resources in the Shropshire Triassic Sandstone aquifer (see Figure 1). Operation is governed by a minimum maintained flow at a control point 200 km downstream of Llyn Clywedog, at Bewdley.

Ignoring canal diversions, demands for abstracted raw water are distributed along the river Severn from Shrewsbury to the tidal limit at Gloucester, where water is transferred into a canal for delivery to Bristol. Most of the demands are for public water supply, although one major abstraction provides cooling water for Ironbridge power station. Support for navigation and for agricultural use is provided, but with limitations during droughts. There is provision for environmental benefits, and for local flood alleviation at certain times of the year, as secondary benefits.

Since its first years of operation in the early 1970s some amendments to the rules governing regulation support have taken place. The most notable change was an increase in the maintained flow at the Bewdley control point from 727Ml/d to 850Ml/d averaged over 5 days. This change was implemented following the drought of 1975/6, when it was recognised that flows in the lower reaches of the Severn fell to very low levels. Steady increases in demand, supported by increased yields from the Lake Vyrnwy water bank and the phased introductions of the Shropshire Groundwater scheme, added to the need to review the maintained flow.

Operational experiences during 1975/6 also highlighted several problems associated with the tactical management of releases from headwater reservoirs to support demands distributed along the whole river Severn. For details of these problems, and a very comprehensive system description and bibliography, see Goodhew (1982). Most of the recommendations contained in that paper were implemented by 1989. These included greatly improved hydrometric measurement in the middle Severn using ultrasonic flow gauges, and improved

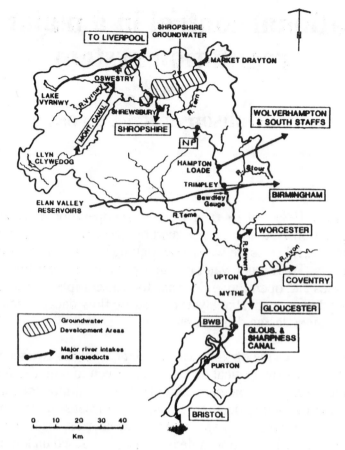

Figure 1   River Severn water resources/supply system

data collection and flow forecasting based on mathematical models (Dobson, Turner, & Eccleston, 1990). The increase of 123 Ml/d in maintained flow was not fully matched by increased resources. This meant that regulation efficiency during protracted droughts needed to be improved to sustain the design drought. Efforts concentrated on minimising excess releases by closer monitoring of river flows and abstractions and by making better use of this information.

Rapid reaction to changes in river flow, especially when flows increase following rain, as well as pre-emptive release variations when significant changes are confidently predicted, requires a quick and easy, but dependable, management system.

Two of the major intakes have small bankside reservoirs adjacent to the river, providing a few days storage to allow supplies to continue in the event of river pollution, or abstraction pump failure. Traditionally these reservoirs have been kept almost full whenever possible. Tactical management of levels in these bankside reservoirs offers a significant potential for release optimisation.

In order to realise this benefit, it was necessary to demonstrate to water undertakers that intake reliability would not be compromised by operating bankside reservoirs below capacity. This was achieved at the end of the 1989 summer, when the policy was adopted as a pre-cursor to a drought order.

The emergence of powerful personal computers, with comprehensive data management software during the 1980s, allowed hydrologists to process the data required for regulation decision-making quickly and without costly or complex programme developments.

Operating rules

The operation of the Severn Regulation system is controlled by simple rules which were amended after 1975/6. The significant features are:

Daily compensation releases of 18.2 Ml/d from Llyn Clywedog, and 25 or 45 Ml/d from Lake Vyrnwy depending on local inflows.

Additional releases from any regulation source to ensure flows at Bewdley are maintained above 850 Ml/d averaged over any 5-day period, and above 650 Ml/d averaged over any single day.

Maximum obligatory discharge of 500 Ml/d can be exceeded at the discretion of the scheme operator if resources permit.

Abstraction rates are limited once regulation commences to a cumulative volume over a 100-day period.

These operating rules were derived using a resource simulation model for the whole River Severn system,

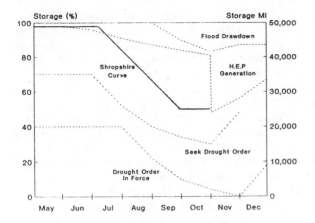

Figure 2   Llyn Clywedog control rules

and concentrated on defining a maintained flow at Bewdley which would provide sufficient support for river abstractions, and at the same time allow an acceptable residual flow in excess of 1000 Ml/d into the tidal Severn estuary in a design drought. Linear programming techniques in this simulation model ensured that a range of criteria were satisfied during a design drought, using the available resources.

To conserve surface water during droughts, a series of reservoir control rules was a product of the same simulation model. The control rules relating to summer operations assume replenished surface storage by 1 May. It is most unusual to have significant demands on storage before June but when augmentation starts, demands can increase rapidly, and be sustained for more than four months.

Because the contribution from the early phases of Shropshire Groundwater was only modest, it could not be held in reserve until late in the season by overdrawing on surface sources. The control rules currently encourage the start of Shropshire Groundwater quite quickly in a season when surface storage comes under early pressure (see Figure 2).

The start-up and use of Shropshire Groundwater is costly, and this mitigates against its early season use. This dilemma will retreat as more groundwater phases are commissioned, allowing a more traditional late season conjunctive use of surface and ground-water resources.

Regulation operations

River regulation provides a balance between inputs and outputs to keep flows consistently at or above a maintained flow. Outputs including abstractions for industry, water supply and agriculture have to be balanced at times of low flow by regulation releases from surface and groundwater reservoirs. Major water supply abstractors upstream of the control point include South Staffs. Water Co. at Hampton Loade and Severn Trent Water Ltd. at Trimpley. Operational problems associated with daily regulation of the Severn are recognised by the definition of a five-day

running mean for the maintained flow, to give a degree of flexibility in daily mean flows at Bewdley. However, problems can be encountered achieving a stable five-day mean when any contributing daily mean flow falls too low or rises too high. Accordingly, the five-day flow is viewed as a safety net to allow for unexpected reductions in flow from day to day. Sources of unexpected fluctuations include sudden increases in agricultural abstractions in the tributaries upstream of the control point.

To optimise the assessment of required release rates it is necessary to consider all factors which govern the residual flow in the river at the Bewdley control point. In its simplest form this requires an accounting procedure which recognises the constraints imposed by the fixed operating rules, and matches these to known or predicted factors of river flow and abstraction demands.

Traditionally, this approach was slow and cumbersome when using manual calculation methods. In 1989 a spreadsheet package was employed to prototype an operational control algorithm to streamline and extend this accounting procedure (see Figure 3). This enabled the duty hydrologist to assess regulation releases more objectively, with greater speed, and allow more rigorous assessment of alternative release strategies.

Data management spreadsheet

A spreadsheet solution using SMART software was produced for an office-based PC with the provision for loading onto portable Toshiba computers. A spreadsheet exists for each month of the regulation season, usually May to October. A link exists between each sheet to cater for release lag time calculations over month ends.

There are four component parts to each month's spreadsheet :

River flows

The spreadsheet requires flow information from

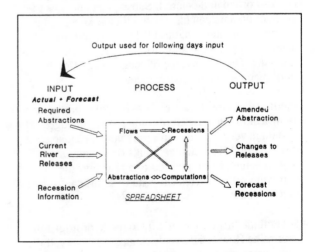

Figure 3   Spreadsheet input, process and output

Bewdley control point and three other gauging stations upstream. This information is used to estimate time of travel of releases, and natural flow trends.

River abstractions

Abstractions fall into two main categories: measured and unmeasured. Anticipated demands by major abstractors are provided a week in advance and are reviewed daily when demands are fluctuating. The operational data handling in the spreadsheet is flex-ible enough to cope with these amendments, and also acts as an archive of changes in abstraction demand.

Unmeasured abstractions provide a problem for the hydrologist. Spray irrigation is now recognised as a major loss to river systems. The MAFF service *Irriguide*, provided primarily for farmers, is valuable to the hydrologist who strives to relate river fluctu-ations to the rates and timing of irrigation demand. The spreadsheet does not make provision for unmeas-ured abstractions, so the duty hydrologist adjusts anticipated flow trends in the light of Irriguide.

Natural flow changes

Data entry is made on a daily basis to the flow and abstraction sections of the spreadsheet. A third area of the sheet calculates observed natural trends at gauging stations, (based on river flows), abstractions, and augmentation releases.

Data processing

The first three components of the spreadsheet deal with the major measured inputs and outputs to the river system upstream of the Bewdley control point. The fourth, and most detailed area of the sheet, combines values derived from the previous three areas with regulation release requirements.

Changes to the abstraction section of the sheet will be reflected in calculations of natural river flow trends on the fourth section. The best estimates of trends cannot be finalised until actual abstractions have been recorded and entered. Subsequent changes to abstraction data can have a significant knock-on effect on calculated natural flow trends, future abstraction potential and ultimately regulation release volumes. The importance of accurate and timely data in decision making is paramount.

Predicted natural flow trends at Bewdley are the most significant factor in determining release changes. The system is very sensitive to errors here, because each day's natural flow change builds on the previous day's change. Over a period of a few days the compounding of errors can lead to significant over or under releases.

Several methods are available to the hydrologist to determine flow trends, including using observed flow trend from one day upstream, to confirm the arrival

of release changes or responses to rainfall. This information is incorporated automatically for the next day's calculations, but for future days the natural river flow changes are assessed using information from the flow forecasting system.

FFS becomes invaluable when judging the river's response to heavy rainfall both on the rising and falling hydrograph. Frequent minor events can allow significant reductions in regulation releases; a very wet period can allow sustained reduction in releases, with consequent resource savings.

Tactical release and abstraction management

When all available data have been entered and the hydrologist has estimated natural flow trends, the spreadsheet will show if flows are sufficient to support planned abstractions without changes to release rates. To optimise abstraction and release changes, the spreadsheet is now used in simulation mode to assess the range of options to satisfy abstraction demands, and maintain the Bewdley target flow for the subsequent 4-7 days. There are two main options which may be used individually or in combination to achieve the required balance :

Amended abstraction rates

Once natural flow trends have been forecast, the requirements of abstractors are reconsidered, to assess whether the originally planned abstraction can be satisfied by current release rates. Operations over the past two years have shown that by keeping Hampton Loade bankside storage drawn down within agreed limits in the regulation season, any over-release or unforeseen natural flow increase in the river can be intercepted hours upstream of Bewdley.

Conversely, flows can be preserved when recession rates fall steeper than predicted by restricting abstractions as far as the storage drawdown limit, until increased regulation releases arrive at Bewdley. Spreadsheet calculations quickly simulate the potential for abstraction control using bankside storage and predicted demands.

Changes to reservoir releases

When no further scope for abstraction control exists, regulation releases need to be increased. Current river releases are manually entered from the day of release, and are lagged in the calculations by the time of travel currently being used. The time of travel of regulation releases depend upon a number of factors, including volume of release and the current flow in the reach. A suitable whole number of days' travel time is assumed for simplicity.

Best use of releases can be made if variable discharges are made from Llyn Clywedog whilst the limited storage at Lake Vyrnwy is used as a constant background release steadily increased when required, and as storage allows. Shropshire Groundwater is used only when surface storage is judged insufficient to sustain demands, but this decision may be required early in the season.

Spreadsheet calculations are very quick and straightforward, so many different regulation release scenarios can be investigated before a change of release is decided upon. Any change in inputs or outputs can be simulated rapidly in the office or at home, so that the potential for prompt release changes exists at any time of day.

Operational experiences in 1989/90

The first prototype for real-time operational control was devised during the developing drought of 1989, when the earlier manual calculation method proved too cumbersome. The first prototype demonstrated three main features :

1. The spreadsheet enhanced the hydrologists' ability to respond rapidly to changed conditions, and this improved regulation proficiency. Target flows at Bewdley were achieved with greater precision, despite the efforts of spray irrigators to reduce tributary flows without warning. Excess releases for the season due to forecasting errors were about 7%; a significant improvement compared with 1975/6. This is in part due to a combination of improved river flow hydrometry and flow forecasting capability as well as the introduction of this system (see Figure 4a).

2. Spreadsheets are quick to establish and versatile at carrying out many individually trivial calculations on a small amount of data. The time taken to assess a proposed change in release, and/ or abstractions, was reduced from many minutes to a few seconds. Updating the result as new or corrected data became available was similarly trivial, in stark contrast to the manual system.

3. Spreadsheets are not particularly user-friendly, and, although easy to establish for PC-literate

hydrologists, they are difficult to package in a form which allows casual users to pick up the system on their weekend's duty, having possibly not used it for several weeks. This was particularly true at the overlap between months, but attempts to concatenate all the regulation season into a single spreadsheet soon highlighted the limitation of spreadsheet size and speed of execution within the chosen package.

Having demonstrated a general increase in regulation proficiency, developments concentrated on improved operation of the bankside storage reservoirs. This achieved further optimisation in release utilisation and so reduced again the excess releases during 1990 (see Figure 4b).

The prototype spreadsheet was redesigned for 1990 to incorporate improvements identified during 1989. It was made more usable by adding "casual user" data entry procedures and was successfully used by all duty officers that summer.

In its second year of operation, total excess releases were halved (see Figure 4b). Part of the improvement can be explained by more predictable weather; it stayed dry for longer compared with 1989, and any rain was sustained for longer. Nevertheless, the greatest improvement can be ascribed to the operation of bankside storage, to ensure that when flows did respond to rainfall subsequent to releases being made, much of that response could be taken into storage. This helped to halve the excess releases due to "subsequent rainfall" from 12% in 1989 to 6% in 1990. Excess releases due to forecasting error were also cut again, mainly due to improved familiarisation with the technique. These two areas of improvement enabled regulation to be sustained without the need for Drought Orders, and avoided the need to utilise the Shropshire Groundwater contribution.

Conclusions

Regulation of the river Severn is made difficult because the control point is some three or four days

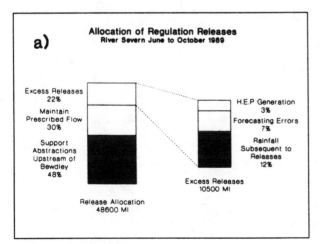
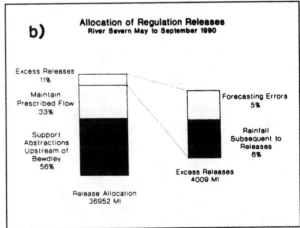

Figure 4.   Allocation of regulation releases, 1989 and 1990

time of travel from the main resource. The demands are distributed throughout a long length of river, and flows have to be maintained at the control point against a background of natural recessions and the unpredictable activities of irrigators and other water users. Although the concepts involved are not complex, the practical difficulties are considerable.

Introduction of a simple, readily available PC spread-sheet package has replaced a formerly cumbersome accounting procedure. The resultant package has reduced response time from hours to minutes. It has released hydrologists to concentrate on interpretation of the data and results rather than be involved with endless calculation.

The implementation was possible in stages, using the package to develop a prototype, and then refining the original with the benefit of experience. This approach to small system development allows the users to influence the outcome, and builds on their operational experience.

This pragmatic approach has been tested in two significant drought summers. Although the technology is modest, it represents a significant step forward in operating this system. It has enabled the better information about river conditions to be used to influence release decisions. By so doing, a demonstrable improvement in regulation efficiency has been achieved, by reductions in excess releases. Some of the improvements would have arisen anyway, as a result of improved hydrometry at the control point. However, by building these hydrometric improvements into a credible management system, the NRA has streamlined its tactical operations.

The information resulting from the introduction of this modest, but effective, technology are now being fed back to the resource planners for incorporation into the long term planning models. The main areas for consideration in this feedback are redefining the simulation model to include revised operation of bankside storage reservoirs, along with more realistic assumptions about errors in release rates.

Further improvements are now being sought, including extensions of real-time monitoring of irrigation and water supply abstractions, and of effluent discharges. This extra hour-by-hour information would enable a more detailed model of the whole river Severn system to be built.

Extensions to include river quality indicators, as remote sensing technologies improve, would be valuable for the lower Severn reaches. As the operational model becomes more extensive, incorporation of "expert systems" to evaluate the presently unpredictable elements of the system may be appropriate.

The present rather crude approach has demonstrated that even simple decision control algorithms, built into a readily available software package, can provide worthwhile improvements.

Acknowledgments

The authors acknowledge the assistance and comments of colleagues during the development stages. The co-operation of Severn Trent Water Ltd and South Staffordshire Water Co. in agreeing modifications to operation of bankside storage is recognised.

The paper is published with permission of Dr. G. Mance, Regional General Manager, NRA Severn-Trent Region. The opinions are those of the authors, and not necessarily of the National Rivers Authority.

References

Dobson, C., Turner, A. and Eccleston, A. 1990. A real time environmental monitoring and fore-casting system. In *Total Solutions for Measurement and Control*, SIRA Communications, Chislehurst.

Goodhew, R.C. 1982. Performance of a major river regulation resource system under design conditions. In *Optimal Allocation of Water Resources*. IAHS Publication No. 135, 337-355.

A low flow management procedure for the River Derwent, West Cumbria

H. Smithers

Abstract

The paper describes the procedure currently being developed by North West Water Ltd for regulation of the River Derwent, Cumbria, to support abstractions near Workington. Water is released from Thirlmere Reservoir and travels around 50 km to the control point, passing through a natural lake. Current management strategy is to avoid regulation by reducing the abstraction rate, so releases are small and infrequent. These factors have led to the choice of a relatively simple set of release rules which will be refined with further operating experience.

Introduction

The River Derwent drains the northern part of the Lake District and reaches the sea at Workington. Water is abstracted by North West Water Ltd (NWW) at Barepot, and further downstream by British Steel. The NWW abstraction is supported at times of very low flow by regulation releases from Thirlmere Reservoir. Releases travel down St John's Beck, through the Rivers Greta and Derwent and into Bassenthwaite Lake. There is no control structure at the lake outlet into the lower part of the Derwent. The abstraction control point is downstream of Camerton, 50 km from the release point. The catchment area of Thirlmere is 41 km², which is 6% of the total to Camerton. The paper presents the operational procedure for regulation and discusses the development of the release rules.

Derwent low flow management procedure

On the formation of the National Rivers Authority (NRA), responsibility for the management and operation of the Derwent Regulation Scheme passed to NWW. Because of the nature of the scheme, operating rules have until now been ill-defined. Hence a procedure is currently being developed at NWW for management of low flows on the Derwent. The licence held by NWW authorises 34 Ml d⁻¹ abstraction at Barepot without regard to the rate of flow in the river. In addition, when the measured flow at Camerton gauging station exceeds 191 Ml d⁻¹, up to half the excess can be abstracted, up to a maximum of 57 Ml d⁻¹.

Previous regulation and modelling experience

Records of previous regulation and modelling were examined to assess their value in the current investigation. A series of controlled releases was made in the early seventies in order to measure travel times and losses. However, the results were in most cases affected by rainfall, particularly at the lower end of the catchment. As a result of the release experiments, the use of a fixed "catchment" recession constant was abandoned in favour of one determined by recent data.

A model was then developed by consultants based on unit hydrograph principles; it appears that the model was not particularly successful. In 1977 an alternative stepped release scheme was proposed, by which releases should begin 24 hours before the flow rate was forecast to fall below the maintained flow at Camerton, and increased when necessary as natural flows declined.

Releases were made in 1980, 1982, 1983, 1986 and 1989 but provided very little data uncontaminated by rainfall. In 1984 and 1989 there were periods of very low flow but abstractions were less than 34 Ml d⁻¹, so no regulation took place.

Extensive daily simulations had also previously been carried out using NWW's suite of computer programs for hydrological analysis (NWW, 1981) to develop a water resources strategy for West Cumbria, including the Derwent. However experience indicated that a daily simulation model was not suitable for investigation of the catchment response to regulation releases in an operational management context, as travel times were too short and variable. It was concluded that no model remained in a usable form, and that the accumulation of additional data warranted a fresh examination of the catchment.

Development of current regulation model

The Derwent regulation model is required to determine quantities and timing of releases from Thirlmere in order to satisfy the Derwent licence conditions. In designing such a model various requirements must be kept in mind:

(i)   Current management strategy is to keep the Barepot abstraction below the level at which regulation is required, in order to minimise the demand on Thirlmere Reservoir. Regulation is likely to be infrequent and involve small quantities of water. A sophisticated model would therefore result in an unjustifiable use of staff and equipment, both in development and maintenance. Considerable refamiliarisation would be necessary at the beginning of each regulation episode.

(ii) The catchment is complex, particularly because the released water has to travel through a natural lake to reach the regulation point. Changes in hydrograph shape and volume, particularly below Ouse Bridge, also suggest significant amounts of bank storage capacity.

(iii) All the readily-available measured flows have an artificial component, due to Thirlmere Reservoir, and the direct supply abstraction from Crummock Water on the Cocker.

Data availability

The first stage in designing a model was to review the available data. This was divided into two categories: historic records; and those which will be available to the hydrologist in the real-time regulation situation. In addition, some information was available about previous releases, as discussed above.

Measured flows are available for the regulation point at Camerton since September 1960. This is a velocity-area station which is known to be insensitive at low flows. Thirlmere compensation and releases have been measured at St John's Beck since January 1973 when a compound Crump weir was installed, and flows have been measured at intermediate stations since the early seventies. Camerton and St John's Beck are linked to the Regional Telemetry Scheme (RTS) and data is therefore available in real time. Data from the intermediate stations is available for historic analysis.

Rainfall information is also useful, particularly in real time at the end of a regulation period. The gauge at Dale Head Hall near Thirlmere is linked to the RTS and provides an indicator of conditions in the upper part of the catchment.

Evaporation data is sparse. The only readily available information is provided by fortnightly Met. Office reports produced using MORECS (Thompson *et al.,* 1981), which give potential evaporation for both real land use and grass and also soil moisture deficit values on a 40km-square grid. Analysis of this data for recent years indicated the general range but specific values proved to be too coarse, both temporally and spatially, to use on a real time basis.

The information is however useful in building up a general picture of the situation in conjunction with Met. Office forecasts.

Forecasting information

In controlling regulation the hydrologist must decide when to begin releases, how much to release, and when the releases can safely be terminated. In order to develop guidelines for this decision-making process, recession rates, travel times, attenuation and losses were examined, both in natural events and in releases for regulation or experiment. Catchment response to rainfall at low river levels was also investigated. Throughout these analyses the need to provide simple indicators was paramount.

Recession rates

The recession constant is given (e.g. Barnes, 1939) by

$$Q_t = rc\,Q_0$$

where Q_t = discharge on day t
Q_0 = discharge on day 0
rc = recession constant

and thus has units of time. It is usually calculated over 24 hours. Ineson and Downing (1964) pointed out that for many British rivers the recession "constant" in fact declines throughout the summer. They suggest that as the summer progresses water drains from areas more remote from the river channel. As Walker and Pearson (1985) suggested, recession rates at Camerton appear to be closely related to the prevailing discharge; there is substantial variation between events, however.

Regression analyses using data from 1984 and 1988 suggested only a weak relationship between recession constant and the available MORECS evaporation parmeters. The reach between Portinscale and Ouse Bridge contains Bassenthwaite Lake, which is 6.4 km long with a surface area of 5.28 km². Evaporation from the surface is estimated to reach a mean value of 3.7 mm d^{-1} in July, resulting in a drop in outflow of around 6 Ml d^{-1} at low lake levels. Changes in evaporation rate could thus have a small but measurable effect on the Camerton recession rate.

Regression equations were produced to predict flow at Camerton using various discharge parameters and also Dale Head rainfall. These all explained over 90% of the variation in Camerton flow.

Using Camerton data only

$$Q_{t+1} = 14.17 + 0.954Q_t \quad (R^2=0.917, SE=60.57)$$

where Q_t = discharge on day t
Q_{t+1} = discharge on day t+1
R^2 = coefficient of determination.

Including Dale Head rainfall gives

$$Q_{t+1} = 5.20 + 0.954Q_t + 5.79R_t \quad (R^2=0.928, SE=56.12)$$

where R_t = rainfall on day t.

Other equations were produced, but the parameter values would not be available in a real-time situation, and there was little improvement in prediction. All these regressions suffered from the constraint of fixed parameter values, so it was considered more appropriate to use the prevailing 24-hour recession constant, thus allowing implicitly for changing conditions. However, values of the recession constant when calculated on a 24-hour basis were extremely unstable. This was not only due to physical variations but was also affected by the insensitivity of measurement. In order to damp down the fluctuations for forecasting purposes the recession constant was taken to be the mean of the previous three 24-hour values.

Travel times

Travel times were analysed by dividing the river into reaches between the gauging stations and taking each separately. Here it is necessary to distinguish between releases, which can be thought of as a wave travelling down the channel, and hydrographs from natural events, which generally result from widespread rainfall and thus tend to grow in speed and volume downstream, particularly when there is a considerable tributary inflow along the reach. However, as release data was extremely limited, data from natural events was also used.

Travel times calculated were those between peaks, as these are generally easier to identify. However when the effect of storage is substantial, as in the reach between Portinscale and Ouse Bridge, due to Bassenthwaite Lake, the time of peak is less well-defined. Indeed for natural events it was found that Camerton often peaked before Ouse Bridge due to runoff from the Cocker catchment. Mean travel time from Southwaite Bridge to Camerton is 5.5 hours, but from Ouse Bridge to Camerton it is 8.5 hours.

Despite attempts to relate travel times to flow conditions in the river, a lack of suitable data meant that for most reaches use of the mean time provided the best estimate. Adding the individual times suggested a range of 27 to 45 h for the maximum effect of a release to reach Camerton, the uncertainty arising mainly from Bassenthwaite Lake. Releases must therefore be started two days before they are required at Camerton, although some effect may well be noticed sooner.

Losses and attenuation

Volumetric calculations are also best carried out using release data; natural events tend to increase in volume downstream, and regulation periods end with heavy rainfall. In June 1973 a maximum of 97% of the Thirlmere release rate was recorded at Low Briery, and 93% at Portinscale. By Ouse Bridge the maximum reached 60% after 120 hours, and at Camerton it was 57% after 120 hours, and still rising, when rain intervened. Losses in Bassenthwaite Lake were thus around 33% but the water was released at the natural discharge rate of the lake over the next few days. Losses between Ouse Bridge and Camerton were initially 12%, reducing to 3% after 120 hours, possibly as bank storage became saturated.

Catchment response to rainfall at low river levels

The Derwent catchment shows considerable variation in its response to rainfall after a dry period. The shape of the Camerton hydrograph depends largely on the areal distribution of the rainfall. Significant precipitation over the whole catchment gives an inital sharp peak due to flow from the Cocker, followed by a longer, more gentle rise due to the main river. If rain falls only over the Cocker or lower Derwent catchment below Ouse Bridge, the peak will be rapid and the river will soon return to its previous low levels. If, on the other hand, rain falls only above Ouse Bridge, the rise at Camerton may be delayed by 24 hours.

The Camerton flow data was examined in conjunction with rainfall from Dale Head Hall. Camerton generally responded the same day to amounts over 10mm, with the rapid rise due to rain over the lower part of the catchment. During a release period this would lead to an over-release; however in the absence of reliable weather forecasts this is unavoidable, as the decision would have been made two days previously. A daily rainfall of 10mm spread generally over the catchment results in a Camerton rise of around 70 Ml d^{-1} at low river levels, so theoretically the release rate could be trimmed by the same amount. Actual losses will depend on the hydraulic gradients between river and bank storage, and the level of Bassenthwaite Lake.

Regulation procedure

A regulation procedure has been developed, based on the analyses described above. It has two levels of activity, routine monitoring and periods when flows are approaching or below the regulation level.

Routine monitoring

Routine monitoring will be carried out weekly by a hydrologist from NWW's Hydrological Management Section. Daily and hourly flow rates at Camerton, abstractions at Barepot, and rainfall at St John's Beck will be obtained via the RTS. For much of the year no further action will be required.

Procedure during low flow periods

Low flow periods are most likely during summer droughts, but very cold spells with sub-zero temperatures may also cause a substantial reduction in runoff. An automatic alarm has been set to 300 Ml d^{-1} at Camerton. This gives adequate warning at the lower regulation levels and for recession rates above 0.93.

Once the alarm limit has been reached, or routine

monitoring reveals Camerton flows at or near the limit, further action will be required. A hydrologist from Hydrological Management will contact local supply staff with a request to reduce the abstraction below 34 Ml d^{-1}. If this cannot be achieved, Hydrological Managment will inform local staff that releases will probably be required within 5-7 days in the absence of significant rainfall. Local supply staff will then inform riparian land-users along St John's Beck that river levels may shortly increase substantially as a result of additional releases from Thirlmere. This allows time for livestock to be moved where necessary.

Daily monitoring via telemetry will now be required. Each day the Camerton 24-hour recession rate must be calculated, and the mean of three days' recession rates used to forecast the flow one, two and three days ahead.

When the three-day forecast reaches the regulation level a 24-hour warning may be given to the local staff. When the two-day forecast reaches regulation level a release must be made that day. Hydrological Management will inform local supply staff by telephone and telex of the timing and volume of the release. Local supply staff will in turn inform the NRA that releases are to be made. Based on the analyses discussed above, the size of the release is determined by the forecast shortfall two days ahead, allowing for a 50% transmission loss, and assuming that the first 20 Ml d^{-1} is entirely lost. Release volumes should then be rounded up to the nearest 30 Ml d^{-1} as smaller increments are not operationally manageable; they also imply an unwarranted degree of precision in the forecast.

Catchment conditions and the Met. Office weather forecast will be monitored at frequent intervals by Hydrological Management, and any changes in the release rate notified to local staff. Careful records of all release times and quantities will be kept by local supply staff and notified to Hydrological Management by 0900 on the day following the change. This will assist in fine-tuning the release volume, and ensure that maximum benefit can be obtained from the data.

Releases will be terminated by local supply staff at the direction of Hydrological Management when either:

(i)   Abstraction at Barepot falls significantly below 34 Ml d^{-1} and will remain so until the river recovers,
       or
(ii) The river rises naturally due to significant rainfall. A daily total of 10 mm spread generally over the catchment will allow termination of releases up to 60 Ml d^{-1}.

Assessment and maintenance of the procedure

When significant autumn rain and high river levels mark the end of the release season, Hydrological Management will produce a report summarising the releases made during the year and recommending any changes to procedures in the light of experience. At the beginning of each year contact lists for NWW personnel, NRA and local landowners will be checked.

Conclusions

This paper has described aspects of the hydrology of the Derwent catchment. Analyses of historic and current data have been used to develop a regulation procedure.

The Derwent is unusual amongst British regulated rivers in two particular respects: the infrequency and small volume of releases, and the presence of a natural lake between release point and control point. These together determined the approach taken in this investigation.

Despite all the work carried out on the Derwent and all the data collected over the years, very little of the information relates closely to the regulation situation. This has necessitated the use of very wide margins of error. It should therefore be expected that the results and "rules" presented here will be revised in the light of further experience. A more sophisticated model and enhanced telemetry network could only be justified if the abstraction rate at Barepot were to be significantly increased.

References

Barnes, B.S. 1939. The structure of discharge-recession curves. *Trans. Am. Geophys. Union* 20, 721-725.

Ineson, J. & Downing, R.A. 1964. The groundwater component of river discharge and its relationship to hydrogeology. *J. Instn Wat. Engrs. Sci.*, 18, 510-541.

NWW 1981. An introduction to the RP suite of programs. Internal report.

Thompson, N., Barrie, I.A. & Ayles, M. 1981. *The Met . Office Rainfall and Evaporation Calculation System (MORECS)*. Hydrological memorandum 45, Met 08 Bracknell.

Walker, S. & Pearson, D. 1985. River recession analysis in the operational management of lake abstraction. *J. Instn Wat. Engrs Sci.*, 39, 244-253.

Low flow management of the Lower Thames

C. M. Glenny & J. H. Kinniburgh

Abstract

The River Thames is a major source of water supply for London, it receives the effluents returned, and supports recreational and environmental uses. These uses conflict at times of low flow. The paper shows how this conflict is resolved with reference to the 1990 drought when flow was less than 50% of average. A drought assessment package is used to predict flows, reservoir levels, and abstractions. The effect of low flows on dissolved oxygen concentrations in the Thames estuary is also predicted. Short-term procedures (improving effluent quality, ceasing abstractions, use of the Thames Bubbler) are used to manage the situation. The need for close liaison between water undertakers and the National Rivers Authority is stressed in order to manage the conflict in an integrated manner.

Introduction

The natural mean annual flow of the River Thames at Kingston is $6700 \times 10^3 m^3 d^{-1}$, of which about $1700 \times 10^3 m^3 d^{-1}$ are abstracted. The natural flow is the measured (or gauged) flow at the ultrasonic gauging station at Kingston, plus the quantity abstracted from the Lower Thames, i.e. between Windsor and Teddington. The locations of the abstraction points are shown in Fig. 1. During an average summer 50% of the flow in the Thames is abstracted (about $1500 \times 10^3 m^3 d^{-1}$) but in a drought year this can increase to over 80%. The water is abstracted for London's potable supply by three companies of whom Thames Water Utilities (TWU) is the largest, abstracting approximately 80% of the total. Any shortfall in abstraction to meet the water demands is made up from storage reservoirs in London which hold 100 days' supply and are filled during the winter.

Most of the water supplied to London is returned, after use, to the sewage treatment works at Beckton, Crossness and Mogden (Fig.1), which discharge a total of $2000 \times 10^3 m^3 d^{-1}$ to the tidal Thames (known

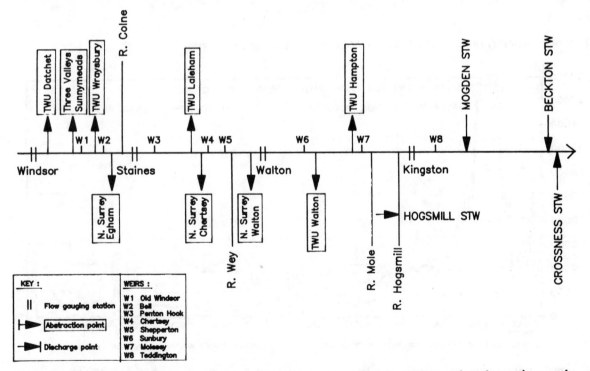

Figure 1 *Schematic of Lower Thames to show location of flow gauging stations, weirs, abstractions and major discharge points*

as the tideway). The works are operated by TWU. When flows over Teddington weir are low (less than $800 \times 10^3 m^3 d^{-1}$) the quality of the tidal Thames may deteriorate due to the impact of these discharges and overflows from the sewerage system.

At times of low flows, these uses of providing potable supply and maintaining quality in the tideway, conflict. Demand for water supplies increase in hot dry summers but abstraction from the river must be carefully regulated to leave sufficient flow to maintain water quality. Head water levels in the river must also be maintained for navigational purposes. This paper outlines how this situation is managed with specific reference to the 1990 drought.

The drought of 1990 was severe in terms of rainfall, but less so in terms of river flow. Rainfall in the Thames region was below the 1941-70 average for every month from March to December 1990. Total

rainfall for the nine months from March to November inclusive was the lowest for these months since records began in 1904 (287 mm compared with an average of 546 mm or 63%). May 1990, with 6.2mm was the driest May on record (Fig.2). River flows at Kingston were not quite so extreme, mainly because of the heavy rainfall in December 1989 and February 1990. Natural flows at Kingston were at their lowest in September (when the mean was $1600 \times 10^3 m^3 d^{-1}$ compared with the average September figure of 2950 $\times 10^3 m^3 d^{-1}$) and remained less than 50% of average from October to December. In terms of lowest ever recorded flows, these compare favourably with the August 1976 mean of $954 \times 10^3 m^3 d^{-1}$ (Fig.3).

Low flow management is based on the use and interpretation of models and operational data and close liaison between water undertakers and the National Rivers Authority, Thames Region (NRA). This is now described in more detail.

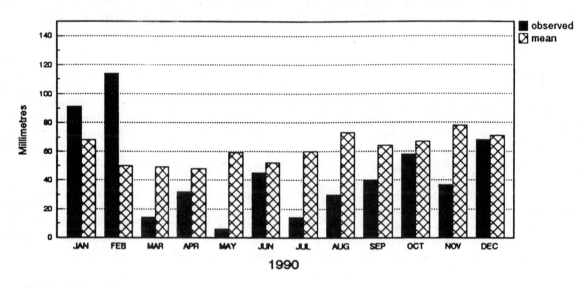

Figure 2   Monthly rainfall (1990) for the Thames upstream of Teddington

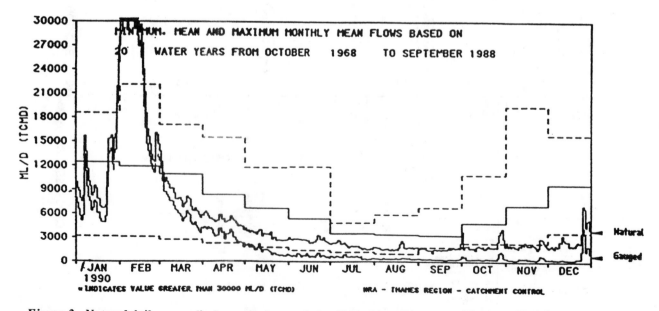

Figure 3   Natural daily mean discharge hydrograph for 1990, River Thames at Kingston (Teddington)

Managing flows and abstractions

An "operating strategy" determines how much water can be abstracted from the Lower Thames and what the residual flow over Teddington weir should be. Normally, reservoirs are filled by April each year, and if possible are maintained full during the summer. The strategy specifies that when reservoir levels are falling, one of a series of target residual flows over Teddington weir is maintained, depending on the quantity in store and the time of year (Fig.4). The flow can be set at 800, 600, 300 or 200 x 10^3 m^3d^{-1}. Details of the strategy were given at the public enquiry into the Teddington Flow Proposal (Thames Water, 1986).

This operating strategy is incorporated into a drought assessment package. This package was developed by Thames Water Authority and is now used by both TWU and NRA. The package integrates a rainfall/runoff model with a model of the Lower Thames abstraction and reservoir system. The rainfall/runoff model generates natural flow at Teddington weir for the next 12 months using average rainfall, 75% average rainfall (a 1 in 10 year event based on annual rainfall totals) and 60% average rainfall (a 1 in 50 year event). It enables a forecast to be made of when and if reductions to the target residual flow over Teddington Weir are likely to be required and to identify the level of restriction on potable water use which may be required.

When predictions have been made, and the need for reducing Teddington flow has become apparent, discussions between TWU and NRA on the practicalities and desirability of implementation commence.

The actual storage in the London reservoirs in 1990 is shown on Fig.4. The reservoirs were full until the beginning of July as shown by the coincidence of the 1990 storage line with the adjusted full storage level (allows for practical problems in achieving theoretical full storage level). After July, reservoir storage reduced significantly as less flow was available for abstraction and demands increased significantly, but flows could be reduced at Teddington weir to allow greater abstraction (Fig. 4), and demand could also be restricted at this time. Flows were reduced to 600 x 10^3 m^3d^{-1} on 4th June, to 300 x 10^3 m^3d^{-1} on 23rd July, and to 200 x 10^3 m^3d^{-1} on 18th August.

Operational considerations

The day-to-day rate of abstraction by TWU at each intake is discussed with the NRA, who balance the need for abstractions with the need to maintain statutory river levels and maintain the flow target at Teddington.

At low flows, maintaining river levels is operationally difficult because of water loss through weir gates, locks, and fish passes. Achieving the target residual flow at Teddington is also difficult because the tributary flows of the Mole and Hogsmill rivers contribute over 200 x 10^3 m^3d^{-1} downstream of the lowest intake. If the target flow is 200 x 10^3 m^3d^{-1}, then all flow upstream of Molesey Weir can theoretically be abstracted! Practically this is not possible because of the need to maintain head levels in Molesey reach and hence residual flows at Teddington often exceed their targets at low flows. The target flow of 200 x 10^3 m^3d^{-1} was achieved for only a few days in September 1990, at other times it was above 250 x 10^3 m^3d^{-1}.

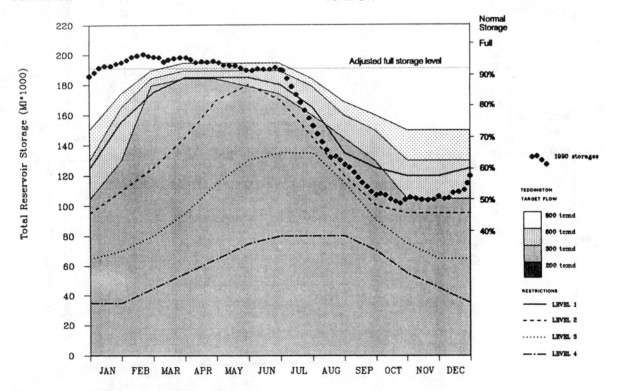

Figure 4   Lower Thames operating strategy

The flows are continuously monitored using ultra-sonic flow gauges at Windsor, Staines, Walton and Kingston, and the results are telemetered to the NRA control centre. This allows immediate monitoring of the effects of abstractions on river levels so that an optimal balance can be maintained.

Water quality management of the tideway

Dissolved oxygen (DO) is essential for aquatic life in the tideway and in order to maintain concentrations, the following DO standards must be met:
  >40% DO saturation for 80% time from Teddington to Battersea (22km below Teddington)
  >30% DO saturation for 80% time from Battersea to Mucking (82km below Teddington)

Discharges from sewage treatment works (STW) and storm overflows from the London sewerage system exert demands on oxygen concentrations in the tideway. (Oxygen is used by bacteria breaking down the organics and oxidising ammonia in the discharges). Fig. 5 shows the location of STW and major storm overflows. The two largest STW at Beckton and Crossness are 50km below Teddington while Mogden is 6km below Teddington. The majority of the storm overflows are in the upper part of the tideway. The discharges from STW must meet standards stated in their discharge consents to ensure DO standards in the river are met. This ensures that when storm overflows occur, on which there are no quality controls, critically low DO concentrations and

consequent fish kills are avoided. Such a storm event in 1986 caused DO to drop to 0% saturation and 20 tonnes of fish were killed; DO standards in the river prior to the storm had not been met.

When Teddington flows are reduced to meet demands for water supply, then this has an impact on DO in the tideway. Fig.6 shows the DO predicted by a water quality model of the tideway (Barrett *et al.*, 1978) with progressively reduced flows over Teddington. DO concentrations are reduced due to the longer retention time of effluents in the tideway.

Hence, DO concentrations in the tideway broadly depend on the balance between flows, STW discharges, and storm overflows. In order to help manage this situation, three operating agreements were made between TWU and the NRA as part of the Water Act transfer arrangements in 1989. These relate to short-term procedures for improving effluent quality, ceasing abstractions and using the Thames Bubbler. Their use in 1990 is now described.

i) Improved effluent quality

The essential parts of this agreement are: "In the event of the NRA considering that environmental circumstances are such that they are likely to cause the dissolved oxygen concentration in the tideway to fall to a figure of less than 30% ... the NRA may request TWU to make arrangements to improve the quality of effluents from any one or more of the

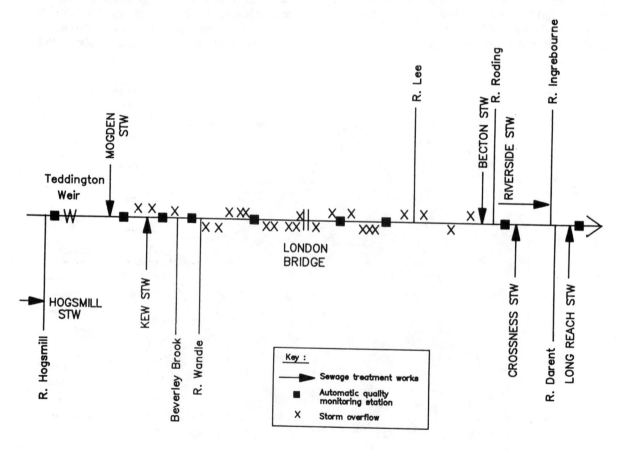

Figure 5 Schematic of Thames tideway to show location of discharges and automatic monitoring stations

2.32

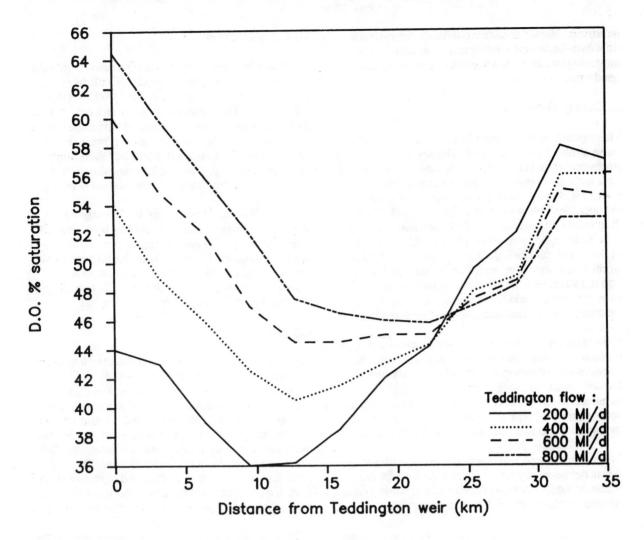

Figure 6   Effect of flow on dissolved oxygen: tideway model output

sewage works to the improved standard specified."
(Transfer Scheme, Thames Water, 1989). The
improved standards are given in Table 1.

Normally, the works must meet the consent
standards. However, when the operating agreement
is invoked, TWU must endeavour to meet the
improved standards. In 1990, because of low flows

in April, high temperatures, and deteriorating DO
concentrations, the NRA requested TWU to improve
effluent quality on May 4th. Fig.7 shows the DO
recorded by seven automatic quality monitoring
stations located in the tideway on April 28th, before
the request for improved effluent, and two weeks
after the request. It shows that it takes about two
weeks for performance at the sewage works to be

Table 1 Improved effluent quality standards **

	*BOD (ATU) (mgl⁻¹)	Ammoniacal Nitrogen (mgl⁻¹)
Mogden	11 (23)	1.0 (7)
Kew	5 (16)	0.5 (7)
Beckton	6 (22)	1.0 (6)
Crossness	10 (25)	7.0 (16)
Riverside	15 (31)	20.0 (44)
Long Reach	20 (50)	25.0 (53)

* Biochemical oxygen demand, suppressed by allyl thiourea
** Expressed as 50 percentiles with consent standards (95 percentiles) in brackets

improved. Hence, prediction of likely reductions in flow over Teddington are necessary to ensure that improvements at the sewage works are requested in good time.

ii) Ceasing abstractions

This agreement allows the NRA to request TWU to cease abstracting in the Lower Thames so that more freshwater flow is available to the tideway. The extra flow helps to disperse oxygen demanding loads down river. Fig.8 shows tideway DO after a storm on 2nd October 1990 when storm overflows caused DO to drop from 40% saturation to 20% saturation. Flows over Teddington were $300 \times 10^3 \, m^3 d^{-1}$ so the effects of the storm were only dispersing slowly. A further storm was forecast for the following day, and if this was to cause the same effect as the first storm, DO concentrations would become critical. Extra freshwater flow could help alleviate the situation.

A decision on whether one day's abstraction in a drought (approximately 60% of a day's demand in London) should be sacrificed for the quality of the tideway when the salmon run was occurring was required. Since it was October and one could expect some autumn rains, a decision was made by the NRA to request TWU to cease abstraction for 24 hours.

In the event, the second storm was not significant and it was not necessary to restrict abstractions for the whole of the 24 hours, so the quantity of water lost to storage was less than 25% of a day's supply.

iii) Thames Bubbler

The Thames Bubbler injects oxygen directly into the river at a rate of 30 tonnes per day (Griffiths *et al.*, 1985). It is owned and operated by TWU but the NRA has a role in requesting its use and determining its location for maximum effect. At the same time as a request for ceasing abstractions was made in the above event, the Thames Bubbler was mobilised. These actions helped restore DO concentrations to 40% saturation by October 4th, as shown in Fig. 8.

The overall effect of managing the tideway during 1990 in the ways described is evident from river DO data. For the period July to September, the upper tideway exceeded 48% saturation for 80 percent of the time, and the mid-tideway exceeded 35% saturation for 80 percent of the time. Hence, despite low flows, the DO standards were achieved.

Conclusion

This account demonstrates the conflicting demands for water in a drought; for public supply and for maintaining river levels and water quality. In order to predict likely situations, several models are used. However because of the underlying assumptions and approximations in models, it is necessary to interpret the results carefully and to combine these with daily situation reports from telemetered data. This requires close liaison between modellers and operational staff. Furthermore, because the responsibilities for water supply in London and the river environment are split

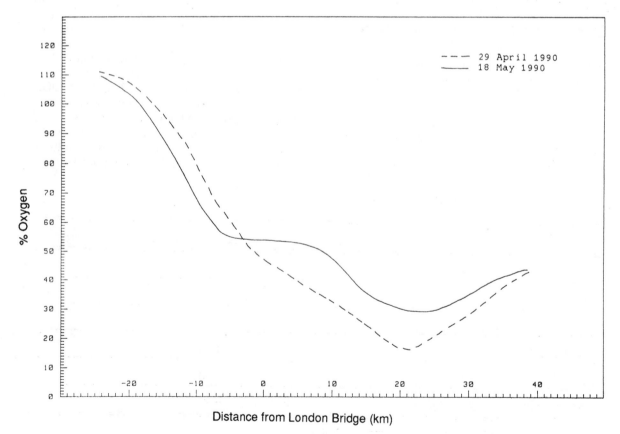

Figure 7 Dissolved oxygen in the tideway measured by automatic quality monitoring stations

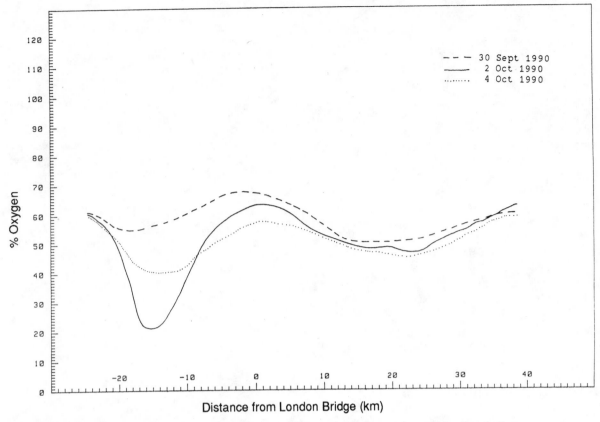

Figure 8 Dissolved oxygen in the tideway measured by automatic quality monitoring stations

between TWU and NRA, open liaison and co-operation between these two parties is essential.

Liaison takes time and often time is short; counter-acting the effects of storms on tideway quality cannot be delayed a day or so - fish die quickly! Daily telemetered monitoring and reporting of the situation have helped us to respond quickly. Good working relationships between TWU and NRA have been built up. The 1990 situation, when tideway quality standards were achieved at the same time as water supply needs were met, demonstrates that this system, of working together in an integrated manner, resolves the conflicts experienced during a drought.

Acknowledgements

The authors wish to acknowledge the assistance of their colleagues in the Catchment Control Department of the National Rivers Authority, Thames Region, in the preparation of this paper and for the comments of Water Resources Department, Thames Water Utilities. The authors would like to thank the National Rivers Authority for permission to publish this paper and wish to state that the views expressed are their own and not necessarily those of the Authority.

References

Barrett, M.J., Mollowney, B.M., & Casapieri, P. 1978. The Thames model - an assessment. *Prog. Wat. Technol.*, 10, 409-416.

Griffiths, I.M. & Lloyd, P.J. 1985. Mobile oxygenation in the Thames Estuary. *Effl. Wat. Treat. J.*, 5, 165-169.

Thames Water 1986. Teddington Flow Proposal, Statement of Case. Internal publication of Thames Water. 80pp.

Thames Water 1989. The Water Act 1989, Transfer Scheme of Thames Water Authority. Agreement B2.

Rehabilitation of the Wallop Brook and Bourne Rivulet

P. Midgley & C. R. C. Jones

Abstract

The Wallop Brook and the Bourne Rivulet are two of the tributary streams of the River Test in Hampshire. For many years they have suffered excessive flow depletion during droughts which can be traced at least in part to the effects of licensed abstractions. In early 1990 the NRA gave both streams a high priority for investigation and remedial works to improve summer drought flows, and subsequently let a contract to Mott MacDonald to carry out the investigation and cost potential remedial measures. This paper describes the problems involved, the computer simulation and modelling, and the costing work and rehabilitation proposals.

Introduction

The Wallop Brook and the Bourne Rivulet are two of the tributary streams of the River Test in Hampshire (Figure 1), which itself is the premier game fishing river in England and which is also very important for public water supply abstraction. Its quality and quantity of flow are hence vital to the NRA. Since the Test (in common with most Chalk rivers) has few tributaries, conditions in the Wallop Brook and Bourne Rivulet are also vital. From at least 1965 both these tributaries have suffered excessive flow depletion during drought years which can be partially traced to the effects of abstraction licences of right granted under the terms of the 1963 Water Act.

In early 1990 the NRA national list of 'over-abstracted' catchments was published which gave both streams a high priority for investigation and remedial works. The latter might include revocation of licences, lining of channels, groundwater augment-ation and artificial recharge. After a short internal study the NRA let a contract to Mott MacDonald in the autumn of 1990 to investigate and cost remedial measures to improve summer drought flows in both the Wallop Brook and the Bourne Rivulet.

The Wallop catchment area is some 61 km² and the groundwater divide is largely coincident with that of the surface water. During winter and early spring the Wallop Brook rises about 1 km to the northwest of Over Wallop and flows into the Test some 12 km further down the valley (Figure 1). In dry summers it rises between Over and Middle Wallop at the site of some old watercress beds, disappears through the bed adjacent to Broughton Pumping Station, and reappears at Bossington just short of the confluence

with the Test. The natural perennial section is thus quite short, being only some 2 km long. Typical accretion profiles are shown in Figure 2.

Within the Wallop catchment there are 18 licensed sources which authorise abstraction of about 9% of the annual average recharge to the valley. The one groundwater source for public water supply at Broughton Pumping Station comprises over 90% of this abstraction. The remaining licences are small non-consumptive agricultural and domestic abstract-ions. The Broughton abstraction is largely non-consumptive in that a good percentage of the water is used within the valley and returned to the aquifer via septic tanks or local sewage treatment works. In overall terms the Wallop valley is thus not heavily abstracted but it is the siting of the Broughton abstraction boreholes which causes the problem.

Abstraction from these boreholes commenced in 1949 (the source was licensed in 1963), when the primary concern was to maximise the yield of good quality water to feed an expanding population, hence its siting immediately adjacent to the Brook. In water supply engineering and hydrogeological terms this made sense but it causes the cone of depression around the pumping boreholes to draw down water from the Brook through the bed. Whilst this is not a problem in winter or in average and wet summers when sufficient amounts of water are available, it means that in dry summers such as those of 1976, 1983, 1989 and 1990 the Brook disappears by the pumping station and what is normally a village amenity within Broughton is lost.

The Bourne catchment area is about 140 km² and again the groundwater and surface water divides are coincident; however the Bourne Rivulet is a higher order tributary than the Wallop Brook and the perennial section is much larger, being some 10 km out of a total channel length of about 16 km. In wet winters it can rise as far up the valley as Upton although its more normal winter head is in the Hurstbourne Tarrant area (Figure 1). Its summer head is normally between St Marybourne and Stoke but its normal dry season head is probably in the centre of St

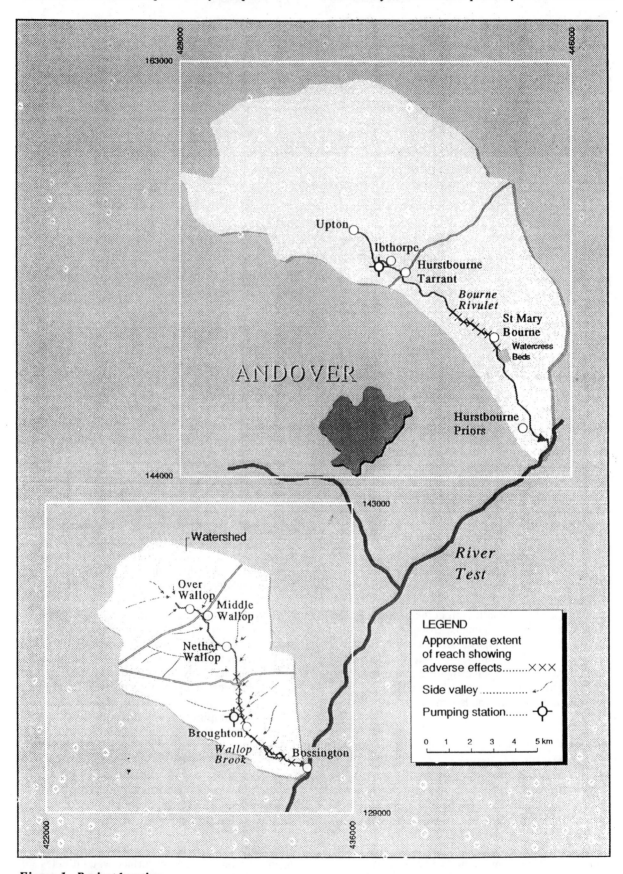

Figure 1   Project location

2.38

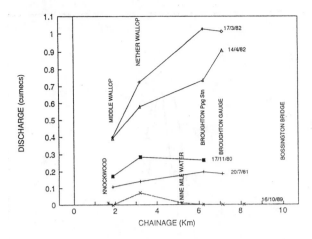

Figure 2 Discharge profile of Wallop Brook

Marybourne. Since the 1970s the drought head has migrated downstream to the foot of the watercress beds below St Marybourne on several occasions. Similar events were alluded to in several 19th century documents, particularly Stevens (1888) and Cobbett (1830), although correlation with observations of the watertable at Chilgrove indicates a high return period for this type of behaviour prior to groundwater abstraction taking place.

Within the catchment there are 48 licensed abstractions which are authorised to take some 29% of the annual average recharge. Of these only two are of any size, and both are from groundwater. One, for watercress below St Marybourne, accounts for about 84% of the abstraction and the other, for water supply at Ibthorpe, accounts for 13%. The remaining licences are small agricultural and domestic sources.

Although abstraction is heavier than in the Wallop Valley it is again in percentage terms not particularly high, particularly if the almost 100% return from the watercress beds within 300 m of the abstraction point is taken into account. Here again it is the siting of the main abstraction boreholes which appears to cause the problem. Both licences are 1963 Act Licences of Right and abstraction began in the early 1950s. The Ibthorpe supply boreholes are in the non-perennial section and are unlikely to effect the permanent spring head. The watercress beds were mainly river fed until about 1960 when they changed over to groundwater supplies because of quality problems. It appears that the large groundwater abstraction from the watercress boreholes has moved the stream head downstream such that the effluent discharge from the watercress beds now forms the drought head of the Bourne Rivulet.

Hydrogeological Studies

Hydrogeological studies included downhole flow logging at Ibthorpe and at a watercress bed borehole to identify the main inflow horizons, and a review of water level fluctuations in the valley gravels overlying the main Chalk aquifer. Analysis of the

Hydrogeological Map of Hampshire and the Isle of Wight (British Geological Survey, 1979) allowed the long sections through the valleys to be drawn and the major boreholes and inflow zones included.

The long sections show that the Wallop catchment is relatively simple, with the Upper Chalk having a saturated thickness of over 50 m and the main inflow to the boreholes at Broughton Pumping Station occurring from the base of the Upper Chalk or the Chalk Rock. The water levels and valley floor levels follow similar profiles, in a classic winterbourne configuration. The accretion profile appears to be governed by an area of low permeability in the Chalk running across the valley along the axis of an anticline. This forces throughflow up to the surface and relatively high and sustained stream flows are observed. Downstream towards Broughton, the Chalk is much more permeable and the stream flow diminishes as water seeps away as throughflow. Indeed, it may be speculated that the Broughton Pumping Station was sited in a known losing reach because it was recognised that Chalk permeabilities must be higher at that point.

The Bourne catchment is hydrogeologically complex. At the downstream end, the dip of the Chalk is steeper than the valley floor and so the maximum thickness of Upper Chalk is developed at the confluence with the River Test. Further upstream the boreholes at the watercress beds appear to derive their yields from the Upper Chalk or Chalk Rock. The latter formation outcrops in the section from Stoke to Vernham Dean and so the boreholes at Ibthorpe probably obtain their yield from the Melbourn Rock, assuming that the depth of this bed, as derived by interpolation from the BGS map, is an over-estimate.

The section also suggests that the occasional spring flows at Vernham Dean are probably influenced by preferential flow horizons through the Chalk Rock, i.e. a perched watertable relative to the Melbourn Rock. The alternative explanation of a single piezometric surface would require water level fluctuations of 40 m in the main aquifer. At the watershed with the Thames Valley, the dip of the strata and piezometric surface are such that the Melbourn Rock itself may be unsaturated in some places.

Computer Modelling

The study of over-abstraction in the Wallop Brook and Bourne Rivulet has involved the development of an integrated catchment model that simultaneously calculates groundwater and stream flows in each catchment. Recharge estimation was carried out independently of the integrated catchment model using the Stanford Catchment Model.

The integrated model combines a straightforward finite difference model of the aquifer with a simulation of the flows in the stream throughout the length of the valleys.

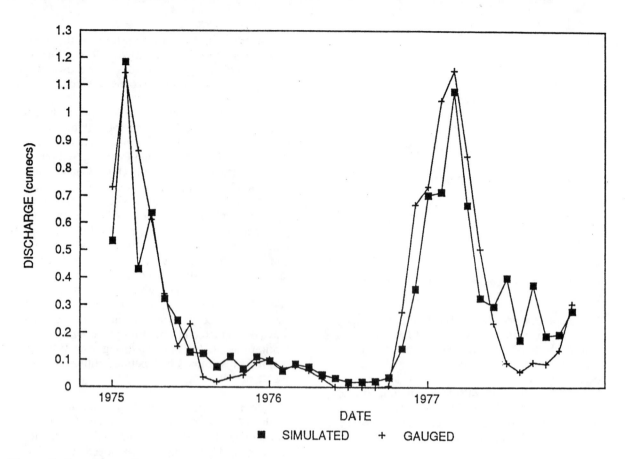

Figure 3   Low flows - Wallop Brook, 1975 to 1977

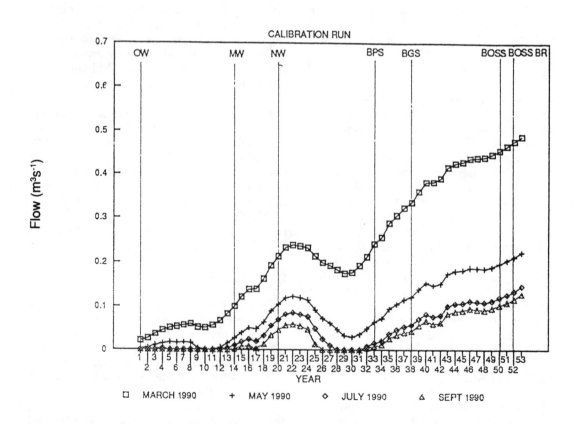

Figure 4   Flow profiles (March to September 1990) showing calibration (this page), no abstraction at Broughton (opposite, top) and with compensation at Nether Wallop (opposite, bottom)

2.40

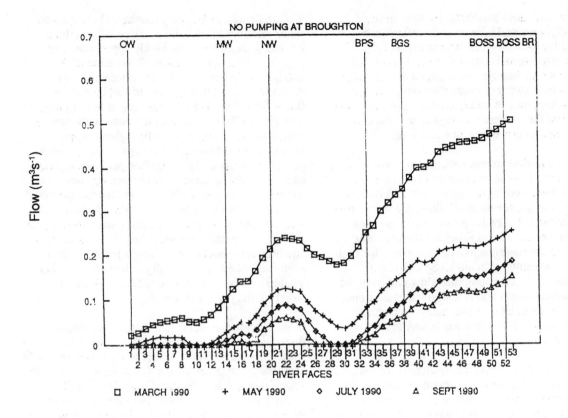

NO PUMPING AT BROUGHTON

□   MARCH 1990   +   MAY 1990   ◊   JULY 1990   △   SEPT 1990

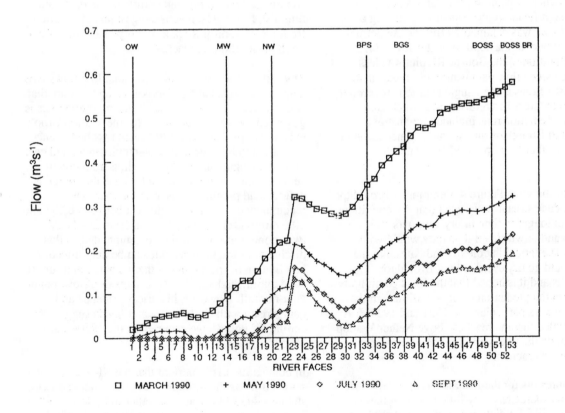

□   MARCH 1990   +   MAY 1990   ◊   JULY 1990   △   SEPT 1990

LEGEND

OW	OVER WALLOP	BGS	BROUGHTON GAUGING STATION
MW	MIDDLE WALLOP	BOSS	BOSSINGTON
NW	NETHER WALLOP	BOSS BR	BOSSINGTON BRIDGE
BPS	BROUGHTON PUMPING STATION		

Figure 4   (continued)

2.41

Within the main aquifer (that is, the bulk of the catchment), horizontal inflows and outflows are calculated for each flow cell depending on the hydraulic gradient and connection to adjacent cells. Vertical recharge into the cell is added during each one month time step. For every time step, a water balance is computed by calculation of all inflows and outflows and the change in storage within the cell corresponding to the change in water level.

In the vicinity of the stream line, the distribution of cells and flows is more complex as flows into and from the stream itself through the river face nodes are calculated. For the stream itself, flows are incremented or decremented in each cell according to flows from groundwater. Stream flows are then adjusted according to the stage discharge relationship for each reach and the resulting stream levels calculated. These in turn affect the computed flow rate from the aquifer and thus water levels within the aquifer and so the whole set of calculations has to be repeated iteratively until a flow balance is achieved for the time step in question.

The model has been calibrated by analysis of over 25 years of observed flows in the perennial and winterbourne reaches as well as groundwater levels, as shown in Figure 3. Calibration has overcome the general absence of pumping test data in the catchments. A significant improvement in matching of observed flows was obtained by forcing the permeability to vary over the depth of water level fluctuation. Calibration of the Bourne Rivulet was less satisfactory since flow data is monthly rather than daily and the flows at the gauging station are strongly influenced by cress bed return flows which are ungauged. Prediction runs included no-abstraction at Ibthorpe and Broughton and stream augmentation of 100 ls^{-1} at Nether Wallop based on a satellite borehole.

Results are shown in Figure 4. Pumping at Broughton tends to reduce stream flows such that dry conditions persist both longer in time in dry summers and further up and downstream than they would without pumping. The modelling clearly indicates that the stream would go dry even without Broughton abstractions and it is hoped that the local community can confirm the prediction of dry conditions in the pre-pumping era particularly in 1921 and 1934. It is also concluded that the reaches above Nether Wallop which include the true winterbourne portion are not affected by abstraction.

The model results for the Bourne Rivulet show that the Ibthorpe source has very little effect on the accretion profile. Prediction runs were not made to study the effect of the watercress beds on the reach to St Marybourne because the calibration did not mirror the drying up of this reach in sufficient detail.

Conclusions and recommendations

Environmental studies confirm the high quality of the Wallop Brook, particularly its channel margin and water meadow habitat and amenity in Broughton. Remedial measures seem highly appropriate and several options were studied. Revocation of the Broughton licence would help restore the stream to its 'natural' condition but would still lead to low flows. Southern Water would need to invest more than £0.5 million to connect the nearest alternative source at Horsebridge to the Broughton supply system. Channel lining in the losing reaches would be very expensive at £0.3 million per km and would have a significant adverse environmental impact on the water meadows. Collection and recycling treated sewage effluent to Nether Wallop would only yield 4 ls^{-1} and therefore does not justify investment by the NRA. Augmentation by recycling river water from downstream would involve longer pipelines than from satellite boreholes in dry valleys near Nether Wallop which, costing around £0.33 million, is therefore the preferred option.

In the Bourne Rivulet catchment, the increased frequency of the spring head moving down to the watercress beds and the failure to flow in winter at St Marybourne appears to be a direct result of the large abstraction at the beds. The Chalk Rock aquifer actually intersects the valley floor above St Mary Bourne and this effectively enables drawdown at the watercress beds to propagate further upstream and diminish flows. The results suggest that abstraction from the Melbourn Rock at Ibthorpe has little effect on the winterbourne reach.

Environmental assessment shows that low flows have a negative impact at St Marybourne and so remedial action is recommended. The choice of alternatives is governed by similar factors as for the Wallop Brook except that revocation of the watercress bed licence is thought to be undesirable on employment and cost grounds. Augmentation by recycling from downstream is the preferred option because the source is assured and pipeline costs are moderate. The recommended scheme would cost between £0.37 and £0.6 million for discharges from 50 to 200 ls^{-1}. A two-month pumping trial is recommended so that discharge of the final scheme can be determined. A key finding of the studies is that recharge and runoff have diminished since 1971 as a result of lower and later rainfall. However, historical evidence and comparison with Chilgrove water levels suggest that similar droughts have occurred in the 1850s and in 1895.

In both cases it is important that the NRA does not set itself up as the ultimate arbiter of what level the streams should flow at or whether they flow at all. The local community and other interested bodies should be made aware of the options available and their relative costs. The latter are particularly important as it is the water consumer who is likely to foot the bill indirectly for the remedial measures through increased water charges. It is only when general agreement with regard to remedial measures has been reached that these should begin.

The River Aled regulation system - reconciling the reconcilable

A. E. Weston & B. P. Hodgson

Abstract

The River Aled is the major upland tributary of the River Elwy, having at the top of its catchment a reservoir system that augments the low flow during the summer months. It has provided a source of raw water to Glascoed water Treatment works for distribution to Rhyl and the surrounding area since the 1930s. The river serves as an important salmonid recruitment area crucial to the maintenance of migratory fish stocks for the Elwy system as a whole.

Dry summers and increasing demands for water during the mid-1970s created the situation where Drought Orders were applied in three successive years which dramatically reduced the residual flows. This in turn impacted unfavourably upon the fisheries resources. A series of changes to the statutory and abstraction licence conditions since that time has now not only secured the requirement for water supply but has also reduced the concern of local riparian interests about river flows and has virtually eliminated the need for drought orders. This was achieved by a process of consultation which has now been formalised in the shape of a Consultative Group under an Operating Agreement.

Introduction

The River Clwyd and its major tributary the Elwy run through some of the most picturesque and valued countryside in North Wales. The hard rock, barren terrain of the upper catchment on the Denbigh Moors is replaced by well-wooded valleys eventually widening to a meandering, largely agricultural flood plain before the rivers discharge to the estuary close to the coastal resort of Rhyl. Only a small amount of light industry operates in the area, none of which abstracts directly from the rivers.

The rapid changes in river levels following rain creates a highly mobile river channel with large gravel movements and erosion problems in many areas. Nonetheless the high river quality and the largely nutrient-rich run-off produces an environment that is ideal for a productive salmonid fishery as well as creating the habitat for a diverse range of wildlife.

The Clwyd system has long been recognised as one of the most productive mixed salmonid fisheries in North Wales, having a consistently high run of sea trout and an important stock of salmon providing excellent sport for the small but energetic body of angling clubs that manage the fisheries. Over the years fish population numbers have also allowed a profitable net fishery to operate in the estuary, with up to eight sling (drift) nets capitalising on salmon and sea trout moving into the river between March and August each year. THE FUTURE OF THE FISHERY ULTIMATELY DEPENDS ON THE SUCCESS OF THE SPAWNING GROUNDS.

Details of the scheme

The River Aled, the major tributary of the river Elwy, plays a crucial role in providing salmon stocks for the river system as a whole. It is the most important salmon spawning tributary on the Elwy system and therefore any changes in flow characteristics can have serious implications for recruitment and the ultimate return of adult stocks to the river.

Until 1979 the River Aled was the only major source of water for a holiday area around the seaside resorts of Rhyl and Prestatyn. Two impounding reservoirs, Llyn Aled and Aled Isaf were built in the headwaters during the 1930s. These reservoirs were originally intended to supply water directly to a water treatment works and then transfer treated water by aqueduct to the coastal demand area. However, a scarcity of financial and technical resources at the time meant that the aqueduct was never built. So, by default, the scheme became one of the first river regulating systems.

The abstraction point at Bryn Aled is some 8 km downstream of the reservoirs, close to the confluence with the Elwy (see Figure 1). The catchment area of 70 km² to Bryn Aled has thin soil cover overlying impervious rocks, so that summer natural minimum runoffs are low, of the order of 3 Mld⁻¹. The water

from Bryn Aled pumping station discharges into a small reservoir called Plas Uchaf and from there it goes by gravity pipeline to the Glascoed water treatment works. Plas Uchaf, together with Dolwen (a further small impounding reservoir), usually provides a large part of the water for the Glascoed water treatment works during the winter.

Maximum demand for water from the river is most likely to occur during the period of lowest natural

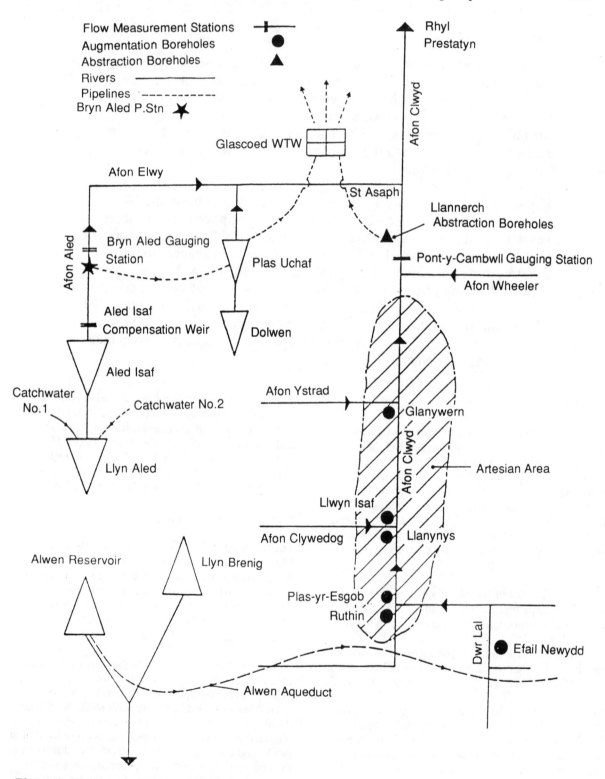

Figure 1 The Aled and Clwyd regulation schemes

2.44

flow, and at times when angling activity is at its greatest in mid-summer. The potential for continuous and increasingly bitter conflict between the water supply and fishing/river interests was considerable.

Fundamental questions associated with a regulated river are:

What residual flows, if any, are appropriate?
What release patterns should there be from the reservoirs?
What is a reasonable quantity to abstract?

These key questions can be answered with quantifiable flow values but the test of the veracity of those chosen lies in less quantifiable aspects such as establishing the impact on the fish populations and on the river environment.

The Aled Scheme, looked at today as a proposed resource development, would require extensive consultation and a detailed environmental impact study. The start of the Aled regulation is little documented, however, with only the enabling Act of 1932 giving the assessed environmental protection measures of the time. These are a fixed reservoir compensation water from Aled Isaf of 2.3 Mld^{-1} and a fixed residual flow rate below the abstraction point of 23 Mld^{-1} when abstraction took place but not at other times. The environmental reasons for the chosen flow rates are not known, but at the time it was assumed that this was a temporary arrangement until a direct raw water supply pipeline was built to the small Plas Uchaf and Dolwen reservoirs.

So what has happened since the inception of the scheme ?

After three consecutive years of Drought Orders (1974, 1975 and 1976) it was very clear:

.. to the Water Undertaker

that the Aled on its own could not be expected to support the then current peak abstraction rates for the Rhyl and Prestatyn demand area, let alone the projected increase in abstraction even though the abstraction licence permitted this. It was also apparent that too much senior management time was being spent on day-to-day operational decisions during dry summers.

.. to the 'Environmental Protection Body'

that the regulation scheme was not operating in a way that would maximise any benefits to the river environment although statutory requirements were being adhered to.

.. to the Anglers

that the regulation scheme was possibly having adverse affects on the fish populations and the water undertaker appeared to have little or no consideration for the environmental implications on the river resulting from the way the regulation scheme was operated.

Relations between the anglers and the water undertaker were at a low ebb. In a way, the process of resolving the situation was made more complicated because the water undertaker and the environmental protection body were the same organisation after the 1973 Water Act, namely the Regional Water Authority.

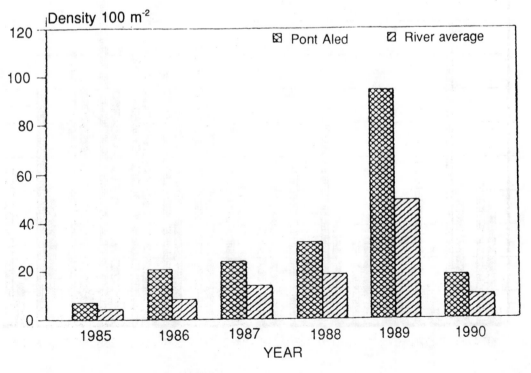

Figure 2   Salmon densities, River Aled 1985-90

Although data are not available, it could be argued that all the dry summers (even those before significant abstraction was taking place) adversely affected the numbers of juvenile progeny as indicated in the continuous data set (1985 to 1990) of surveys of fish less than one year old (see Figure 2). The 'one year lag' of low densities of the young fish is clear. Less clear is the effect on adult fish as indicated by the rod catch returns shown in Figure 3. The question is, "Did the regulation scheme make it so much worse?"

The compensation water is greater than the natural dry summer flow from the reservoired area and so offers flow enhancement during a drought all the way downstream. On the other hand, empty reservoirs at the end of the drought were retaining most of the inflow until the reservoirs spilled, thus depriving the upper reaches of spate flows. The residual flow protected the river below the abstraction point, but each dry summer forced the application for a Drought Order seeking a large reduction in the residual flow. The last Drought Order to be used reduced residual flows to 6.8 Mld[-1], though this was still twice the natural minimum flow for that time of year.

So other factors are important. The physical presence of the reservoirs resulting in a modified flow sequence during regulation and abstraction may be a significant factor, but it is difficult to attribute variations in the fish population year-by-year directly to simple volumes of flow in the river.

The development of reconciliation

By the end of 1976 plans were well in hand to bring in another source to be used conjunctively with the Aled. This was the Clwyd Augmentation Scheme which started operating in 1979. This would satisfy the water supply requirements. The monthly abstractions from 1974 to 1990 for the two sources, excluding Dolwen and Plas Uchaf from before to after the start of the Clwyd augmentation scheme, are shown in Figure 4. From 1979 the supply of water for the area would be increasingly shared between the two sources.

The aim now was to address the environmental issues and thereby to gain the confidence of the anglers and move to a position of broad acceptance of a scheme which could be operated in the best interests of all concerned.

A two-stage process began. First, following the end of the 1976 severe drought and using the limited amount of historic data, a proposal was drafted to amend the operation of the regulation scheme. Members of the then Water Authority's Fisheries Advisory Committee associated with the Aled were asked to meet with the Water Authority Officers to discuss proposals for a change in the operation of the Aled regulation system. This was the beginning of restoring confidence between people approaching a problem from different backgrounds and viewpoints.

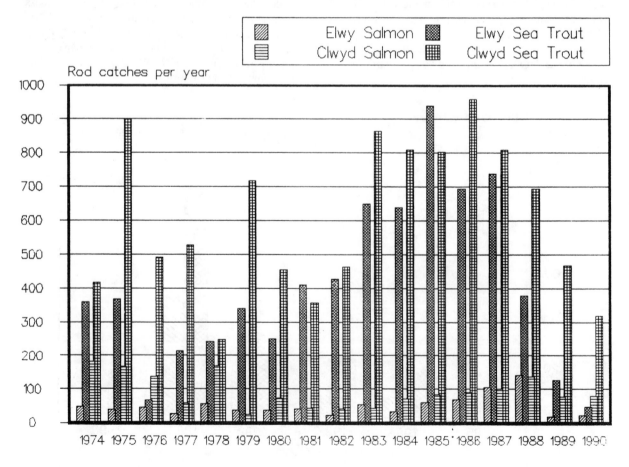

Figure 3 Clwyd and Elwy rod catch

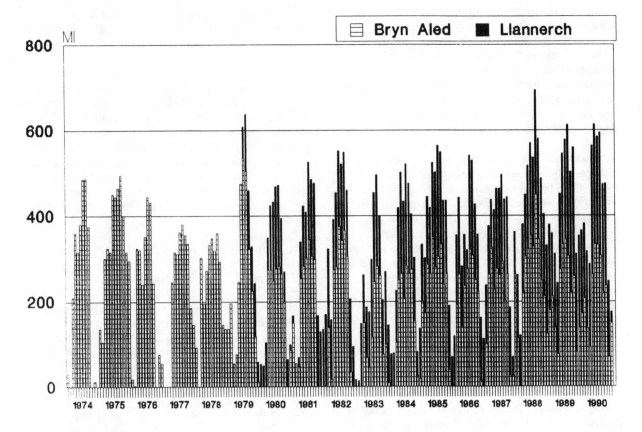

Figure 4 Monthly migrations, 1974 to 1990, at Bryn Aled and Llannerch

The basic proposals were to alter the residual flow of 23 Mld⁻¹ only when abstraction took place to a continuous 18 Mld⁻¹ flow at all times and to make special fisheries releases in the late autumn and early winter to help fish migration. These began in the autumn of 1977 and have continued without fail since then. To propose such a release required the development of reservoir Control Rules (Lambert, 1988) for Aled Isaf and Llyn Aled.

Initial analysis of the reservoired catchment by comparison with nearby long flow records indicated that only very dry autumn/winter periods would

preclude the discharge of significant fishery releases using stored water 'surplus' to the water supply requirements. The 'surplus' is defined as stored water above the 99% probability winter refill line. The first formal control rule therefore contained the fishery release provision and an Action Line to trigger the application for the time consuming Drought Order (see Figure 5a). Although a less-than-ideal control rule, it was a major step forward from the previous control rule. The latter was never written down but could be deduced as having three zones: zone A - "happy"; zone B - "deeply worried" and zone C - "help!"– see Figure 5b.

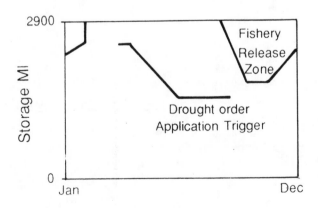

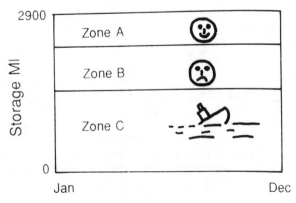

Figure 5a First formal control rule

Figure 5b Previous "unwritten" control rule

The local sub-committee approved the lower residual flow on the basis that a continuous residual flow through the summer of 18 Mld⁻¹ was more conducive to the well-being of the aquatic life than sudden changes from 23 Mld⁻¹ residual flow to much lower natural flows. Moreover, the maintenance of sufficient wetted area of the river bed is considered crucial to the survival of young fish during periods of high water temperatures and low flows.

Amendments to the necessary statutory powers were instigated but did not come into effect until 1983. During this period there were no dry summers so river flows were relatively high and consequently no concern was expressed about low river flows. Also by 1978, all the necessary improved hydrometric measurement facilities had been installed and routine accurate and reliable data collection had been set in place. Indeed, one of the original 'bones of contention' had been the need to block off the gauging weir in summer at the abstraction point to create a deep enough pool for the water supply intake. Modifying the residual flow weir not only resolved the intake problem but also improved the sensitivity of the flow measurement and allowed better control of the regulation releases.

However, the dry summer of 1984 (almost equal in severity to the 1976 drought) showed that the Aled Regulation System still required the need to apply for a Drought Order, even with a reduced residual flow rate. The application for the Drought Order was

approved and residual flows were dramatically reduced throughout August and into early September when the drought ended.

Although 1984 revived memories of 1976, the situation was crucially different. A complete set of hydrometric data was collected and processed which proved invaluable in the ensuing second stage of the consultation process. In addition, when a sub-committee of the then Informal Fisheries Group was convened it was from a point where actions had been agreed (amending the residual flow) and had taken place, and actions had been promised (Autumn fishery releases since 1977) and had been seen to be done.

The consultation took the form of an introductory meeting to reaffirm the physical aspects of the scheme and explore the points of concern. The initial ideas for change were floated. The next meeting was arranged on the basis that written draft proposals were to be prepared in the meantime by the Water Authority Officers. The final two meetings then refined and clarified the proposals for a more flexible regime of river regulation. Approval in principle was then achieved, subject to a final assessment when the advertisements for the statutory notices and licence variation were drafted.

One advantage for the Water Authority, from the point of view of convincing the anglers that the proposal would be carried forward as explained, was

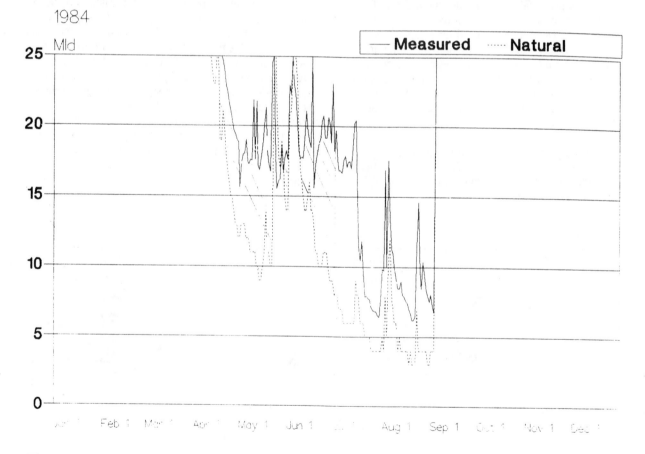

Figure 6   Daily mean flows, natural and measured, 1984

that it had to draft the proposed abstraction licence prior to advertising. This allowed all interested parties to view and to comment on the proposed licence as it would be granted unless called in by the Welsh Office.

The 1984 natural river flows and the measured residual flow at Bryn Aled are shown in Figure 6. This was the key information in the consultations with the sub-committee to see if a modified scheme could be designed that would all but preclude the use of Drought Orders and maximise any benefits river regulation could provide.

In the second stage of consultation it was clearly established that the releases of 327 Ml (hatched area in Figure 6) in April to June of 1984 to maintain 18 Mld^{-1} residual flow had little or no benefit to the fishery. This point had not been fully appreciated in the earlier consultations. Indeed, it could be construed that the river was harmed by the increasing risk of a Drought Order in July reducing the residual flows to 6 Mld^{-1} at a time when low natural flows really needed to be protected and if possible enhanced. Reservoir storage could not support a residual flow anywhere near 18 Mld^{-1} and the water supply requirement of over 11 Mld^{-1} throughout a drought which started in April and ended in mid-October — the end-date which an operator of a water supply scheme must use (Lambert, 1988). How much of the storage should be reserved for water supply? There had to be a starting point for the discussion, and so, because the scheme was originally intended

to be a direct water supply scheme, the calculation was done on this basis.

No amendment to the compensation water at 2.2 Mld^{-1} all year was suggested. A calculation based on a design drought sequence showed that at the beginning of April there would be 350 Ml out of the 2900 Ml total reservoir storage available, on a guaranteed basis, that was not required to maintain the compensation water and water supply releases (11 Mld^{-1} as an average), if the principle of a 'put and take' scheme similar to the Clwyd was acceptable. The 350 Ml would be available for fishery releases throughout the summer but would not normally be used earlier than July. The 'put and take' proposal provided the way to greatly simplify the day-to-day operation of the scheme. It is also simple to understand and to police, as had been proved during the development and operation of the Clwyd augmentation scheme (Lambert, 1981).

In addition, extra releases would be available for fishery, dependent on reservoir storage, if the inflows were higher than the design drought sequence (1984 extended to mid-October). Such a scheme would safeguard the upland storage at the critical time of April to June and provide releases for the fishery from July onwards in dry summers without the fear of drastic cuts from the application of a Drought Order. The Control Rule for the reservoirs in Figure 7 shows the current operating policy based on the aggregated storage of Llyn Aled and Aled Isaf. The reservoir releases during the design drought are

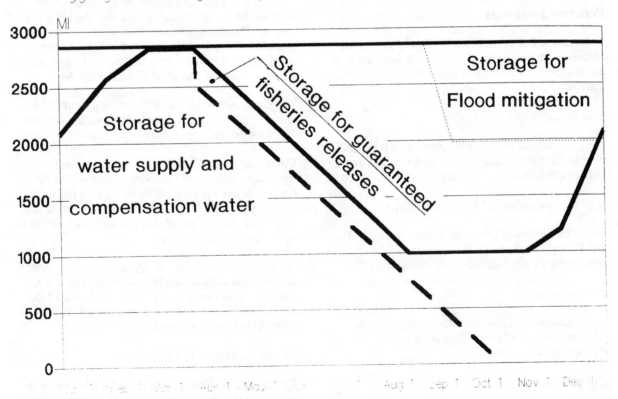

Figure 7 *Bryn Aled Control Rule*

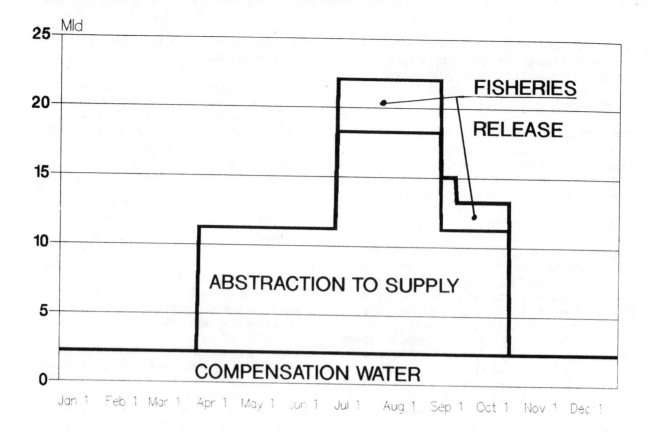

25 Mld

20

15

10

5

0

FISHERIES
RELEASE

ABSTRACTION TO SUPPLY

COMPENSATION WATER

Jan 1 Feb 1 Mar 1 Apr 1 May 1 Jun 1 Jul 1 Aug 1 Sep 1 Oct 1 Nov 1 Dec 1

Figure 8   Releases from Aled Reservoirs

shown in Figure 8. The demand for water is highly seasonal, currently reaching a summer peak of 21 Mld^{-1} in August as the seaside resorts of Rhyl and Prestatyn reach full capacity.

Perceived benefits

Only time and data collection will truly show if the perceived long-term benefits for the fishery are real but the revised scheme now has the following clear benefits:

... to Water Supply

A simpler operational system which requires little or no higher management input on a day-to-day basis, especially during a drought.

... to the Environmental Protection Body

Flexibility of use of the fishery release volume and Drought Orders only in very extreme circumstances during dry winters to aid reservoir refill.

... to the anglers

Guaranteed reservoir storage for summer releases made at a time of their choosing as a flexible seasonal residual flow.

.. in general

In average rainfall years there will be little

problem on the Aled because as well as the compensation flow from the reservoirs in the headwaters there is adequate uncontrolled run-off to the river from the catchment downstream. It is the drought years that will create the greatest concern. In the past the all-too-frequent need for drought orders and the ultimate dramatic reductions in residual flow rates have impacted and reduced fish production levels particularly in the section of river immediately below the abstraction point close to Pont Aled.

The enhanced flows during the summer months will not only protect but positively enhance the juvenile salmonid resource.

Conservation of wildlife is also of fundamental importance and should be safeguarded within the context of any scheme and in the case of the Aled, consistent flows play an important part in protecting otters and other forms of wildlife which are abundant in the well wooded valley.

However, with the complexity of variation in stock size in tributaries especially in drought years, it is important that monitoring is continued over a long period to ensure that the foreseen benefits to the fish populations do actually materialize.

Developments in 1989

The drought of 1989 again tested the Aled but with the new statutory powers in place reduction of the residual flow under a Drought Order was not

2.50

required. The formation of the National Rivers Authority and the Water Services companies brought further change to the Aled.

Section 126 of the 1989 Water Act allowed the National Rivers Authority to enter into Agreements with the Water Service companies on river regulation schemes. The Aled Operating Agreement was concluded in August 1989 together with one for the Clwyd. The Agreement details the management policy for the regulation scheme and authorises the formation of a Consultative Group consisting of two National Rivers Authority officers and two Water Company officers. The first task of the group was to produce an Operating Manual. This was completed in early 1990 and details the way in which the scheme will operate, including points of contact and necessary data transfer between the two bodies. Regular meetings are held, not only to ensure that the scheme is operated in accordance with the aims of the Operating Agreement, but also to encourage attendance and involvement of *ex officio* participants associated with the rivers Aled and Clwyd. The chairmanship of the group alternates between the two bodies annually. This Agreement in many ways formalised the consultation procedure of the previous 12 years.

The adult stocks of migratory fish that run the river in the autumn to spawn must also be safeguarded by the provision of adequate fish passes. The fish pass at the Bryn Aled abstraction point is there to allow unrestricted access to the river by fish as well as to gauge the flow accurately to ensure agreed regulated flows are adhered to. As a site owned by the Water Company, the Operating Agreement ensures the pass is maintained and repaired as required.

The Operating Agreement also formally incorporated the provision of a flood storage volume in Aled Isaf. Some 30% of the total reservoir storage is available during flood incidents and although this represents a small proportion of the total run-off from the whole Elwy catchment, the severity of the peak flow will be reduced. It will give some protection to farmers and their livestock downstream and for some extreme floods will make the difference between overtopping or not of the embankments protecting the vulnerable low-lying parts of the town of St Asaph just above the confluence of the Elwy and Clwyd.

The developments continue

In September 1990 the flexibility of use of stored water 'surplus' to water supply requirements was demonstrated. A sustained 24-hour release of water was used in an attempt to improve fishing quality on the Elwy during a low flow period and some success was achieved. Although the system does not allow great volumes of water to be used in this way, the better understanding of the mechanics of the system can only lead to more beneficial ways of using any special reserve volume which accumulates though the summer.

In July 1991 some 900 Ml (over and above the guaranteed 350 Ml) was assessed as 'surplus' to water supply requirements and made available to the National Rivers Authority for additional fishery releases or extra releases to help mitigate periods of adverse water quality.

Was the consultation process a success?

The scheme is now viewed as follows:

> The water undertaker would have liked one or two more Ml of reliable yield (currently calculated as 11.3 Mld^{-1}) from the scheme but the simplicity of operation is of enormous value.

> The National Rivers Authority is content with the conservation measures but needs to continue to monitor fish populations regularly to see if the expected improvement materialises.

> The anglers would wish for greater volumes of fishery releases but recognise that the scheme is now being operated to actively benefit the river environment wherever feasible.

Above all perhaps, everybody is now willing to participate in discussion and review the scheme in an atmosphere of mutual respect and understanding. The antipathy and grumbling discontent is gone. The experience of the development of this scheme and similar ones in North Wales suggests it would be a rare river regulation scheme that could not be operated better by listening to the suggestions and experiences of local anglers and riparian owners.

How is the Operating Agreement working?

The Aled and Clwyd Consultative Group has met on six occasions since their formation. Each meeting has been conducted in a constructive and amicable manner. Currently a series of meetings is under way to plan a drawdown to empty the lower reservoir Aled Isaf for dam repair works in August 1992. The initial meeting in July 1991 outlined the draft timescale and explored the possibilities of this rare opportunity to provide extra releases to the river.

Summary

This scheme will now operate without Drought Orders or the need of high level management time in all dry summers considerably more severe than those of the last 30 years and provide flexible guaranteed releases for the benefit of the fisheries and the river in general.

The inherent conflict between reservoirs for water supply and downstream fishing interests has been met head-on and resolved within the constraints of the scheme's assets.

The Operating Agreement consolidated the positive approach of the Water Undertaker and Environmental

Protection Body used during the previous 12 years. The Consultative Group can modify the Operating Manual in the light of new developments. This provides an adaptable management tool to accommodate the wide and continuing improvement in knowledge about operating river regulation schemes.

Acknowledgements

The authors wish to thank all National Rivers Authority (Welsh Region) and Dwr Cymru-Welsh Water staff, Northern Division who have been involved in work on the Aled. The authors thank Dwr Cymru-Welsh Water and the National Rivers Authority for permission to publish this paper. Any views or opinions expressed are those of the authors, not necessarily those of Dwr Cymru-Welsh Water or the National Rivers Authority.

References

Lambert A.O. 1988. *An introduction to operational control rules using the 10-component method.* BHS Occasional Paper No. 1.

Lambert A.O. 1981. The river Clwyd augmentation/ abstraction scheme. *J. Inst. Wat. Env. Manage.* 35, 125-134.

The River Allen - a case study

A.T.Newman & R.D.Symonds

Abstract

The River Allen by reputation was once an exemplary chalk stream: a classic habitat for trout. Its character is believed to have been eroded by the groundwater planning techniques of the 1960s and 1970s. These gave rational engineering considerations pre-eminence over a coherent method for environmental impact assessment. The NRA Wessex Region is now confronted with legacies of past resource planning with the Allen of high priority. Linked computer models of the groundwater and surface water are being developed, supported by biological and fisheries studies to establish what may be achieved by changes to resources management. Several instances of flow depletion in chalk streams are under investigation. The ecological parameters for river restoration should be more clearly understood than a generation ago but knowledge remains imperfect in comparison with the economic and engineering certainties of public water supplies. Current research should eventually redress this imbalance. Until then action is imperative with respect to the River Allen.

Introduction

The formation of the National Rivers Authority (NRA) in 1989 coincided with prolonged dry weather when river flows were low throughout the country. It was claimed that some river flows were depleted to unacceptable level from over-abstraction. The expectation was that the NRA would resolve the problems.

The NRA surveyed its 10 regions to assess the extent of the problems. This review (1990) identified 20 sites in England and Wales for priority of attention: emerging from the question "would the current abstraction licences be issued with hindsight of the effect on the river environment?" Most involved public water supply groundwater abstractions, many being Licences of Right.

Three of the 20 sites are in the Wessex Region of the NRA, where recognition of problems pre-dated the survey. One of them is the River Allen in Dorset, where concern for the effect of groundwater abstraction on the river had been expressed for some 20 years. To investigate these claims a three-year programme of study commenced in 1989, to include hydrological analysis of the river and groundwater interface, biological assays, chemical quality surveys and fisheries studies.

The Allen Catchment

The River Allen is a tributary of the River Stour, confluent at Wimborne Minster in south east Dorset.

It rises on the south east slope of Cranborne Chase from ephemeral and permanent springs draining the Upper Chalk. Its tributaries are the Gussage and the Crichel streams. The catchment and relevant features are shown in Figure 1.

Upper Chalk covers most of the catchment, and varies in thickness by up to 300 metres. It dips gently to the south and is overlain at the extreme south east by Tertiary deposits. Along the river valleys there are narrow thin beds of alluvium, sands and gravels. The River Allen is by reputation an exceptional game and coarse fishery, with large populations of grayling, trout, roach and chub.

Near mid-catchment is Stanbridge Mill Pumping Station, close to the river, whence water is drawn from four boreholes for public water supply. Each of the three streams is seasonally augmented by groundwater abstracted from Chalk boreholes: the River Allen from Wyke Down; the Gussage Stream near the village of Gussage All Saints; and the Crichel Stream at Long Crichel.

There are two primary river flow gauging stations: at Walford Mill (catchment 176 km^2), where records commenced in 1974; and at Loverley Mill (catchment 94 km^2) where records commenced in 1970 but influenced by the Stanbridge Mill abstraction. Another two flow gauging stations were commissioned in 1980: at Bowerswain on the Gussage Stream; and at All Hallows on the River Allen.

The River Allen Catchment

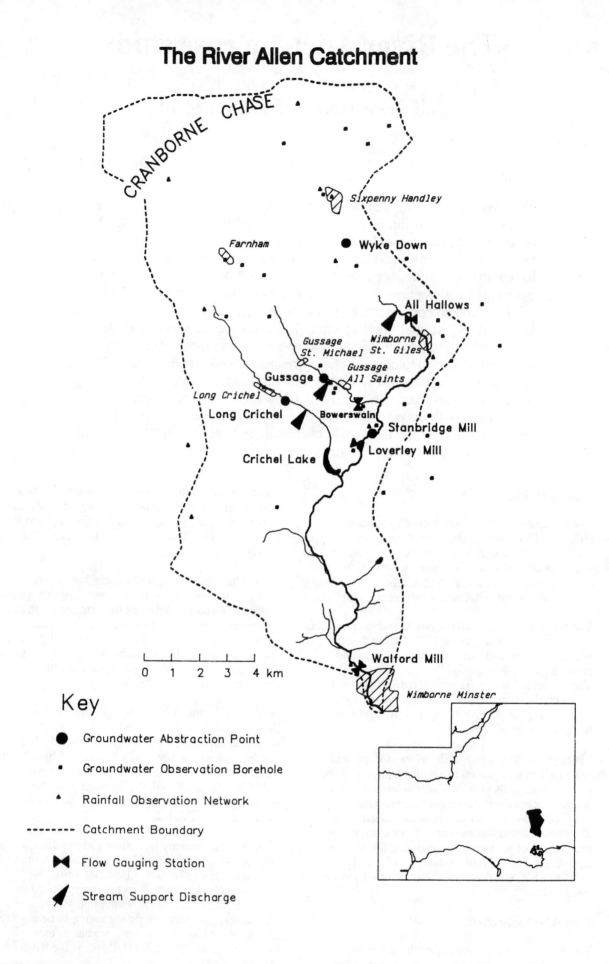

Figure 1 *The River Allen catchment, Dorset*

There are 40 sites within the catchment where records aggregate 900 current meter gaugings. A water level chart recorder is in place at Crichel Lake. The groundwater observation network has approximately 30 stations visited monthly between 1966 and 1981, and thereafter biannually. There are 20 rainfall stations in the vicinity, the earliest record commencing in 1896.

History of groundwater development

At the root of concern about river flows is the operation of Stanbridge Mill as a water supply source, and the now associated stream augmentation boreholes. A condensed history of developments follows in portrayal of the events which have not only increased the yield at Stanbridge Mill but extended the influence of river regulation on a wider basis than an integrated resource development plan might have deemed advisable.

1946 Stanbridge Mill site authorised for 2 boreholes to yield 6.8 Mld^{-1}.
1965 Stanbridge Mill granted Licence of Right for 6.8 Mld^{-1}, and though then abstracting 3.6 Mld^{-1} the water supply undertaking expressed an interest in obtaining 45 Mld^{-1}.
1965 Stanbridge Mill test pumping of two additional boreholes. Total pumping at 22.7 Mld^{-1} reduced River Allen flow at Loverley Mill by 163 ls^{-1} and produced groundwater depression of 2.7m at 320m distance.
1967 Licence approved for 18.2 Mld^{-1} at Stanbridge Mill subject to augmentation of river from source of up to 6.8 Mld^{-1} when flows at Loverley Mill declined to 276 ls^{-1}, conditional only for April to September inclusive.
1971 Reports of derogation of groundwater sources in the Gussage All Saints area and of water levels in Crichel Lake.
1973 Gussage boreholes licensed for 6.8 Mld^{-1} to augment River Allen via Gussage Stream in lieu of stream support from Stanbridge Mill. This released an equivalent quantity from the Stanbridge Mill source for export as public water supplies. Because of leakage from the Gussage Stream, due to pumping from Stanbridge Mill, all but 150m of the watercourse was bed-lined to combat loss of augmentation water. Eastwood, Kenyon and Wilkinson (1977) reported reduced infiltration losses by 95% and various lining techniques displayed little difference in cost or performance. (A further section was lined with bentonite in 1990. Its efficiency is being monitored).
1973 Local water sources derogated by the Gussage boreholes were compensated with mains connections.
1974 Long Crichel boreholes licensed for 9.1 Mld^{-1} to maintain the water level in Crichel Lake and provide a residual flow to the River Allen. Uncertainty about their impact was signalled by a licence condition that suspension of pumping might be invoked at any time.

1977 Wyke Down boreholes added to stream support arrangements to achieve wider management of the catchment's resources: increasing flexibility for river augmentation and utilising storage from Chalk more remote from permanent springs. No separate licence was issued and little evidence recorded of potential effects of pumping on the Allen headwaters at Wimborne St Giles.
1977 The entire water supply undertaking's abstraction rights were merged into a single licence with conditions for augmenting streamflows at occurence of prescribed minimum values at Loverley Mill, All Hallows, Bowerswain and to a water level at Crichel Lake. The licence now stands in total at 55 Mld^{-1} of which 25 Mld^{-1} may be used directly for public water supplies, the remainder being devoted to the various support schemes.

Local protest

The River Allen Association, formed of riparian owners in the early 1970s, claimed low flows had damaged the fishery. Its concern was heightened by the 1975/76 drought, and the extension of works to provide river augmentation. The Association did not object to the 1977 licence; instead seeking assurance that the prescribed minimum flow would be reviewed after five years.

It did object to an application for a fifth borehole at Stanbridge Mill, for 6.8 Mld^{-1} as stream support in replacement of Wyke Down borehole. This application coincided with the agreed review of the licence, completed in 1984, which concluded that there had been no significant depletion of river flows but recognised the possibility of effects upstream of Stanbridge Mill, avoidable with a "hands off" flow at All Hallows. The Association was willing to withdraw its objection on agreed terms for the licence, but the Water Company withdrew its application.

Discussions to agree the operating rules unspecified in the abstraction licence were inherited by the NRA in 1989. Because of circular arguments over alternative policies it was concluded that an environmentally preferred operating policy should emerge from more detailed study of the catchment, to include examination of alternative stream support mechanisms.

Recent publicity has been given to the alleged decline of the river in *The Field* magazine (1990).

Indications of river impairment

Fears for derogation of protected rights, and objections to proposals for the increased quantity at Stanbridge Mill, led to flow protection conditions in the licence of 1969. Even then a forecast 2.5 km radius of cone of depression was not associated with river bed leakage possibly influencing up to 8 km of unsupported streamflows. The benefit of the licence condition for augmenting river flows was isolated to the downstream gauging station at Loverley Mill.

Reports in 1970 of lowered water levels in Crichel Lake continued into 1974 when the Long Crichel boreholes were constructed. These have been unsuccessful in maintaining the lake levels.

Complaints of fishing ruined by low flows led to experimental temporary fabric dams at six locations to raise water levels. Increased anxiety was supported by records supplied by Sir Richard Glyn (1976) of fish caught, showing decline between 1970 and 1975 (Figure 2). Such correspondence recurred during the 1984 drought, when a fisherman with 62 years experience of the River Allen declared flows unacceptable and water levels lower since the early 1970s.

Attention has been focussed on the decline of aquatic weeds, particularly the *Ranunculus* so essential to good habitat for trout. The reduction in valued macrophytes is common to many Chalk streams in recent years. Explanations are several but there is a general charge that it is a consequence of reduced summer flows.

In 1990 the NRA intervened with additional stream support from Wyke Down in response to distressed river conditions downstream of All Hallows gauging station.

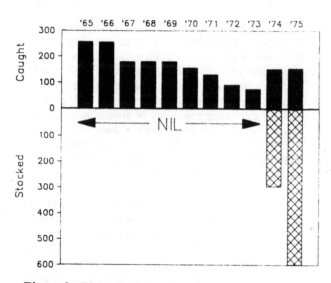

Figure 2   Fish caught on Gaunts Water

Studies in progress

Three studies are in progress on the River Allen: a river basin study of water resources; a biological survey; and a fisheries survey. These are being undertaken in consultation with the Allen Association which has independent advice from a consultant hydrologist and an ecologist.

The water resources study was awarded to Groundwater Development Consultants of Cambridge in 1990 to occupy an 18-month period.

The primary objective of the study is the use of an integrated catchment computer model of the aquifer and river systems in investigation of hydrological responses to past and potential future abstraction regimes. The model will be used to assess the effect on streamflows and groundwater levels of the abstractions in the catchment; individually and conjunctively. It will explore strategies for maximising the efficiency of streamflow support, investigating new works as necessary. The model will be used to examine how appropriate are the prescribed flows to the simulated regime of natural flows.

The biological and fisheries studies will occupy a three-year period, ending in 1992. The biological studies consist of regular examinations of the river to determine the dominant species of weed, and the extent of cover. The presence of species indicative of water quality will be recorded. Standard techniques will be used to identify macro invertebrates present at sampling points throughout the study period. Particular attention will be paid to water chemical quality at times of the year when pesticides and sediments are most expected to influence ecology.

The fisheries study extends to the Chalk streams throughout Dorset and Wiltshire comparable with the River Allen; some similarly developed, and others in more natural regime. The study will provide information on habitat criteria, such as depth and velocity of flow, sediment type, and cover, from which to assess constraints on fishing conditions and range and populations of species.

Science versus Experience

For twenty years riparian owners and others who know the River Allen well have claimed a vital change in the river, and that licence conditions to protect the river have not had the desired effect. The licensing authority has used broad hydrological arguments that groundwater abstraction has not caused such changes. However, there are no firm scientific measures relating flows to healthy river ecology, and little information of river conditions before the critical increased licence in 1967 with which to compare present standards.

Where there is a balance of river ecology sensitive to small changes in flow regime then hydrology can be a blunt instrument in adjudication of change. It is undeniably a crude implement for the assessment of delicate changes, in contrast to the sensual powers of living organisms.

Instinctively we mistrust anecdotal evidence and favour in its place estimating techniques which may be no more consistent with the truth. Post-event surveys without pre-event data may simply serve to raise our level of comprehension to the level of the local initiate. There is a warning here for water resources engineers: a tunnel vision for river flows at specific locations should not create conviction that all will be well at others. A septuagenarian fisherman might have all the answers, if he is to be believed!

Obstacles to change

An initial perspective of the Allen catchment sees abstractions as authorised to the water supply undertaking increased from 6.8 Mld⁻¹ in Licence of Right to 55 Mld⁻¹ within a 12-year period. In the catchment to Loverley Mill the assessed recharge as average annual is equivalent to 108 Mld⁻¹ but in drought (1975/76) only 50 Mld⁻¹. The control of water resources in a highly interactive ground/surface water system appears unbalanced.

If the current studies conclude the river environment to have been impaired then the history of fragmented resource developments since 1946 will operate as an extra-ordinary burden to effective remedies for the following reasons:

(i) The public water supplies from Stanbridge are at near maximum licensed quantity, are of good quality and inexpensive. An alternative source is not immediately available, will be more expensive, and proposals for replacement are likely to carry a high penalty in compensation from the NRA;

(ii) The stream support to Gussage Stream may be argued a prescriptive right for the amenity of riparian owners in residential villages;

(iii) The stream support from Wyke Down has been incorporated into a downstream run-of-river abstraction for fish farming where prescriptive rights may be argued;

(iv) The stream support from Long Crichel to rectify the influence of Stanbridge on Crichel Lake is not effective and the future of this landscape feature is in question for any partial reduction of pumping from Stanbridge.

Other factors

There is a general presumption by complainants of river impairment that all is due to water abstractions. Reports of recent studies of alleged decline in chalk stream environments by the NRA Southern Region (1990) and Wessex Region (1991) identify a number of other primary mechanisms for adverse change in river ecology as follows:

(i) reduced depths of river water resulting from field and river drainage enhancements in the period 1950-1970;

(ii) changes in agricultural land management, particularly arabilisation and intensification, inducing increased rates of sediment mobilisation and its consequent deposition in rivers;

(iii) increased intensity of livestock grazing of riparian meadows with greater mechanical damage of river banks and beds;

(iv) stress to water chemical quality from agricultural and waste water treatment works, notably from rising concentrations of nutrients;

(v) the abandonment of traditional water-meadow systems which contributed to off-stream sediment containment and to early summer localised water storage, and which extended the corridor of visible water environment.

To a degree some of these factors might be an influence in the River Allen controversy but none persuades that the key issue in this case is other than the distributed effects of production and augmentation boreholes, which together infect the catchment with widespread groundwater depressions inducing leakage from stream beds.

Relevance of general NRA research

The NRA has an expansive national R & D programme from which several elements will contribute to a greater understanding of the mechanisms for change to the river environment. One project is concerned with the development of a standard method for assessing the degree to which abstractions have caused low flows; a technique for sensible distribution of funds for remedial works. Another aims to provide a method for the determination of 'minimum acceptable flows', an essential measure for future decisions.

The algorithms for standard analytical techniques must include models which relate visible physical characteristics to biological measures of the river ecosystem. In this respect the NRA research project concerned with 'ecologically acceptable flows' offers high promise for a rational description of habitat requirements for a variety of key aquatic organisms. Such information is vital to the definition of parameters for the reinstatement of rivers, such as the Allen, to an acceptable environmental quality. This project is due for completion in 1993. Individual regions of the NRA are engaged in site-specific investigations which, in answer to local problems, may contribute valuable wider explanation of catchment processes. An example would be studies of the origins and distribution of sediments, which in chalk streams might be of trans-regional significance.

Conclusions

1   The River Allen catchment is deservedly listed as one of the NRA's 'top twenty' low flow problems. The effects of abstractions on the low flow regime have long been recognised, as witnessed from the succession of honourable attempts to augment streamflows.

2   Past attempts at streamflow augmentation have been piecemeal, with narrow goals of prescribed minimum flows at convenient gauging sites resulting in poor provision for the widest consequences of creating influent stream conditions. In addition these projected remedies may have created dependent prescriptive rights from which disentanglement will be difficult.

3   The prime complaint of environmental degradation has been of loss of fishing sport. This is not a trivial concern. The decline of the sport would be antecedent to decline of the fishery. It is an early indicator of environmental impact.

4   While the superficial simplicity of cause of river decline in this catchment removes the need for extensive investigations peripheral to the crucial issue of reduced summer flows, the enigma remains of how to relate the findings of robust hydrological studies with intangible flows for habitat suitability. Wider NRA research aims are not time-compatible with decisions to benefit the River Allen.

5   The River Allen represents a warning to all water resources planners for lateral vision of all conceivable consequences of their decisions. None should be so sure of prowess in an uncertain science to leave no room for correcting mistakes. There is strong argument to eradicate the grant of licences on the evidence of short pumping tests, often conducted in inappropriate conditions. Short tests might better be regarded as substance for a provisional licence, time-limited for a lengthy period of operation to prove the case for permanent status.

Acknowledgement

The authors thank Mr Nigel Reader, Regional General Manager of the NRA Wessex Region, for permission to render this paper for publication. It should be noted however that opinions expressed do not necessarily conform with NRA judgement.

References

Eastwood J.C., Kenyon, W.J. & Wilkinson W.B. 1977. Sealing river beds and its relevance to the development of groundwater resources - with particular reference to the Gussage stream. Seminar on the Ecology of Management of Chalk Streams. WRc (March 1977).

The Field Magazine 1990. Summer Issue, August/ September 1990.

Glyn, R.L. 1976. Private communication on fish catch statistics (letter of 27 March 1976).

National Rivers Authority 1990. Review of rivers suffering from low flows (March 1990).

National Rivers Authority - Southern Region 1990. Proceedings of River Test Forum. Public meeting at Winchester (October 1990).

National Rivers Authority - Wessex Region 1991. River Piddle Investigations: Report and Action Plan. Regional Rivers Advisory Committee (April 1991).

Defining an environmentally acceptable flow regime for the River Darent, Kent

R.P.C. Brown, N. Ironside & S. Johnson

Abstract

The River Darent, situated in north Kent, has been identified by the National Rivers Authority as one of 40 British rivers subject to critically low flows as a result of over-abstraction. In October 1990, NRA Southern Region commissioned W S Atkins to undertake an ecological and hydrological survey to define an Environmentally Acceptable Flow Regime (EAFR) for this river which was capable of supporting a natural chalk stream ecology. The survey identified a stretch (Shoreham) on the river which exhibited high macroinvertebrate Biological Monitoring Working Party scores compared with RIVPACS predictions. Most other sites along the river were characterised by lower, sometimes extremely poor, BMWP scores when compared with the computer predicted results. On the basis that the Shoreham site therefore received flows of sufficient quantity and quality, an EAFR, in the form of a flow duration curve and mean monthly flow annual hydrograph, was standardised by catchment area for translation to other sites along the river.

Introduction

The National Rivers Authority (NRA) has identified 40 rivers throughout the country which suffer from critically low flows. These rivers are all suffering from the effects of over-abstraction and are cause for concern in terms of impacts both on other water users, such as fishing and recreation, and on the natural environment. Of the 40 severely-affected rivers, the River Darent in north Kent has been highlighted as one of the 20 suffering the most serious impact (NRA, 1990).

The River Darent has suffered severe flow depletion as a result of the progressive development of catchment groundwater resources for public water supply over the past 30-40 years. The existing licensed abstraction now exceeds the expected aquifer recharge in an average year. However, actual abstraction has remained relatively constant since the 1960s at approximately 70% of the licensed quantities.

In September 1990 the NRA-Southern Region appointed W S Atkins to undertake a limited survey of the river ecology along the whole of its length, under 1990 drought conditions, and to estimate a suitable environmentally acceptable flow regime (EAFR) for the river. The formulation of an EAFR seeks to balance the restoration of flows capable of supporting a healthy instream environment with the need to maintain a reasonable level of net abstraction from the catchment.

Background to the catchment

The River Darent rises to the west of Sevenoaks, near Westerham, on Lower Greensand deposits. Flowing east, parallel to the North Downs, it turns north at Sevenoaks to run across the succession of Lower Cretaceous beds and on to the Upper Cretaceous Chalk at Otford. Cutting through the North Downs it forms its own valley with wide flood plains to flow eventually into the tidal River Thames at Dartford (Figure 1).

Land use in the catchment is mainly arable and pasture with some woodland. Much of the middle and upper catchment is within the North Downs area of outstanding natural beauty and is characterised by landscape of very high quality. 10-15% of the total surface catchment is urbanised, primarily by Sevenoaks and Dartford. The lower part of the catchment contains many open water gravel pits and a landscape somewhat typical of an urban fringe.

The river is reputed to have been an excellent trout fishery in the 19th century, with numerous contemporary descriptions of large catches of fish. Its initial demise in the early part of the 20th century appears to have been due to deteriorating water quality (Halcrow, 1988). The quality of river water has greatly improved since then but the reduction in water quantity, resulting primarily from abstractions of groundwater, has led to the river drying up completely for several kilometres between

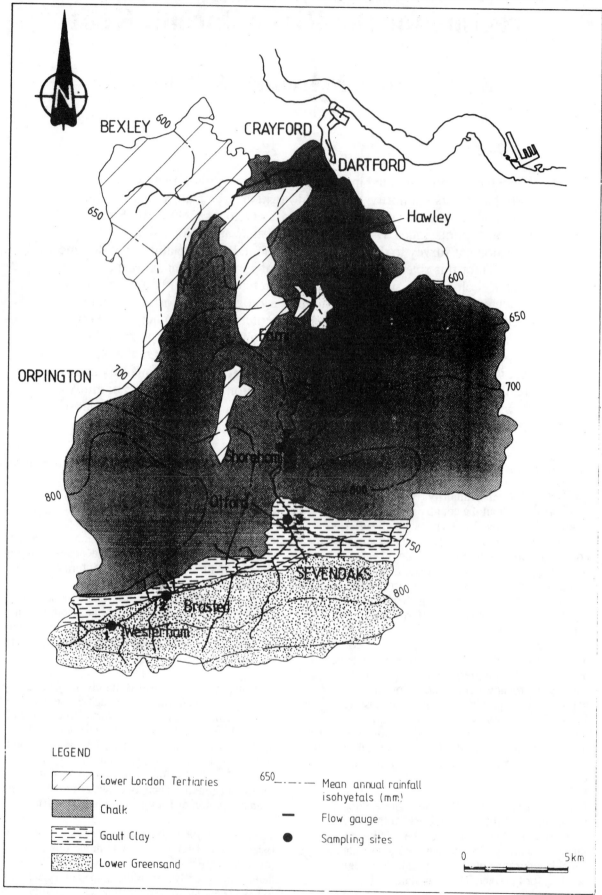

Figure 1   River Darent catchment hydrology and hydrogeology

LEGEND

(hatched)	Lower London Tertiaries
(stippled dark)	Chalk
(dashed)	Gault Clay
(dotted)	Lower Greensand

650 _____ Mean annual rainfall isohyetals (mm)

— Flow gauge

● Sampling sites

0   5km

Farningham and Dartford in the summers of 1976, 1989, 1990 and 1991.

The river is gauged at three gauging stations: Otford, Lullingstone and Hawley. The surface catchment area to Hawley, the most downstream of the three, is 191.4 km². Figure 2 presents the flow duration curves for the three sites. The mean flow of the river at Hawley is less than that at Lullingstone, and the low flows at Hawley are less than those at both Lullingstone and Otford. The influence of groundwater abstraction is apparent in both the Hawley and Lullingstone flow duration curves where they dip down at the low flow end.

Background to EAFR'S

In recent years there has been increasing interest in the concept of environmentally acceptable flow. This involves establishing a flow which will maintain the biological and general environmental integrity of the river under other than natural discharge regimes. It entails determining the minimum flow requirements of the various aspects which together determine the river's ecological character. These include flora, fauna, water quality, fisheries and amenity.

The main effects of a reduction in flow in a river are changes in water velocity, level, temperature, sub-stratum and water quality. Temperature affects growth and development; water quality affects nutrient budget; velocity affects siltation and breeding conditions; level affects depth and wetted area, and substrate affects colonisable habitat, resulting in a less diverse invertebrate community.

Management strategies in the past have tended towards maintaining viable populations of sport and commercial fisheries, the assumption being that adequate habitat for target fish would ensure habitats for other organisms. Gore (1989) concluded, however, that this may not be the case and that it is very important to consider the requirements of benthic invertebrates separately.

Although the theory behind the concept is sound, it is difficult to quantify exactly what an EAFR should be in any particular stretch of river. For example, requirements for salmonids are not simple to define. Changes in flow result in changes not only in velocity, depth, width and wetted area, but also in transport of food and dissolved oxygen. Salmonids also have a range of flow requirements related to different stages in their life cycle.

Thus there must be sufficient flow to stimulate spawning, protect the feeding habitats of fry and juvenile fish and support both upstream and down-

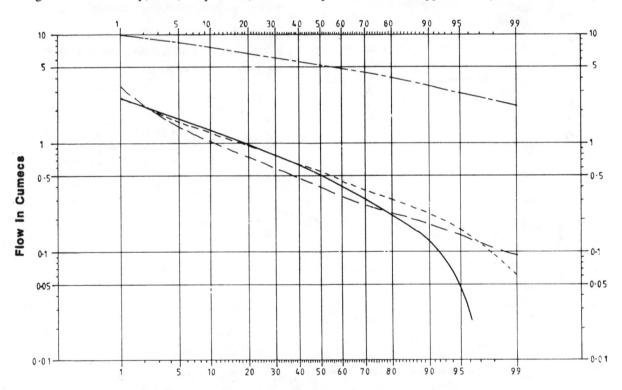

KEY

——— Darent at Hawley. Area 191.4 km²   —··— Darent at Lullingstone Area 118.4 km²

— — Darent at Otford. Area 100.5 km²   —·— Itchen at Highbridge and Allbrook. Area 360.0 km²

Figure 2   Flow duration curves for the River Darent

stream migration (e.g. Brayshaw, 1966; Stewart, 1968).

The overall environmental requirements for many benthic invertebrates are even less well known. The major problem is quantifying the wide variety of factors which affect them, such as competition, predator-prey relationships, substrate type, water chemistry, discharge regime, and river management. Causal relationships are therefore difficult to define, and predictive modelling is even less tangible.

Models (such as PHABSIM) built to assist objectively in the derivation of ecological flow requirements are still at an early stage of development and have yet to be proven in this country. Moreover, they are intended as management tools to indicate relative requirements rather than to define quantities (Brown, 1989).

It is, however, the attempt to synthesise all the combined requirements of the whole aquatic ecosystem which leads to the assessment of an environmentally acceptable flow regime. An EAFR seeks to mimic the natural seasonal variations in flows and moves away from the more traditional approach to regulated flow management which has always tended towards subduing not only extreme flows but also the seasonality of flows.

Fieldwork and results

A preliminary field assessment was undertaken throughout the catchment in order to select sampling sites for environmental characterisation. Nine sites were selected to be representative of either characteristic river reaches and/or characteristic habitat types encountered along the length of the river. Their locations are indicated on Figure 1. Factors considered in the selection included channel morphology, substrate, underlying geology, type of flow (pool/riffle/run), river and bankside vegetation, riparian management and surrounding land use. Hydrometric, chemical, and biological characterisation of each site was undertaken during fieldwork between 10 and 12 October 1990.

Invertebrate Biological Monitoring Working Party (BMWP) scores were calculated for each site from the samples taken. Predicted BMWP scores (Wright et al., 1984) were also obtained for each site from the Institute of Freshwater Ecology's computer program RIVPACS. Results of both sampled and predicted BMWP scores and average score per taxon (ASPT) for each site are presented in Figure 3. Of the nine sites, only sites 1, 3, and 4 (Westerham, Otford gauging station, and Shoreham) had sample scores within the confidence range of the single season RIVPACS scores. Of these only sites 3 and 4 had sample scores proximal to the predicted mean. A visual assessment of the emergent and bankside vegetation also showed that sites 3, 4, and 9 displayed abundant and diverse macrophytes.

Water quality analysis indicated that water was generally of a very high quality where it was present.

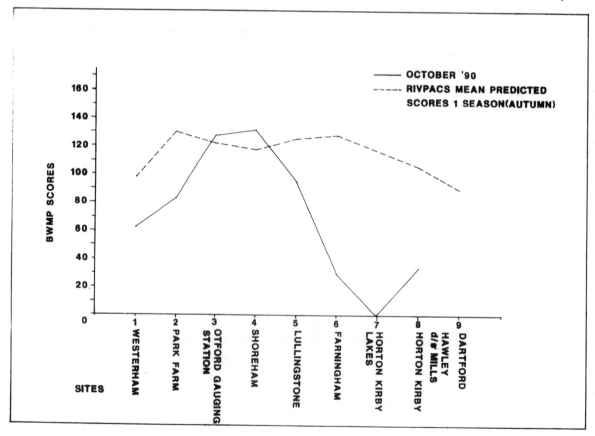

Figure 3   River Darent invertebrate scores

This reflects the almost total lack of effluent discharges to the river, due primarily to the presence of the trunk sewer from Sevenoaks to Dartford. This sewer collects the majority of sewerage generated within the catchment and exports it directly from the catchment via the Longreach treatment works at Dartford. This effectively exports some 20Mld^{-1} from the catchment.

Of the nine sites selected, three were on Lower Cretaceous beds (sites 1-3) and six were on the Chalk (sites 4-9). The catchment areas and flow profiles are shown in Figure 4. It can be seen that flows were around the 95th percentile of the flow duration curve over the period of field work. The flow profile also demonstrates the nature of flow depletion in a downstream direction. Mean flows at the gauging stations are derived from the gauged flow records. These records commenced in the 1960s, since which time groundwater abstractions from the catchment have been at a maximum.

The results indicate that there remain stretches of the river, particularly in the Shoreham area, where biological quality is very good, as indicated by their diversity of flora and fauna. These stretches also retain the visual characteristics of a chalk stream.

For the remainder of the river, however, the sampled BMWP and ASPT scores fall far short of those predicted by RIVPACS. This is particularly noticeable downstream of Lullingstone where low or no flows have had significant effects on the ecology of the river.

Macrophytes are also an integral part of a riverine environment: they provide colonisable habitats for invertebrates and shelter for fish. Their removal, either through flood defence or other riparian management (including agriculture practice), is therefore likely to influence the extent of habitat available, and ultimately the productivity of the macroinvertebrate community. The majority of sites had a low diversity of macrophytes, except for Otford, Shoreham, and Wilmington. It is notable that those sites above Shoreham where flow remained reasonable but which were impoverished from a macrophyte point of view, also displayed impoverishment in macroinvertebrate scores.

Defining an EAFR

Given the uncertainties of adequately defining the flow requirements for a riverine ecosystem, and the discovery of a river reach that displayed all the natural characteristics of a chalk river, a pragmatic approach to defining an EAFR was adopted. This sought to utilise the stretch on the River Darent which currently experienced sufficient flow to maintain a healthy chalk stream ecology as an index site.

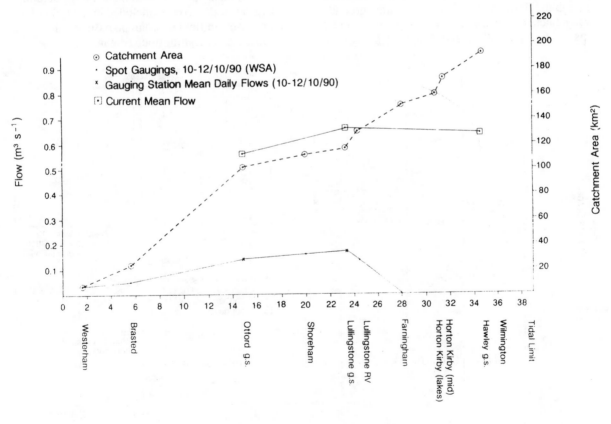

Figure 4 *Darent flow profiles and catchment areas*

The macroinvertebrate sampling and chemical analysis undertaken in this study indicated that site 4 at Shoreham received sufficient flows of good quality water to enable a healthy aquatic community to be sustained: Shoreham was also the only site at which trout were found (albeit possibly stocked). The fact that the ecology of the river both upstream and downstream of this site was less healthy also tends to suggest that Shoreham only just receives the flow regime and management required to support its ecology. Shoreham was therefore deemed to experience an EAFR in its current flow regime and was therefore taken as the index site.

The catchment above Shoreham contains less than 25% Chalk, and may not therefore be viewed as geologically representative of the catchment as a whole, which is approximately 52% Chalk. Nevertheless, the site exhibits all the characteristics of a chalk stream, and probably represents a mean geology of the river, being about halfway down the course of the river and having something of everything that outcrops in the catchment as a whole.

Contributing surface catchment area was therefore adopted as the characteristic by which to standardise the EAFR for transfer to other sites along the river. Although this is less attractive than using natural channel width, it does provide a pattern of increasing flows downstream broadly in line with natural expectations. It is, however, less applicable on chalk catchments where surface water runoff contributes very little to the flows in the river. Contributing groundwater catchment area would hold more meaning but this is difficult to define, and complicated where

there is more than one aquifer in the catchment (as here), as well as impermeable strata contributing surface runoff.

Shoreham lies more or less midway between Otford and Lullingstone gauging stations. It was therefore relatively straightforward to define the flow regime at Shoreham from these two flow records and results obtained during fieldwork (Figure 5). The mean flow at Shoreham (approximately Q30 on the derived fdc) is estimated as $0.65m^3s^{-1}$, equivalent to 185mm of runoff per year.

Standardising the flow duration curve by catchment area allows it to be transferred to other sites along the river. Figure 6 compares estimated natural mean flows (using a rough water balance approach), EAFR, and current gauged flow statistics along the river. It can be seen that the EAFR represents a substantial increase in both mean and low flows in the lower half of the catchment, and a slight improvement in the upper half. For example the proposed EAFR mean flow at Hawley is $1.12m^3s^{-1}$ which is some $0.49m^3s^{-1}$ (42 Mld[-1]) improvement in the current mean flow. The EAFR mean flow is still estimated as $0.31m^3s^{-1}$ (47 Mld[-1]) below the estimated natural mean flow for Hawley, and this would effectively remain available for abstraction.

Seasonality in flows, indicated earlier as being necessary to support the various life stages of different fauna, as well as to maintain the natural character of the river, is included in the form of a monthly mean flow hydrograph based on that experienced at Lullingstone (Figure 7).

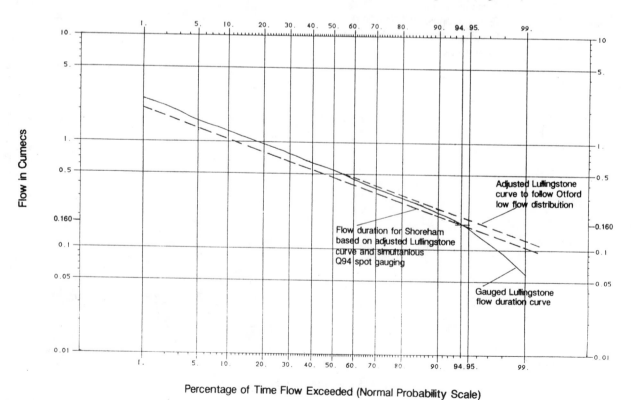

Figure 5 Derivation of Shoreham EAFR flow duration curve

Implications for the river

The implication for the river of defining the EAFR as discussed are considerable. The proposed EAFR represents a significant increase in mean and low flows downstream of Shoreham and will therefore require the introduction of additional flows back to the river. The NRA has commissioned a detailed study to determine the most feasible and economic means of achieving this increase in flows and managing the EAFR.

The regime is also set with respect to the prevailing very high standards of water quality: should this decline then increased flows are likely to be required.

It is difficult to quantify the benefits to the river from its surrounding bankside vegetation in terms of provision of habitat and shelter. However, the survey found that where this vegetation was present and properly managed, there was significant improvement in macroinvertebrate communities. The implications for the future provision and maintenance of such vegetation will therefore need to be considered in conjunction with the restoration of flows. Similarly, the reasons for the noticeable deviation from the expected geomorphological character of the river downstream of Shoreham will also need to be considered, as will the implications of increased flows on the geomorphology in these reaches.

Conclusions

The River Darent has suffered from flow depletion due to groundwater abstraction for public water supply since before the commencement of flow records in the 1960s. In the summers of 1976, 1989, 1990 and 1991 the river between Farningham and Dartford dried up for some or all of its length, and has received considerable media coverage recently due to this problem.

In this study, nine sites along the River Darent were selected to represent characteristic stretches of the river. Fieldwork undertaken at these sites characterised the biological, chemical and hydrological attributes of the river.

One site on the river, Shoreham, site 4, was identified as having good BMWP and ASPT scores compared to RIVPACS predictions. This site also displayed the generally accepted natural characteristics of a chalk

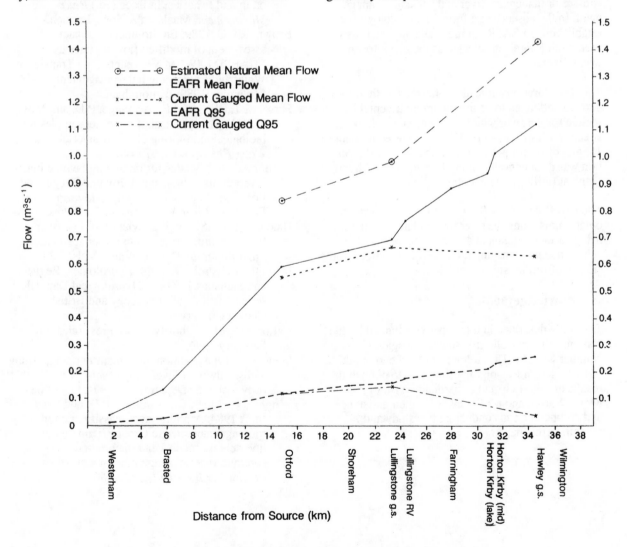

Figure 6   Comparison of estimated, natural, EAFR and observed mean flows, and Q95s

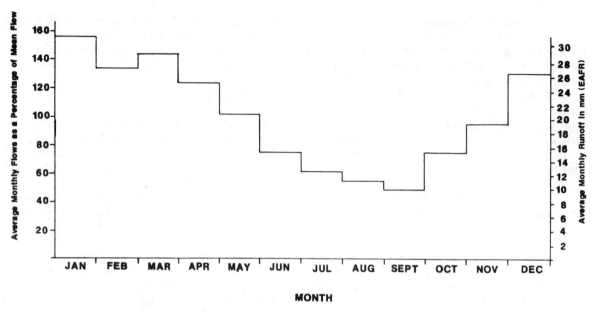

Figure 7   Seasonality of flows at Lullingstone gauging station

stream. Most other sites had macroinvertebrate scores below, or well below their predicted scores. This was deemed to be due to either or both extreme low flow stresses or inadequate river and bankside management. In the absence of a formal methodology for establishing an EAFR, an index site approach was used, with Shoreham selected as the index for the whole river.

The flow duration curve at Shoreham was therefore derived and taken to be the minimum acceptable flow regime for the river which could sustain a chalk stream ecology, i.e. an EAFR. This was equivalent to 185mm of runoff per year. A seasonal flow distribution was defined as the monthly mean annual hydrograph at Lullingstone gauging station.

The EAFR defined at Shoreham was transferred to other points along the river by standardising the fdc using surface catchment area, but the means of achieving and managing the EAFR in practice are the subject of further studies by NRA.

Acknowledgements

The study described in this paper was funded by the National Rivers Authority Southern Region (Job Number K0756). The authors would like to thank the NRA Southern Region for permission to publish the results of this study and in particular wish to thank Mr G. Warren and Mr S. Oakes for their assistance and co-operation in conducting this study and in compiling this paper.

References

Brayshaw, J.D. 1966. The effects of river discharge on inland fisheries. In Isaac (ed.) *River Management*, Maclaren & Sons, London.

Brown, R.P.C. 1989. Environmental impact assessment of modified flow regimes using PHABSIM. IWEM 89: Technology Transfer in Water and Environmental Management, 12-14 September 1989, Birmingham.

Furse, M.T., Wright, J.F., Armitage, P.D. and Moss, L. 1981. An appraisal of pond-net samples for biological monitoring of macroinvertebrates. *Water Research* 15, 679-689.

Gore, J.A. 1989. Modes for predicting benthic macro-invertebrate habitat suitability under regulated flows. In Gore and Petts (eds) *Alternatives in Regulated River Management*. CRC Press.

Halcrow. 1988. Study of alleviation of low river flows resulting from groundwater abstraction. Final Report to Thames Water. Vols. 1,2,8.

Institute of Hydrology. 1988. Hydrological Register and Statistics 1981-85. Hydrological Data UK series. Institute of Hydrology and British Geological Survey.

National Rivers Authority. 1990. Press release, February 1990.

Stewart, L. 1968. Salmon movement in rising, falling and steady river levels. Lancashire River Authority Fisheries Department report, July 1968.

Wright, J.F., Moss, D., Armitage, P.D. and Furse, M.T. 1984. A preliminary classification of running water sites in Great Britain on macro-invertebrate species and the prediction of community type using environmental data. *Freshwater Biology* 14, 221-256.

Towards the setting of ecologically acceptable flow regimes with IFIM

A. Bullock & I. Johnson

Abstract

Minimum Acceptable Flows have until now been prescribed in the UK
using hydrological data which takes no clear account of ecological
requirements. By predicting how physical habitat changes with discharge,
IFIM introduces consideration of habitat requirements of aquatic species in
the identification of Ecologically Acceptable Flows. This paper reports
upon an application of the Instream Flow Incremental Methodology (IFIM)
in the United Kingdom, and issues pertinent to the setting of flow regimes.

Introduction

The consideration of a Minimum Acceptable Flow in
the setting of prescribed or compensation flows
below impounding reservoirs, surface abstractions or
regulation schemes, has largely been founded upon
discharge statistics in the United Kingdom, applying
the concept of a Dry Weather Flow. Statistics
commonly used include fixed percentages of the
mean flow, the 95 exceedance percentile or mean
annual minimum low flows; historically they have
also been linked to reservoir yield.

In an ecological context, a single discharge statistic
pays little cognisance to the instream flow requirements of biological species. It has long been demonstrated that aquatic species (fish, invertebrates and
macrophytes) exhibit preferences for different habitat
types and physical parameters, some of which are
discharge-dependent. The Instream Flow Incremental
Methodology (IFIM) represents a quantitative
management model for recommending flow regimes
which consider ecological demands. IFIM, which
incorporates the Physical Habitat Simulation
(PHABSIM) system, provides an estimate of habitat
loss/gain with changes in discharge.

This paper reports upon issues arising from the initial
application of IFIM in the United Kingdom on the
rivers Blithe (Staffordshire) and Gwash
(Leicestershire) which are pertinent to the setting of
Minimum Acceptable Flows from the viewpoint of
the ecologist, and worthy of consideration in
negotiating against other demands. Furthermore, the
paper elaborates upon research developments within
an ongoing National Rivers Authority-funded project
aimed at developing the IFIM for setting ecologically
acceptable flow regimes in the rivers of England and
Wales.

Methods for setting Minimum Acceptable Flows in the UK

Dry Weather Flow is an undefined discharge but is
indexed by a low flow discharge, typically either the
95 percentile exceedance flow duration statistic
(most common in eight of ten NRA regions), or the
mean annual minimum seven-day flow frequency
statistic (commonly used in Severn-Trent and
Yorkshire regions). Only recently in the U.K. have
resource planners given fuller recognition to the
ecological value of low flows. The Yorkshire region
of the NRA, for example, employ an environmental
weighting scheme which sets prescribed flows as a
proportion of the Dry Weather Flow (DWF). The
DWF is weighted according to a range of environmental characteristics and used to calculate the
Environmental Prescribed Flow (Drake and Sherriff,
1987). Fish management models tend to be more
scheme-specific in nature as, for example, in the
fisheries study downstream of Roadford Reservoir
which commenced in 1984 to develop operating rules
to minimise detrimental impacts upon salmonids in
the rivers Tamar and Torridge (British Hydrological
Society, 1988).

Instream Flow Incremental Methodology (IFIM)

Procedures for evaluating the impacts of streamflow
changes on ecology were first developed in the
United States and have advanced considerably in the
period 1974-1991. Central to these advances has been
the concept of instream flow requirements, which
recognises that aquatic species have habitat preferences, with habitat defined by physical properties
(flow velocity, water depth, substrate and vegetal/
channel cover). Because some of these physical

properties which determine habitat vary with discharge so species have different preferences for different discharges. Development of the IFIM (Bovee, 1982) by the Aquatic Systems Branch of the U.S. Fish and Wildlife Service has allowed the quantification of species preferences for the full range of discharges that may be experienced within a river. This quantification of habitat preferences and the relationship with river flow gives potential for setting optimal flows for ecological management. Defining Minimum Acceptable Flows in this manner complements purely water-quantity or cost-management objectives by recognising physical habitat requirements.

The IFIM has been applied in several countries outside the USA, including Canada (Mathur *et al.*, 1985), New Zealand (Scott *et al.*,1987), Australia (Gan & McMahon, 1990), Norway (Heggenes *et al.*,1990) and France (Souchon *et al.*,1989). The first application in the United Kingdom was undertaken on the River Blithe in Staffordshire and the River Gwash in Leicestershire/Lincolnshire (Bullock *et al.* 1991, Bullock & Gustard, in press). For this application habitat suitability (preference) curves were derived by the Institute of Freshwater Ecology (Armitage & Ladle,1990) and the Institute of Terrestrial Ecology (Mountford & Gomes, 1989).

Model calibration

The Physical Habitat Simulation (PHABSIM) software is a key component of IFIM and is in the public domain. It is driven by field survey information, being a transect-based method in which the physical parameters of depth, mean column velocity, cover and substrate type are measured at each of a number of sampling points across each transect within a specified study reach. Application of the PHABSIM model to a particular instream flow study follows the following steps:

(i) selection of study reach/reaches

(ii) placement of transects

(iii) bed elevation survey

(iv) coded observation of cover and substrate type

(v) measurement of water surface elevations and mean column velocities at different calibration discharges.

Details of each of these steps in the application of PHABSIM may be summarised thus:

(i) Study reach selection

At the outset of an IFIM study it is necessary to define the limits of the hydrological area to which the required instream flow must apply. The stretch of river within this area must now be studied so as to identify the range of geomorphological features and different habitat types present. Within this larger stretch a smaller reach or number of reaches, referred to as "study reaches", are selected. To represent fully the features of the larger stretch, the study reach must contain all of those geomorphological features and habitat types present. For this reason the study reach is referred to as a "representative reach".

(ii) Placement of transects

Placement of transects within the representative reach must reflect the need to model the reach well in both hydraulic and ecological terms. Some transects must be placed so as to represent the range of different geomorphological features e.g. riffles, pools, runs. Others are placed to sample different habitat types e.g. areas with overhead cover or instream vegetation. Data requirements of the hydraulic models used within PHABSIM require the most downstream transect to be placed at a point which acts as a hydraulic control, above which there is a unique stage-discharge relationship. At least one transect should be placed with the sole goal of providing a good estimate of the stage/discharge relationship.

(iii) Bed elevation survey

Across each transect a number of points are defined so as to best represent the shape and thalweg of the channel. The bed elevation is measured at each of these points using standard surveying techniques.

(iv) Substrate/cover classification

At each sampling point coded observations of substrate and cover must be made. The hydraulic model may be thought of as being cell-based, with cells stretching from a point half-way to adjacent points and likewise half-way to adjacent transects. However, it is not appropriate to view observations of substrate/cover as being cell-based. A more appropriate and practical approach is to view observations as point samples restricted to a small area around the sampling point. Within PHABSIM this local information is mapped to cover the whole of the reach by applying different weights to the data collected at each transect. For the initial assessment on the Blithe and Gwash cover and substrate codes were assigned using the conditional criteria scheme proposed by Trihey and Wegner (1981).

(v) Water surface elevation and velocity measurement

A number of different hydraulic models are available within PHABSIM to predict water surface elevations and/or velocities. The water surface elevation is assumed to be constant across each transect whilst velocities vary from point to point. Different models have different minimum data requirements but the basic data requirement may be summarised thus:

- averaged water surface elevation at each transect

- mean column velocity at each wetted point for each transect

These data must be recorded for at least three different discharges. To achieve the best possible calibration (and to permit simulation over the full flow regime experienced in the stream without over extrapolation), these calibration flows should represent as wide a range as possible.

Model limitations

It must be recognised that the application of PHABSIM is not appropriate in situations where it is thought that a parameter other than physical habitat is limiting to populations of aquatic species. Water quality and temperature are examples of such parameters. When the model is run over a range of simulation discharges, care must be exercised to avoid extrapolation too far beyond calibration discharges.The model does not have the capacity to incorporate any time-dependent biological response to changes in available habitat, for example extended periods of low flows.

Issues pertinent to the ecologist in setting flows

Optimal flows can be extracted from the habitat versus flow relationships and it is seemingly logical to argue for the peak of the function or significant thresholds or inflections. There are several concepts that must be borne in mind (Bovee 1982), and these are discussed with reference to data from the River Blithe (Figures 1-3).

(1) A flow change that is beneficial to one life stage may be detrimental to another life stage

The shape of the WUA/Q curves for Brown Trout at Blithe Dam is a foundation for arguing that an

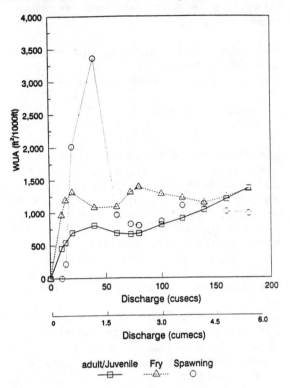

Figure 2   Weighted Usable Area (WUA) vs discharge (Q) for roach at Blithe Dam

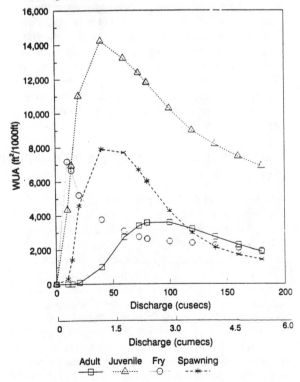

Figure 1   Weighted Usable Area (WUA) vs discharge (Q) for brown trout at Blithe Dam

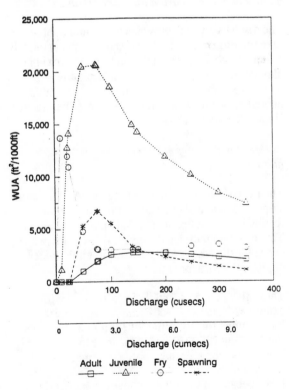

Figure 3   Weighted Usable Area (WUA) vs discharge (Q) for brown trout at Hamstall Ridware

increase in flows from 0.5 m³s⁻¹ up to around 1.5 m³s⁻¹ would be beneficial for spawning, juvenile and adult life stage, but that such an increase would prove detrimental to the fry life stage.

(2) A flow change that is beneficial to one species may be detrimental to another species

An increase in flows at Blithe Dam upwards from 1.5 m³s⁻¹ would be beneficial to the adult life stage of roach but detrimental to adult brown trout.

(3) Various life stages and species may require different amounts of water at different times of the year

Brown trout spawn late in the year, typically November to December, with the critical period for the fry stage being in the spring. Most coarse fish spawn in the spring, typically May to June, with the critical period for the fry stage being in the summer. In the case of Brown Trout at Blithe Dam, flows of approximately 1.5 m³s⁻¹ in early winter would provide optimal habitat for the spawning stage, whereas fry would benefit most from a decrease in flows to approximately 0.5 m³s⁻¹. At other times of the year, flows should be set to optimise habitat for the juvenile and adult stages. It is clear that to decrease flows in the spring to provide optimal habitat for fry brown trout would introduce conflict with the demand to maintain flows at 1.5 m³s⁻¹ to maintain habitat for spawning roach.

(4) A flow that maximises usable habitat in one part of the stream may not maximise, and may decrease, habitat in another part of the same stream.

The discharge which provides maximum habitat for juvenile brown trout at Blithe Dam is approximately 1.5 m³s⁻¹, while at Hamstall Ridware (approximately 5km downstream), the maximum habitat is provided by approximately 2.5 m³s⁻¹. To maximise usable habitat at Blithe Dam will not maximise habitat at Hamstall Ridware.

(5) More water does not necessarily mean more habitat

The peaked nature of many of the WUA/Q relationships means that above certain thresholds more water results in a reduction in available physical habitat. This is due to individuals having decreasing preferences for the associated increases in either water depth, velocities, or both.

These five concepts, and their illustration with examples from the River Blithe, have important implications for the setting of Minimum Acceptable Flows using IFIM. It is possible to recognise three key issues which must be borne in mind;

First, because a flow change that is beneficial to one life stage may be detrimental to another life stage, and because various life stages and species may require different amounts of water at different times

of the year, it is essential that seasonally-varying Minimum Acceptable Flows are considered. Combining WUA/Q relationships with time series of historical flows to give a time series of WUAs can demonstrate the seasonal variability of physical habitat.

Second, because a flow change that is beneficial to one life stage may be detrimental to another life stage, it is essential in advance of the application of the IFIM methodology that the priority target species are identified and, if necessary ranked.

Third, it has been shown that a flow that maximises usable habitat in one part of the stream may not maximise habitat in an adjacent part of the same stream. The practice of choosing Prescribed Flow points (commonly gauging sites, abstraction/discharge points or river confluences), could introduce significant bias into the prescribed flow regime by not recognising the wider characteristics of the upstream and downstream river reaches. Application of the IFIM would be more appropriate to setting flow regimes in river reaches than individual points.

Each of these recommendations has implications for the conduct of an instream flow study, in that there is an essential stage prior to any field work being undertaken in which interested parties achieve prior agreement on target species and the reach limits. Prior agreement must also be achieved concerning competing demands on the river water, such that all parties concerned with the study reach register an interest. For once the IFIM study is completed and WUA/Q relationships have been generated, the ecologist or hydrologist concerned with optimising habitat must utilise this information in a negotiating forum against competing demands (Wilds, 1985). Because ecological demands have been related to discharge, the application of IFIM has the merit of equipping the negotiator with both a quantitative basis and equivalent terminology to other water resource demands.

Issues pertinent to the setting of Minimum Acceptable Flows

The forum and decision-making process for prescribing new Minimum Acceptable Flows in the United Kingdom is yet to be established post the 1989 Water Act. Whilst negotiation amongst concerned organisations is commonplace in the United States, the first occasion on which a Minimum Acceptable Flow is set in this country with ecologically acceptable flows as an issue will no doubt provide valuable frameworks and strategies for future cases. Key questions in setting ecologically acceptable flows include: What organisations are to be involved? What needs are represented? What role will each assume? What resources does each have? How will the final decision be made, if no acceptable agreement can be reached? Who will likely dominate? What laws are involved? Wilds (1985) describes five factors which will affect the likelihood of success in mediating environmental negotiations, and which offer guidelines to concerned organisations: despite their American origin and association with different water management frameworks they bear repetition.

(1) The participants must have some incentive to negotiate with each other, and must believe that the end result will achieve more than an imposed formal legislative procedure.

(2) Negotiators should attempt to identify the specific interests that underlie stated positions, and then to bargain based on those interests.

(3) There is little documentary evidence that the number of participants involved, or the presence/absence of a deadline, affects the likelihood of success, contrary to popular wisdom. Instead, how the participants prepare for the negotiation, and their willingness to cooperate and bargain in good faith, are crucial.

(4) The most significant factor to achieving success is whether or not the organisation responsible for implementing the agreement, once reached, directly participated in the process.

(5) The presence of a mediator facilitates the process greatly, especially when the mediator is both willing and able to conduct an assessment of the particular negotiating situation before beginning dispute resolution.

Future research developments in the application of the IFIM

Work commenced in October 1990 under a three-year R&D commission 'Ecologically Acceptable Flows' from the NRA. The scope of this commission is to assess the applicability of IFIM to the range of river types found in England and Wales by application on ten different rivers in England and Wales. The choice of study rivers was guided by the desire to represent the full range of different ecological and hydrological features present and different types of water resource problems, e.g. rivers subject to compensation flows, rivers regulated artificially by weirs and sluice gates, rivers subject to the effects of groundwater abstraction etc.

In order to choose rivers representing a full range of different ecological types, data from the RIVPACS database were used to divide all UK rivers sampled into ten different ecological classes. Having selected potential study rivers, representative study reaches were then chosen to meet the following criteria:

(i) being within 10km from a RIVPACS sampling site;

(ii) being within 10km from an operational gauging station with a good flow record;

(iii) having a catchment area of less than 150 km^2
(iv) being representative of the river in hydrological/ecological terms for at least 10 km up/downstream from the study reach.

The provisional list of study rivers is as follows :

RIVPACS Group	River	NRA Region
1	Exe	South West
2	Wye	Welsh
3	Hodder	North West
4	Blithe	Severn Trent
5	Rother	Southern
6	Lymington	Southern
7	Frome	Wessex
8	Lambourn	Thames
9	Gwash	Anglian
10	Great Ouse	Anglian

The Great Ouse is an exception to the third criterion, selected to be representative of a large lowland river which is intensively regulated.

During the course of this research it is intended to develop the model in a number of ways to make it more applicable to UK conditions. These are summarised thus:

- To develop a more sophisticated coding system for observations of cover and substrate type. A new coding system has been applied at field sites but now needs incorporating in the modelling procedure.

- To develop software enhancement for ease of analysis and presentation of results.

- To investigate the seasonal effects of vegetation growth on the hydraulic modelling.

- To develop more refined preference curves for target species. The Institute of Freshwater Ecology are liaising on this part of the project and will be using both information from the literature and occurrence data from on-site sampling in this task.

- To combine WUA vs Q relationships with time series of flows to provide information for assessing time dependent instream flow requirements.

- To develop a quantitative framework for setting ecologically acceptable flows.

Acknowledgements

The initial assessment of IFIM involving studies on the rivers Blithe and Gwash was commissioned by the Department of The Environment. Work reported under 'Future Research Developments' was commissioned by the National Rivers Authority. For the same section we acknowledge the assistance of

Dr Robert Milhous and the Royal Society for the funding of his research fellowship.

References

Armitage, P.D. & Ladle, M. 1989. Habitat preferences of target species for application in PHABSIM testing. Unpublished report to the Institute of Hydrology.

Bovee, K.D. 1982. A guide to stream habitat analysis using the Instream Flow Incremental Methodology. Instream Flow Information Paper No. 12. U.S.D.I. Fish & Wildlife Service, Office of Biological Services. FWS/OBS-82/26

British Hydrological Society. 1988. Aspects of hydrological studies in S.W. England: monitoring and resources. BHS *Circulation* No.17, 4-6.

Bullock, A., Gustard, A. & Grainger, E. 1991. Instream flow requirements of aquatic ecology in two British Rivers. *Institute of Hydrology Report No. 115*

Bullock, A. & Gustard, A. In press. Application of the Instream Flow Incremental Methodology to assess ecological flow requirements in a British lowland river. In *Fluvial Dynamics Of Lowland River Channel And Floodplain Systems*, Proceedings of British Geomorphological Research Group Symposium, Loughborough, September 1990.

Drake, P.J. & Sherriff, J.D.F. 1987. A method for managing river abstractions and protecting the environment. *J. Water and Environ. Manage.* 27-38.

Gan, K. & McMahon, T. 1990. Variability of results from the use of PHABSIM in estimating habitat area. *Regulated Rivers: Research & Management*, 5, 233-239.

Heggenes, J., Braband, A., & Saltveit, S.J. 1990. Comparison of three methods for studies of stream habitat use by young brown trout & atlantic salmon. *Trans. Amer. Fish. Soc.*, 119(1).

Mathur, D., Bason, W.H., Purdy, E.J.,jr. & Silver, C.A. 1985. A critique of The Instream Flow Incremental Methodology. *Can. J. Fish. Aquat. Sci.* 42, 825-831

Mountford, O. & Gomes, N. 1990. Habitat preference of river water crowfoot (*Ranunculus fluitans lam.*) for application in PHABSIM testing. Unpublished report to the Institute of Hydrology.

Scott, D. & Shirvell, C.S. 1987. A critique of The Instream Flow Incremental Methodology With observations on flow determination in New Zealand. *Regulated Streams: Advances in Ecology*, Plenum Press, New York, 27-43.

Souchon, Y., Trocherie, F., Fragnoud, E. & Lacombe, C. 1989. Les modèles numeriques des microhabitats des poissons: application et nouveaux developments. *Revue des Sciences de L'Eau*, 2, 807-830.

Trihey, E.W. & Wegner, D.L. 1981. Field data collection procedures for use with The PHABSIM System of The Instream Flow Group. Cooperative Instream Flow Service, Fort Collins, Colorado.

Wilds, L.J. 1985. A negotiator's checklist: success through preparation. *Hydro Review*, (Winter) 56-60.

Advances in low flow estimation and impact assessment

A. Gustard & A. Bullock

Abstract

The estimation of low flows at ungauged sites has traditionally been based on relationships between flow statistics derived from gauged data and catchment characteristics. This paper describes three main advances in low flow estimation which have followed the publication of the first national study of low flows in 1980. First, research into automatic techniques for the derivation of catchment characteristics which have been implemented on a MICRO LOW FLOW software package for rapid and consistent low flow estimation for all reaches in a hydrometric region. Second, the 1991 Low Flow Study which analysed a considerably larger national data set, recent extreme events and improved catchment characteristics to generate revised regional regression equations. Third, investigations into techniques for assessing the impact of water resource schemes upon downstream flows, including studies which have assessed the impact of point abstractions upon low flow regimes, and different scenarios of reservoir operation. Each of the three principal areas of development is summarised and case studies are presented which illustrate the potential of new techniques for hydrological impact assessment.

Introduction

The Low Flow Studies report(Institute of Hydrology, 1980) describes the first national study of low river flows in the UK. The report presents:

1. Procedures for deriving a number of low flow measures from daily mean flow data

2. Techniques for estimating low flows at sites in the UK without data

3. Recommendations on how to combine short flow records, spot current meterings and local flow data in the estimation procedure

The report presents a number of different ways of describing the low flow regime of a river, because a low flow event can be expressed in terms of several different parameters: a threshold discharge, an accumulated volume, a length of time spent below a threshold or a rate of recession. The frequency of an event can be expressed as a proportion of time (the flow duration curve) or as the proportion of years (the low flow frequency curve derived from the annual minima series). Finally most forms of analysis can be repeated for different durations or for different threshold discharges.

The Base Flow Index (BFI) provided a key stage in estimating low flows at the ungauged site. The index provides a measure of the proportion of runoff that is derived from stored sources and can be calculated from daily mean flow data. Although examples of how to derive procedures for estimating BFI at the ungauged sites were given in the report a formal procedure with national coverage was not provided.

Advances in low flow estimation

Indicators of improvement in low flow estimation include development of new low flow measures, extended spatial coverage, finer spatial resolution, reduced errors of estimation and improved ease of estimation. In addition to the national Low Flow Study carried out by the Institute of Hydrology (IH) a number of regional investigations have been completed. These include a study by the Southern Water Authority (1979) which combined the IH method with that based on a low flow per unit area and included the production of the first BFI map for a Regional Water Authority area. Regional methods were subsequently developed for the Severn-Trent region (Pirt & Douglas, 1982) which used a dry weather flow per unit area and relationships between low flow statistics and both soils and catchment geology. Other local techniques were developed but remain unpublished, for example in the South-West for estimating the flow duration curve from soil type, and elsewhere rules-of-thumb were applied such as assuming Q95 to be 10% of the mean flow.

New low flow variables were derived in developing a national methodology for estimating runoff accumulation times, and seasonal flow duration curves have been published in reports 2.3 and 2.4, supplements to the original Low Flow Studies.

Data from Northern Ireland were not included in the 1980 Low Flow Study, and this omission was addressed by the subsequent development of a low flow estimation technique for the province (Gustard & Sutcliffe, 1986). The first revision of the 1980 Low Flow Study was the development of a regional methodology for low flow estimation in Scotland (Gustard et al., 1987). A further 68 stations were analysed with data periods extended by a further 10 years. The standard error of the regression equations was reduced, as illustrated in Table 1, and the revised equations enabled the influence of lakes to be incorporated. The production of the river network map of BFI for Scotland (Figure 1), published at a scale of 1:625,000, considerably simplified the task of estimating BFI and hence low flow statistics at an ungauged site.

Table 1 Reduction in errors of low flow estimation (units m^3s^{-1})

1980 Low Flow Study

$$Q95(10)^{\frac{1}{2}} = 8.60BFI^{\frac{1}{2}} + 0.00377AREA^{\frac{1}{2}} + 0.0414SAAR^{\frac{1}{2}} - 3.22$$

$$R^2 = 0.552 \quad s.e. = 0.956$$

$$MAM(10)^{\frac{1}{2}} = 9.39BFI^{\frac{1}{2}} + 0.00199AREA^{\frac{1}{2}} + 0.144SAAR^{\frac{1}{2}} - 2.89$$

$$R^2 = 0.667 \quad s.e. = 0.855$$

1987 Low Flow Estimation in Scotland

$$Q95(10)^{\frac{1}{2}} = 8.81BFI^{\frac{1}{2}} + 0.0248SAAR^{\frac{1}{2}} - 2.40FALAKE^{\frac{1}{2}} - 2.66$$

$$R^2 = 0.665 \quad s.e. = 0.57$$

$$MAM(10)^{\frac{1}{2}} = 9.44/BFI^{\frac{1}{2}} - 2.80FALAKE^{\frac{1}{2}} - 2.27$$

$$R^2 = 0.761 \quad s.e. = 0.54$$

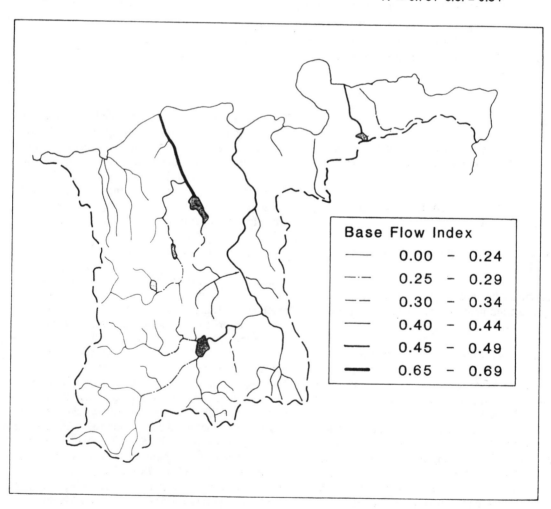

Base Flow Index

———	0.00	– 0.24
—·—	0.25	– 0.29
— —	0.30	– 0.34
———	0.40	– 0.44
———	0.45	– 0.49
━━━	0.65	– 0.69

Figure 1 Illustration of the Base Flow Index map of Scotland for Hydrometric Area 97

Subsequent regional low flow estimation methods were undertaken in the North West region (Bullock & Gustard, 1988), which included the definition of a modal flow index, and in the South West region (Bullock & Gustard, 1989). Both studies made significant advances not only in developing improved regression equations, but more so in the ease of application by providing estimates of key low flow statistics at many ungauged sites: 4,000 in the case of North West and 14,000 in the case of South West. This was achieved by application of the river network overlay method, which is described in the following section.

The 1991 Low Flow Study (Gustard et al., 1991) was commissioned by the Department of the Environment in 1987 to revise the original Low Flow Study. Developments and improvements lie in three main areas: first, the analysis of data to the end of 1989 includes several extreme low flow events which were excluded in the original study which analysed data to the end of 1975, thereby omitting the major 1976 and subsequent drought events. Second, the opening of new gauging sites means that data from 1100 stations are now adjudged suitable for analysis of daily data compared to only 456 previously. Third, the availability of improved catchment characteristics, especially the 29 class Hydrology Of Soil Types (HOST) classification (Boorman & Hollis, 1990) which offers both better spatial resolution and the improved grouping of soils classes at the extremes of hydrological response compared with the earlier five-class Winter Rainfall Acceptance Potential scheme.

The 1991 Low Flow Study presents a register of the quality classification of all permanent gauging stations in the United Kingdom. 1643 catchments in the Surface Water Archive have been graded in two ways: first, according to the hydrometric quality of low flow measurement based on station sensitivity, scatter of low flow gaugings and other factors including weed growth and siltation; second, according to the degree of artificial influence exerted upon the flow regime by discharges, abstraction and regulation schemes. Hydrometric quality and degree of artificial influence are each graded from A to C. Figure 2 depicts those catchments which have acceptable quality of low flow measurement (Hydrometric grade A or B). Figure 3 depicts that

area of the country which combines good quality measurement with relatively natural gauged low flow regimes (Hydrometric quality is graded A and Degree of artficial influence is graded A).

Revised regional regression equations for low flow estimation at ungauged sites are based upon the key variables Q95 and MAM(7), which have been related directly to the 29 HOST classes. The necessity to estimate BFI at an ungauged site is replaced by a requirement to calculate the fraction of HOST classes, either from 1:250,000 (or other scale) soil maps or from a national HOST gridded database. Table 2 presents provisional results of calculated Q95 and MAM(7) with significant parameter values, for some example HOST classes. Revised internal relationships allow the improved estimation of flow duration curves and low flow frequency curves, from knowledge of either Q95 or MAM(7) respectively.

Automatic derivation of catchment characteristics

A general drawback of the application of regional design techniques is the requirement upon the user to estimate catchment characteristic values at the ungauged site of interest. This is a problem, particularly in large catchments with numerous soil classes, which is not only time-consuming but which can also suffer inconsistency between users. Automatic techniques for the derivation of catchment characteristics depend upon the capability to construct a catchment boundary above the site of interest for superimposition upon thematic maps in digital form.

Although techniques have been developed for deriving digital catchment boundaries from a hydrologically consistent digital elevation model (Morris & Heerdegen, 1988), the derived boundaries are not yet available on a national basis. An alternative strategy has been to derive synthetic catchment boundaries from the 1:50 000 digital river network data which is currently more widely available. In the river network overlay technique (Sekulin et al., in prep.) the catchment boundary is constructed by identifying the nearest river reach for every 0.25 km grid square in a given hydrometric area. The method incorporates catchment boundaries

Table 2 Provisional Q95 and MAM(7) values for a selection of HOST classes

	Q95 (% of mean flow)	Standard Error	MAM(7) (% of mean flow)	Standard Error
HOST Class 1	39.2	1.5	45.6	1.7
HOST Class 2	64.6	4.5	65.4	5.0
HOST Class 3	31.0	3.4	33.1	4.0
HOST Class 4	54.0	4.8	57.7	5.6
HOST Class 5	20.8	2.9	22.2	3.4
HOST Class 15	4.8	2.8	4.6	3.3
HOST Class 23	8.7	1.5	8.8	1.8

Figure 2 Gauged catchments with acceptable quality of low flow measurement

Figure 3 Gauged catchments which combine good quality of low flow measurement with relatively natural low flow regimes.

above gauging stations which have been drawn and digitised in the conventional way. The derived catchment boundary is then overlaid onto gridded databases of catchment characteristics enabling the automatic calculation of catchment area, standard period (1941-1970) average annual rainfall, average annual evaporation and fractions of HOST classes.

The river network overlay technique was used for the estimation of key low flow statistics at many ungauged sites in North West and South West regions. In these two studies, the user is required to extract a river segment identification number from a 1:50,000 river network to use as an index in a register of estimated statistics. The overlay methodology has since underpinned the development of the MICRO LOW FLOW software system, which considerably improves the speed of access and quality of hard-copy output. The user is prompted to enter a river by selecting one of the several entry options, which includes river name, and is then presented with a graphic display of the river's network. The vectored nature of the network allows the user to roam interactively around the network, aided by a mouse-driven cursor, to access different river reaches. At the selected reach, hard-copy output of the selected river network with superimposed gauged and estimated flow statistics and flow duration curves can be produced.

MICRO LOW FLOWS was used to estimate the mean flow at 314 ungauged sites for the National River Biological Classification in Northern Ireland (Dixon & Bullock, 1990). The system has been installed in the South West region and will be installed in Anglian and Severn Trent regions of the National Rivers Authority within six months. South West NRA report that in a 40-day period, using traditional manual low flow estimation methods, 72 requests were processed, with a delay in returning requests of up to 30 working days. Using the river network overlay method, the backlog was cleared and 273 requests were processed in an equivalent period. In a catchment-based validation exercise, South West NRA further report that there is a very good relationship between observed (by spot current metering) and predicted Q95 values, although there was a general tendency to overpredict by about 20%. Local minor abstractions are likely to contribute to this discrepancy and this aspect will require further study. The quality of the estimates is frequently maintained at very low discharges, as illustrated by the data (Table 3) assembled during an application for an abstraction licence in a small stream. Also, discussions have taken place between the NRA and the regional water company to use the methodology as standard for low flow estimation.

In addition to improving the speed and consistency of estimation of natural low flow statistics, MICRO LOW FLOWS can identify and display additional information regarding artificial influences upon the flow regime (Figure 4). At present, the software can retrieve information relating to abstractions,

Table 3. Comparison of spot current meter gauging and estimated low flows at ungauged sites in the South West region in a small abstraction study

SITE		Gauged (l/s)	Estimated (l/s)
	A	1.3	1.4
	B	2.9	2.6
	C	2.3	2.6
	D	2.6	2.6
	E	9.4	10.0
	F	11.2	10.0

discharges and reservoirs, as well as gauging stations and spot low flow current meterings that may be archived on, or upstream of, any reach. These data inform the user of upstream water uses and observed flow data to enable adjustments to be made to the natural flow estimates.

Hydrological impact assessment

Investigations into the hydrological impact of man's activities upon low flows can be ascribed to three categories; analysis of gauged flow data; simulation of the impacts of land-use change by applying hydro-logic models to manipulate gauged time series; simulation of impacts at ungauged sites. Examples of these approaches are outlined in Table 4. Development of the capability within MICRO LOW FLOWS to go beyond the archiving of information on a single reach towards the identification of all water use activities upstream of any stretch means that the system has made a significant contribution to the third category of quantifying impacts at ungauged sites.

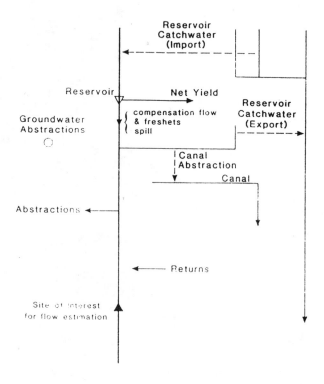

Figure 4 Artificial influences upon low flow regimes

Table 4 Summary of human impact studies upon low flows undertaken by the Institute of Hydrology

HUMAN IMPACT & LOCATION	SUMMARY
1. Analysis of gauged flow data	
Reservoir compensation flows, UK (Gustard *et al.*, 1987)	Compensation flow releases and flood flows below impounding reservoirs are compared with the natural low flow and flood regime
Hydropower generation, Scotland (Gustard 1991)	Details of the level and pattern of compensation releases below 23 hydropower schemes, & assessed in relation to natural downstream flows
Land drainage, UK (Robinson 1991)	The effect of drainage appears to consistently increase the dry weather flow
2. Application of hydrologic models	
Forestry, Mid-Wales (Gross et al. 1989)	The effect of afforestation on flow duration, low flow frequency and storage yield was assessed by application of a conceptual land-use model.
Abstractions, Welsh NRA (Bullock 1991)	The impact of current and licensed abstraction rates is assessed using gauged time series of daily mean flows
3. Simulation of impacts at ungauged sites using Micro Low Flows	
Abstractions, Welsh NRA (Bullock 1991)	The impact of current and licensed abstractions on residual flow diagrams comprising 191 river segments and flow duration curves at five ungauged sites.
Water Resource planning, N.Ireland (Gustard *et al.*, 1991)	The hydrological impact of different proposed reservoir schemes is assessed upon the volume and duration of downstream flows.
Peat extraction, N. Ireland (Bayfield *et al.*, 1991)	The impact on downstream mean flows of the reduction in actual evaporation due to peat drainage and cutting has been simulated at several ungauged sites.

Conclusions and further research

The principal advances in low flow estimation have been towards improving the ease of application of low flow estimation techniques at the ungauged site.

Underpinning this has been the development of a number of digital data sets including catchment boundaries, river networks, HOST, precipitation and evaporation data and methods for digital overlay. Thus, whilst the 1980 Low Flow Study benefited from the advances in the ease with which over 400 flow records could be analysed, the development and application of the methods for estimation at the ungauged site were essentially manual. The advances in digital cartography since 1980 have led to the capability of rapid flow estimation at all river reaches eliminating the need for time consuming manual calculation of catchment characteristics and derived flow variables. A note of caution is however warranted in that it is essential that the results from automated techniques are interpreted by hydrologists with experience in the strengths and limitations of flow estimation and practical local knowledge of river systems.

In response to the importance of the artificial controls on low flows and the background of previous studies focussing on natural catchments the National Rivers Authority have commissioned a three-year low flow study. This project has the objective of developing methods to evaluate the impact of surface water abstractions, discharges, groundwater pumping and land use change on estimates of low flow statistics.

The accurate assessment of the discharge regime is essential for a number of hydrological design problems for example dilution of domestic and industrial effluent or estimating the frequency of an observed drought. However for setting ecologically acceptable flows it is the combination of depths, velocities, substrate and cover characteristics which are the most critical physical variables which determine a suitable habitat for instream communities of fish, invertebrates and macrophytes (Bullock *et al.*, 1991). The development of physically based habitat models to assess the impact of low flow regimes on freshwater ecology requires a multi-disciplinary approach to low flow research in the 1990s.

Acknowledgements

The views expressed in this paper are those of the authors and not necessarily those of the Institute of Hydrology or funding organisations. The 1991 Low Flow Study has been funded by the Department of Environment, local investigations by NRA regions and the Department of the Environment (N. Ireland). The National Rivers Authority are now funding studies of the Artificial Influences on Low Flows and Ecologically Acceptable Flows.

References

Bayfield N.G., Picozzi N., Staines B.W., Crisp D.T., Tipping E., Carling P., Robinson M., Gustard A, & Shipman P. 1991. Ecological impacts of blanket peat abstraction in Northern Ireland. Report to the Countryside and Wildlife Branch, DoE(NI).

Boorman D.B. & Hollis J.M. 1990. Hydrology of Soil Types. A hydrologically-based classification of the soils of England and Wales. MAFF conference of river and coastal engineers, Loughborough University.

Bullock, A., Gustard, A. & Grainger, E. 1991. Instream flow requirements of aquatic ecology in two British Rivers. *Institute of Hydrology Report No. 115*

Bullock A., Gustard A. & Sekulin A. 1989. Average and low flow estimation in the North West Water region. Confidential report to North West Water.

Bullock A. & Gustard A. 1989. Average and low flow estimation in the South West Water region. Confidential report to South West Water.

Bullock A. 1991. Hydrological impacts of abstraction in the River Frome, Herefordshire. Confidential report to the NRA, Welsh region.

Dixon J.M. & Bullock A. 1990. Discharge categorisation of selected Northern Ireland rivers for the National River Biological Classification Survey. Confidential report to the Department of the Environment (Northern Ireland).

Gross R., Eeles C.W.O. & Gustard A. 1989. The application of a lumped conceptual model to FREND catchments. FRIENDS in Hydrology Conference, Bolkesjø, Norway, *IAHS Publication No. 187*, 309-320.

Gustard A. & Marshall D.C.W. 1983. *Runoff accumulation time: description and estimation manual.* Low Flow Studies report 2.3, 60 pp.

Gustard A. & Sutcliffe M.F. 1986. *Low flow study of Northern Ireland.* Institute of Hydrology, Wallingford.

Gustard A., Jones P. & Sutcliffe M.F. 1986. *Base Flow Index map of Scotland.* Institute of Hydrology, Wallingford.

Gustard A., Cole G.A., Marshall D.C.W. & Bayliss A.D. 1987. *A study of compensation flows in the UK.* Institute of Hydrology Report No. 99, Wallingford, 225 pp.

Gustard A. 1991. The impact of hydropower development on river flow regimes. Paper presented to Hydrology and water power development. BHS and Scottish Hydrological Group, Glasgow.

Gustard A, Bullock A & Dixon J M 1991. *Estimating low river flows in the United Kingdom.* Institute of Hydrology, Report No 108 (in preparation).

Institute of Hydrology 1980. *Low Flow Studies.* Institute of Hydrology, Wallingford.

Morris D.M. & Heerdegen R.G. 1988. Automatically derived catchment boundaries and channel networks and their hydrological applications. *Geomorphology*, 1, 131-141

Pirt J. & Douglas J.R. 1982. A study of low flows using data from the Severn and Trent catchments. *J. Inst. Wat. Engnrs and Sci.* 36, 299-308.

Robinson M. 1990. *Impact of improved land drainage on river flows.* Institute of Hydrology Report No. 113, 226pp.

Sekulin, A. & others (in prep.) The river network overlay technique

Southern Water Authority 1979. Report on low flow studies for the Southern Water Authority area.

Do we make the most of our models?

N.P. Fawthrop

Abstract

A survey of water resources modelling activities within the National Rivers Authority illustrated the depth of knowledge and experience which has been imported to the new organisation, but it also highlighted a number of shortcomings. The issues which impinge upon hydrologists elsewhere in the water industry are discussed.

Introduction

The science of hydrology is fundamental to every aspect of water resources management. A moment's thought given to the spatial and temporal variations in topography, geology, climate, land use, etc. will register the range of processes which affect the movement of water through a catchment. Artificial influences resulting from man's impact upon the environment are superimposed. How can all those interrelated components of the hydrological cycle be disentangled? The answer, more often than not, is by some form of modelling.

Hydrological analysis has always involved repetitive calculation and there is a long history to the development of quantitative techniques (Flemming, 1975). The distinction between data analysis and modelling tends to be blurred. Indeed the term 'modelling' is such a commonplace word that it is perhaps necessary to clarify its meaning. For the purposes of this paper it is taken to be: *Computer software which quantitatively represents the response of a water resource system (natural and/or artificial) to a sample of information.*

Most hydrologists are involved to some extent in modelling, but there is a very wide range of possible viewpoints. For example we have:

- the 'specialist' who develops models in the course of work into one particular facet of hydrology. These could be for hypotheses testing or for operational or design applications;

- the 'systems' hydrologist who works full time on computational hydrology but may not fully comprehend all of the scientific theory;

- the 'universal' hydrologist, responsible for a geographical area rather than a specialist subject. He or she has to have a broad knowledge and uses models as a tool of the trade. There are great differences in mathematical and computational aptitudes and experiences;

- the 'manager' or 'decision maker'. What level of understanding should they be expected to have?

Most hydrological jobs contain a bit of all of these, which makes the task of coming to terms with mathematical modelling all the more difficult.

Is all the time and effort necessary for modelling really worthwhile? Most people would say that it is. Computer analysis allows us to investigate problems which cannot be examined in any other way. We can test and quantify conceptual understanding (Frenkiel and Goodall 1978). However it is possible to waste an awful lot of time and money. This will only be avoided if the people who initiate modelling work know in general terms what is involved, have an appreciation of where effort should be concentrated and are able to maintain close involvement throughout. Without this understanding there is a danger that the results from models are used when they support preconceived ideas but ignored (because "you can't rely on models") when they don't.

The aim of this paper is to discuss aspects of hydrological modelling which are relevant to water resources management. A British Hydrological Society symposium is an appropriate place to reflect on the way in which different parts of the UK water industry interact, and to ask "could we do it better"?

The framework of the paper is based upon the results of a recent survey of modelling activities within the National Rivers Authority (NRA, 1991). It covered not only what modelling work is being done but also *how* it is being done, then looked at the perceived shortcomings and requirements for future developments. Illustrations expand upon aspects of model implementation in practise using examples from the Anglian Region.

A survey of water resources modelling activities within the NRA

Most British hydrologists will be involved at some time or another with the NRA, be it working for the

Authority, their advisors, consultants or the Water Companies. The areas of common ground should be the data and models that we all use, but are they? How many models with water resources applications are there that are widely used by these different organisations and throughout the country? How many times does the situation arise where a potentially useful model exists but for one reason or another it cannot be made available for others to use? Conscious of the need to review the situation within the NRA a survey was recently made of our Water Resources modelling activities. Its objectives were to review:

- *The current usage of models.* To what extent are models actually used in practise? What for and by whom?
- *The origin of these models.* What are the advantages of 'packaged' models over in-house developments? Are programs still written in-house or is bespoke customisation the order of the day?
- *Areas of common ground between the NRA regions.* Are Regions using the same type of model for a given type of job? Should there be greater consistency?
- *Perceived shortcomings and requirements for future developments.* Are people satisfied with the products they use? What is needed in the way of training ?

The survey took the form of a questionnaire plus a proforma to be completed for each model or group of similar models.

The use and origin of models within the NRA

Over 70 models with water resources applications were identified by the survey (Table 1). By no means all of these are in day to day use, indeed perhaps only 60% have been used in anger within the past year.

Of the models which were listed but are little used many were general purpose, commercially available groundwater 'packages' often incorporating contaminant transport routines. These have been acquired by several regions but there has been little opportunity to evaluate them and become familiar with their capabilities. A research and development project has now been set up to progress this work using an outside contractor who will review existing groundwater quality models and assess their suitability for representing subsurface contaminant transport arising from typical UK pollution problems.

Many of the larger resource assessment and economic planning models are also used relatively infrequently, simply because applications do not arise all that often. Most were inherited from the Water Authorities and several have long pedigrees . This type of model is likely to be used more by the Water Companies but there is a need for the NRA to have them as well.

Some of the regional groundwater models are also quite old but most of them are in regular if not frequent use. Without exception all were developed by Birmingham University, WRC or consultants, and not in-house. After the initial development and investigation phase most were handed over for further use at the Water Authorities and now the NRA. Most of the NRA Regions with substantial groundwater resources have staff capable of maintaining and operating these models. They are essential tools for groundwater management. Several new ones are currently under development and it is likely that more will be commissioned in the next few years. The main applications of these models are in assessing the effect of additional or relocated abstractions upon the piezometry and overall water balance of the aquifer. All regional groundwater models address both of these issues but in some cases the emphasis in the past has been on the impact upon other PWS abstractions and not so much upon springs and streamflow .

The use of regional groundwater models highlights a topical issue which has not yet been fully addressed. To what extent should the NRA and the Water Companies share models? The problem has not arisen with the older models because both the NRA and the Companies were entitled to copies at the time of the split, but it will do with new ones in the future. At a technical level it makes sense to use one model of the aquifer, even if the interpretation of the results is open for debate . However, at a political level there is

Table 1 NRA survey of water resources modelling activities

CATEGORY	NUMBER OF MODELS	IN REGULAR USE
REGIONAL GROUNDWATER MODELS	20	16
OTHER GROUNDWATER MODELS	14	0
CATCHMENT SIMULATION / RAINFALL – RUNOFF	7	6
RIVER REGULATION / TRANSFER SCHEMES	6	6
RESOURCE YIELD ASSESSMENT / SYSTEM SIMULATION	15	6
ECONOMIC PLANNING MODELS	3	1
LOW FLOW MODELLING	1	1
GIS APPLICATIONS	3	3

Table 2 Numbers of NRA staff actively involved in water resources modelling

LEVEL OF EXPERTISE	NATIONAL TOTAL	MAX IN ANY REGION
Use 'user friendly models'	44	11
Edit data files and modify programs	28	8
Develop models and write more advanced programs	13	4
Spend >50% of their time on modelling related activities	6	3

a wish for complete independence. A further complication is the issue of intellectual property rights and software licensing. The commercial value of software has been recognised, and this is one of the reasons for the proliferation of models. Each of the organisations represented at this symposium will have their own version of the models they need. Programs are rarely developed to a stage where they can be marketed, but there is a reluctance to give them away in case they fall into the hands of competitors.

In contrast to the groundwater models many of the catchment simulation, rainfall runoff and operational models were developed in house by the NRA and its predecessors. It is probably true to say that surface water systems are in general easier to model. There are several lumped parameter catchment models of varying complexity, each restricted in application to a single region. The only 'packaged' alternative to be mentioned has been bought but not much used by two Regions. Perhaps this, together with the limited use made of the groundwater modelling packages, illustrates a preference for models which can be tailored to a particular application. In-house developments or bespoke customisation allow this, whereas packages do not.

This wish for maximum control over the models we use is understandable, but practical limitations control the degree of involvement which is possible. There are many other demands upon the time of staff with the right combination of technical knowledge and computing expertise. Table 2 summarises the number of people actively involved in water resources modelling within the NRA Regions. This is not the same thing as the number of staff who have computing skills and could be involved. It is not possible or indeed necessary to be too specific, and the numbers should be seen in that light.

Experiences from the NRA Anglian Region

The survey indicated that water resources modelling is carried out by making the best use of available in-house skills supported by outside help when required.

Given that staff with the necessary computing skills are in short supply, how can they best be deployed? Most regions seem to differentiate very clearly between staff engaged in groundwater and surface water investigations. In view of the responses summarised in Table 2 it is clear that modelling expertise must be spread very thinly. Only Anglian has a specialist modelling group working on both surface water and groundwater studies as a service to other staff. (Of course only the larger regions have sufficient staff to contemplate this option). There are advantages and disadvantages. A support group concentrates computing skills and allows staff to focus on modelling full time. This helps to overcome the problem of finding blocks of time long enough to submerge oneself in a modelling problem but it raises another. Can one use a model effectively without understanding the technicalities and theory involved? The role of the group is to use (and help others to use) existing models, and to liaise with instigators/ end users when new models are to be developed. It is not possible, or indeed desirable, for all modelling work within the Region to be carried out by a small team of specialists, but it is felt that a coordinated approach is desirable.

Several regional groundwater models were developed by different Divisions of Anglian Water Authority over a period of 10-15 years. The modelling group has 'inherited' these models and run them in-house to assist with a range of water resources activities. We want to make them more readily available and usable, and to facilitate their updating and maintenance. A contract has been let to the Dept of Civil Engineering at Birmingham University to rationalise our existing models and to establish a 'standard' for future models. This will include:
- common data formats for both input and output files;
- the creation of a common user interface;
- improved graphical presentation of the results;
- improved documentation using a common layout.

In the first stage five existing models will be transferred from the mainframe computer to a VAX workstation.

In the Anglian region (and probably elsewhere) the main aim of regional groundwater models in the past has been to represent flows in the abstraction zones. The surface water response has sometimes been a secondary consideration. The NRA must now have a thorough understanding of the combined surface and groundwater hydrology. The shortcomings of one of our older models certainly became apparent when we tried to use the South Lincolnshire Limestone model to assess the effects of increasing abstraction upon river flows. There were only three spring nodes and one river - groundwater interaction node in a surface catchment of 342km². Improvements to the model are now under way and will place much greater emphasis upon the rainfall - runoff - recharge processes, river - aquifer interaction and subcatchment water balances.

This type of approach has been shown to be possible in the model of the Lodes and Granta chalk catchments near Cambridge (Rushton and Fawthrop 1991) where there are 65 springs and 33 river - groundwater interaction nodes. Developed by Anglian Water Authority and only recently taken over by the NRA, this model was used to examine the feasibility of additional abstractions in conjunction with river support.

None of the water resources models used in the Anglian Region was commissioned as a piece of software development. Usually model development took place at a consultancy, university or research institute as part of a study or investigation. Nowadays it is common for the contract to state that any model(s) developed in the course of the work will be handed over to the NRA upon completion. Anglian Region has received a number of models in this way during the past few years, all from different organisations. At some risk of generalisation it is probably true to say that:
- the organisations did not really expect us to implement the models and do in-house runs of any complexity;

- there were inadequacies in the documentation in terms of interpretation, inaccuracy or incompleteness;
- significant modifications or additions were required before they were usable. This was usually because we had different compilers, graphics libraries or spreadsheets to the developer.

The transfer of software is likely to increase, so it is important to:
- agree the software and hardware specification at an early stage. Try to avoid ambiguities which may lead to misunderstandings;
- the user should be involved throughout the project;
- ensure that adequate documentation is supplied;
- arrange training as necessary;
- recognise the time involved.

The availability of spreadsheets, databases, hydrological applications packages and consultancy services has not removed the need for in-house programming skills. A major consideration is always cost effectiveness but we find a continual requirement to modify code and develop programs at short notice.

Common ground between the NRA Regions

Although the approaches and techniques are similar there are very few models in widespread use throughout the NRA. This is not altogether surprising as until two years ago the Water Authorities acted quite independently. Coupled with the need to customise models to particular applications there was relatively little need for collaboration. Many of the models are related or of the same lineage but few could be easily ported to another Region.

Even now in a national organisation there may be fewer opportunities to use 'standard' models than might be imagined, but there is undoubtedly a wish

Table 3 Computer software used for water resources modelling

SOFTWARE	NUMBER OF REGIONS (OUT OF 9)
Compilers	Fortran (9) Basic (5) C (2) Pascal (1) Clipper (3) Coral (1)
Graphics	Simpleplot (1) GINO (1) Ghost-80 (1) Calcomp(1) Grapher (4) Surfer (4) Freelance (4) Harvard (3)
Spreadsheets	Supercalc (5) Lotus 1-2-3 (5) Smart (1) Symphony (2) Logistix (1)
Databases	DBase (5) Q&A (1) Smart (1) Symphony (2) Rapidfile (1) Dataease (2) Oracle (1)
Statistics	CSS (1) Aardvark (1) SPSS (1)

TYPE	NUMBER OF REGIONS (OUT OF 10)
ICL Mainframe	4
IBM Mainframe	1
Data General	1
Honeywell Mainframe	1
DEC VAX family	7
DEC PDP/11	2
IBM PCs	10
Hewlett Packard PC	1
Mackintosh PC	1
SUN Workstation	1

Table 4 Computer systems used for water resources modelling

to learn more about what is going on elsewhere in the country. This is seen as being to everyone's mutual benefit. It is hoped to organise a series of workshops at which NRA modellers will meet, demonstrate and discuss their software in an informal way. There are many programs which have limited generality but which may be interesting to others. These could be discussed at informal workshops whereas perhaps they couldn't at Institute or Society meetings.

There is similar variety in the software packages which are used in modelling work (Table 3). Many different spreadsheets and databases are in use: Supercalc, Lotus 1-2-3 and DBase being the favourites. Fortran is still the dominant programming language although Basic is widely used. Interestingly C has not made much of an impact yet. The increasing use of graphics is probably the biggest single development in recent years. The presentation of results is much improved and programs can be made much more user friendly. It is therefore interesting to note the wide range of packages in use. No Fortran graphics library is in use in more than one Region. Surfer and Grapher are widely used, particularly amongst the Hydrogeologists. Freelance and Harvard are the favourites for presentation graphics.

The portability of software is not helped by the many different types of computer system in use (Table 4). There is a growing preference to use PCs (universally IBM compatible plus Macintosh at North West and Hewlett Packard at Thames), although even now they are not always sufficiently powerful for modelling applications. Seven of the ten regions use one of the DEC VAX series. The NRA is looking in considerable detail at rationalising its IT functions. This is bound to facilitate the exchange of software and the sharing of experience.

Perceived shortcomings and future developments

The survey invited suggestions about how water resources modelling within the NRA might be improved. The key areas requiring attention are:
- the evaluation of NRA owned in-house modelling software, with a view to transfers between regions, the pooling of experience and the interchange of knowledge;
- the evaluation of existing proprietary modelling software;
- the identification of areas where improved modelling is required and the commissioning of work on behalf of the NRA;
- the identification of appropriate training opportunities.

All of these could be addressed through the NRA workshops. There is some overlap with the national R&D program and close liaison will be maintained.

Conclusions

NRA hydrologists, just like those elsewhere, wish to use state of the art modelling facilities. The extent to which this has been achieved is variable between the regions and between applications. How can the situation be improved ?

The first step is clearly to help ourselves by pooling programs and experience, and organising the necessary training. Beyond that we rely very much upon the specialists and researchers who develop the models that we use. Despite all the years of work on hydrological modelling there is a remarkable lack of commercially available software which is suitable for practical use in water resources and low flow hydrology. This is partly because users need to be able to adapt software for their own particular purpose, but surely no more so than in other aspects of hydrology. Bespoke software is becoming more common, but even then problems can arise in the transfer from the specialist to the practitioner.

So do we make the most of our models? Within the NRA the answer at the moment is probably no, but there are signs of improvement as we capitalise upon being a national organisation. Throughout the rest of the water industry privatisation has led to even greater independence. We must adapt to increasing commercialism and use this to make modelling software more available if our profession as a whole is to benefit.

Acknowledgements

The author wishes to thank Dr Kevin Bond, General Manager of the Anglian region of the NRA and the Regional Water Resources Managers for permission to publish this paper. The views expressed are those of the author and not necessarily those of the NRA.

References

Flemming, G. 1975. *Computer Simulation Techniques In Hydrology*. Elsevier.

Frenkiel, F.N. & Goodall, D.W. 1978. *Simulation Modelling Of Environmental Problems* (SCOPE 9). John Wiley.

National Rivers Authority 1991. Survey of Water Resources Modelling Activities. Water Resources Managers Group.

Rushton, K.R. & Fawthrop, N.P. 1991. Groundwater support of streamflows in the Cambridge area, UK. IAHS Symposium *Hydrological Basis of Ecologically Sound Management of Soil and Groundwater*, Vienna.

Session 3

Hydrograph Separation

Hydrograph separation?

K. Beven

Abstract

"Hydrograph separation", the long-established technique of separating the storm hydrograph into two components representing "storm runoff" and "baseflow", makes subjective assumptions about the sources of the waters which imply a particular process interpretation. To many hydrologists this technique provides the means to finding a linear relationship between "storm runoff" and "effective rainfall" and developing the unit hydrograph as a model of catchment response. In consequence, the Hortonian view, equating storm runoff with surface runoff and baseflow with sub-surface flow, has prevailed despite evidence to the contrary. Hydrograph separation procedures are largely arbitrary and this paper seeks to place them in the context of hydrological response. It is concluded that discharge-based hydrograph separation should be rejected, except for one objective approach.

Introduction

"Hydrograph separation is one of the most desperate analysis techniques in use in hydrology" (Hewlett and Hibbert, 1967)

The technique of "hydrograph separation" has a long pedigree in hydrological terminology and a long and continuing usage in practical hydrology. The term is mostly used to indicate the separation of two components in the storm hydrograph, which we will call for the present "storm runoff" and "baseflow", although occasionally some authors have attempted to carry out multiple component separations (Barnes, 1940). It is a technique I have always tried to avoid, both because of the techniques commonly used in hydrograph separation and because of the continuing tendency to give names to the separated parts that indicate a particular process interpretation. I have never been able to accept that it is objectively possible to distinguish different sources for the waters of the hydrograph, when the only information available is the hydrograph itself.

However, it should be noted that many hydrologists would argue that this is not the point of using hydrograph separation; the point is to obtain a more linear relationship between "storm runoff" and the equivalent volume of "effective rainfall" deduced from a hyetograph separation. In fact, the history of hydrograph separation is inextricably linked with the search for such linearity and the development of the unit hydrograph as a model for catchment response. This has, perhaps, been to the great detriment of hydrological theory (if not necessarily to

hydrological practice) since the rapid sequence of the seminal papers by Sherman (1932) setting out the elements of a linear analysis of hydrographs, and Horton (1933) demonstrating the estimation of effective rainfall as that in excess of the infiltration capacity of the soil, has resulted in a link being drawn between "storm runoff" and infiltration excess overland flow. Such an equivalence has been pervasive in hydrological thought despite the fact that even a cursory field observation carried out in the rain would show that it is all too often totally incorrect.

In what is commonly now called the Hortonian view of catchment response, the storm runoff component is equated with a surface runoff process, while the baseflow process is equated with subsurface flow. This view has prevailed despite the fact that in the 1930s and 1940s C. R. Hursh and his co-workers were pointing out that in many catchments hydrograph responses could not be ascribed to surface runoff. More recent texts (e.g. Linsley, Kohler and Paulhus, 1988; Bedient and Huber, 1988; Ward and Robinson, 1989) allow that there may also be some contribution to storm runoff from subsurface stormflow/throughflow/ interflow (what Horton, 1942, called "concealed surface runoff") and the name "direct runoff" is frequently used for these combined fast flow responses.

Nearly all the procedures available for hydrograph separation are, to a large extent, arbitrary; the desperation referred to by Hewlett and Hibbert is readily apparent from the selection of recent textbook illustrations shown in Figure 1. Their successful use in very many case studies and applications suggests that perhaps the choice of technique itself is not so important relative to other causes of possible error in the hydrograph modelling process (and in particular the associated technique of determining "effective" rainfalls). The objective of this review of hydrograph separation is, therefore, to place some of the different procedures available into the context of the processes of hydrological response from the perspective of a non-user.

Methods of hydrograph separation

Traditional methods

"The most widely used separation procedure consists of extending the recession before the storm to a point under the peak of the hydrograph (AB, figure 1b). From this point a straight line is drawn to the hydrograph at a point N days after the peak. The reasoning behind this procedure is that as the stream rises, there is flow from the stream into the banks. Hence baseflow should decrease until stages in the stream begin to drop and bank storage returns to the channel." (Linsley, Kohler and Paulhus, 1988, page 198). And if there is a net positive lateral contribution into the stream? This is just one example of the lingering underlying perception of the domination of storm runoff by surface runoff, and trying to justify an arbitrary procedure by means of muddled physical reasoning that, while believable in some cases, cannot be generally accepted. Other examples can be found in a variety of hydrological texts, although, thankfully, increasingly qualified by recognition that some storm runoff may be the result of subsurface flow processes.

Another technique that has been widely used derives from work by Hewlett, originally in forested catchments in which little overland flow is expected to occur. Hewlett and Hibbert (1967) separate "quickflow" from "delayed flow" by using a straight separation line from the point of rise of the hydrograph with a constant slope of 0.05 ft³/mile²/h or 0.000546 m³/km²/h or 0.01967 mm/h. Hewlett and Hibbert argue (page 280) that:

"since an arbitrary separation must be made in any case, why not base the classification on a single arbitrary decision, such as a fixed, universal method for separating hydrographs on all small watersheds?"

Their method was simple and conveniently programmed for their IBM7094 computer. Their value of the slope coefficient has been widely used in different areas of the world, despite the fact that it was derived as appropriate for a relatively specific set of catchments in the eastern US. Other studies have used the same technique but have modified the value of the constant. A similar "universal" technique was used by Nash (1960), again a simple straight line drawn from the point of rise to a point on the recession limb at a time three times the time of rise of the hydrograph. This technique ensures a unit hydrograph, for better or worse, with a base time three times the time to peak. Linsley and Ackerman (1942) had earlier argued that this base time should be related to the area of the catchment as:

$$T = 0.8 \, A^{0.2} \qquad (1)$$

where T is the time to the end of storm runoff measured from the time of peak discharge in days, and A is catchment area in km².

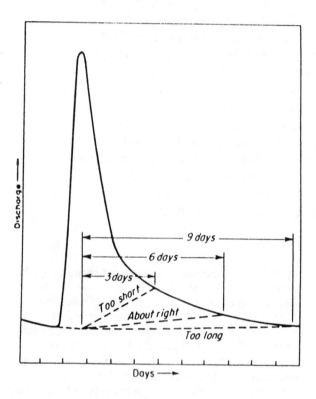

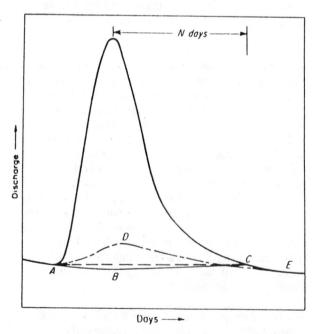

Figure 1 Some simple baseflow separation procedures (from Linsley, Kohler & Paulhus, 1988)

Perhaps one of the strangest techniques of separation is that employed in (at least early versions of) the US Corps of Engineers HEC1 modelling package (Feldman *et al.*, 1981) in which the initial recession is continued until the time at which discharge reaches some (generally higher) "recession threshold" at which the storm runoff is assumed to stop. The separation is completed by a straight line drawn vertically from this threshold discharge to the extra-polated recession of the previous storm (see Figure 2a)! Strange, but published and presumably used!

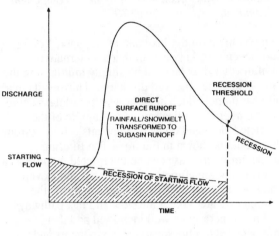

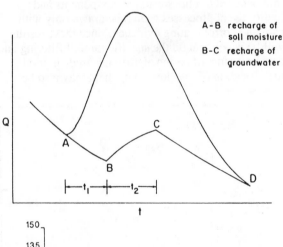

A-B recharge of soil moisture

B-C recharge of groundwater

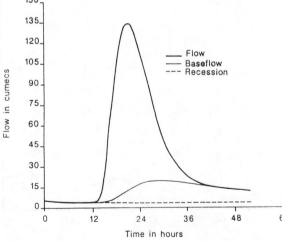

Figure 2 Some more complex baseflow separation procedures. A. from Feldman et al.(1981), B. from Dooge (1973), C. after Boorman (1990).

Moving towards a more theoretically acceptable technique, Dooge (1973) has argued that the baseflow component can commonly be described by means of a linear storage element with mean residence time K. Until the time of peak discharge this "baseflow" Q_b might continue to decline at a rate estimated by assuming no inputs to the store so that

$$Q_b = Q_A \exp \{ - (t - t_o) / K \} \qquad (2)$$

where Q_o is the discharge at the time of hydrograph rise t_o, and t is time. Following this, if a constant input rate of recharge q is assumed then the baseflow discharge will rise as

$$Q_b = (Q_B - q) \exp \{ - (t - t_B)/K \} + q \qquad (3)$$

until a time t_2 when, after rainfall stops and allowing for a delay in the unsaturated zone, significant recharge ceases. Equation (2) is then applied again, given the starting values Q_C at t_2. A typical result is shown in Figure 2b. The technique requires the specification of three variables: K, q and the time t_2.

Recently, Boorman (1989) has used a technique that gives a smoother pattern of changing baseflow discharge with a storm. The technique usually gives a very gradual decrease in storm runoff and a peak in baseflow usually within the period of storm runoff. It requires that the time period T of storm runoff be chosen *a priori*. The baseflow is then described by

$$Q_b = \{t/T\} \{W(t)/W(T)\} \qquad (4)$$

where $W(t) = 0.95\,S(t) + 0.05\,s(t)$
        $s(t)$ is the storm runoff at time t
and $S(t)$ is the cumulative storm runoff at time t.

This gives the pattern shown in Figure 2c.

Choosing one of these separation techniques

Don't.

Avoiding separation in linear analyses: taking first differences

Alternative analyses of storm hydrograph response are possible that avoid the need to choose a separation technique by working with first differences in time of the observed discharge and identifying a transfer function between effective rainfalls and differenced discharges. This is the basis of the DPFT approach (see for example Guillot and Duband, 1981; Duband *et al.*, 1988), which is now used for operational flood forecasting in more than 30 medium sized catchments in France by Electricité de France (EDF). The ordinates of the transfer function are identified from data from multiple events using a ridge regression technique. Differencing of the discharges has been shown to increase the stability of the identification algorithm, although smoothness and positive ordinate constraints are generally applied (Rodriguez *et al.*, 1988). There is an implicit assumption about the baseflow component in this technique, that the change in baseflow between successive time steps is small or constant.

An interesting recent use of this technique has been to use the identified transfer function in a deconvolution step to estimate the effective rainfall sequence for a given storm (Rodriguez *et al.*, 1989). A similar study has been made independently in the UK by Boorman (1989). This allows a search to be made for an appropriate model of the effective rainfalls that can be used for prediction. Experience suggests that the effective rainfalls identified in this way may be dependent on the method of baseflow separation used and that the search for an adequate model of effective rainfalls has far to go.

Avoiding separation in linear analyses: time series analysis techniques

A recent paper by Jakeman *et al.* (1990) has applied Simple Refined Instrumental Variable (SRIV) time series analysis techniques to the rainfall-runoff problem. They found that with a suitable pre-filtering of the rainfall data to take account of seasonal and antecedent rainfall effects they could successfully identify a linear transfer function relating the filtered rainfall to the total discharge without any arbitrary hydrograph separation. Such transfer functions have been used in the past as a way of identifying the unit hydrograph, but in this study the resulting models for two small catchments in Wales exhibit a second

order structure which can be decomposed into two components in parallel with different time constants. Jakeman *et al.* (1990) comment that:

"[an] advantage of the approach ... is that baseflow (slow response) separation is an integral part of model identification and not, as in some methods which derive a unit hydrograph for quickflow only, a necessary prerequisite. The product of the method described here is an IUH corresponding to total streamflow and this IUH can be resolved into its slow and quick components. Convolution of each IUH component with effective rainfall yields component stream hydrographs." (page 297).

In a comment on the Jakeman *et al.* paper, Young and Beven (1991) point out that an alternative rainfall filter may be used by simply multiplying the rainfalls by the observed discharge. This results in a bilinear model which also shows a parallel structure in a number of applications. An example of the predicted slow and quick components resulting from this model is shown in Figure 3. The filtering algorithm in this case can be interpreted directly as a contributing area function, but Young and Beven point out that the coefficient which controls the amount of water taking the slow and fast pathways will not generally be well identified and that inferences about the separated components and hydrological processes should be drawn only with care and corroborating evidence, since these results will be dependent on the specific rainfall filtering and parameter identification algorithms used. A good identification of the slow component may also be

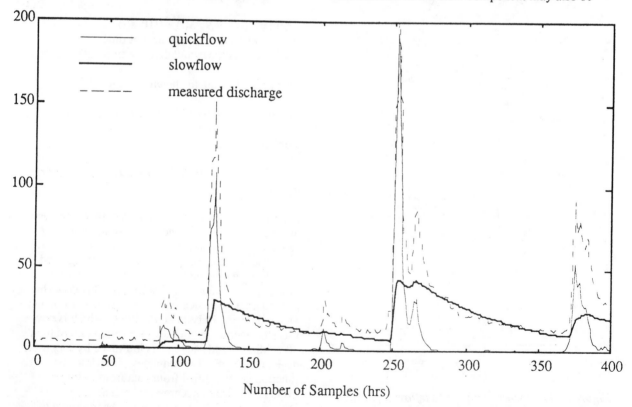

Figure 3 Results of a bi-linear model relating total discharge to total rainfall, showing the parallel slow and quickflow components

dependent on the availability of a sufficiently long period of continuous records and I suspect that both of these procedures may be more difficult to apply in catchments in which interstorm discharges become very small or zero.

Using additional data: observation well records

One obvious way of identifying baseflow responses during storm rainfall is to directly observe water table levels. There are two reasons why this does not generally lead to an acceptable method of hydrograph separation. The first is that the response of the water table can vary dramatically at different points within a catchment, governed primarily by the intial depth of unsaturated zone through which any "wetting fronts" must pass before recharge to the water table takes place. It might therefore be thought that observation wells close to the stream might provide the best guide to baseflow additions to total streamflow. This leads to the second problem, however, in that in such locations it has often been found that the water table may respond to rainfall inputs just as fast as the streamflow, suggesting significant contributions to storm runoff from the saturated zone. Examples have been provided, for example, by Hursh and Brater (1941), O'Brien (1980) and Germann (1986). This does not therefore facilitate hydrograph separation in these catchments; it undermines the whole concept of separating flow components instead.

Using additional data: environmental tracers

If, therefore, it may not be possible to separate components of the hydrograph taking different pathways through the hydrological system, the increasing use of chemical analyses of streamflows has permitted in the last decade or so the widespread application of mixing equations to try and separate the hydrograph into water that was stored in the catchment prior to an event (pre-event or "old" water) and that input to the catchment during the event ("new" water). The environmental isotope tracers of ^{18}O and Deuterium have been particularly successful in the respect, although other constituents such as silica and chloride and mixtures of different elements have also been used. Sklash (1990) provides a useful recent review of the work with environmental isotopes. The conclusions of many studies have been that in humid areas "old" water forms a considerable proportion of storm hydrographs (see for example Figure 4), leading to the conclusion that storm runoff is often controlled by subsurface flows.

In evaluating this conclusion, however, it is as well to be aware of the crude assumptions that are made in the two component mixing model used to separate the old and new water components. The mixing model is based on two mass balance equations, one for discharge and one for the particular chemical constituent under study. Thus:

$$Q_s = Q_o + Q_n \qquad (5a)$$

and

$$Q_s C_s = Q_o C_o + Q_n C_n \qquad (5b)$$

where Q is discharge, C is concentration and the subscripts s, o and n refer to the total streamflow, old and new components respectively.

Combining these equations results in

$$Q_o = Q_s (C_s - C_n)/(C_o - C_n) \qquad (6a)$$

$$= Q_s R$$

where $\quad R = (C_s - C_n)/(C_o - C_n)$

and $\quad\quad Q_n = Q_s - Q_o \qquad (6b)$

The implicit assumptions in these equations are that:

a. The concentrations associated with both old and new components are constant in space and time. This is known to be only both approximately true: successive sampling of rainfall inputs have shown significant variations in isotope concentrations (e.g. Sklash *et al.* 1986, Fig. 4), while there may be significant differences in "old" water concentrations between water stored in different parts of the catchment and in the vadose zone relative to the saturated zone.

b. The denominator in equation 6a must be significantly greater than zero, i.e. there must be a significant difference in the concentrations of old and new water.

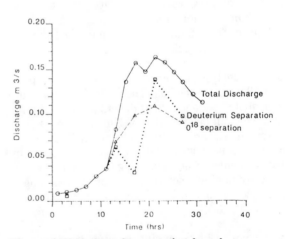

Figure 4 Hydrograph separation based on environmental isotope data for the White Oak Run catchment, Virginia (after Vreeland, 1983)

Sensitivity to both assumptions can be evaluated by carrying out an error analysis, taking account of any uncertainty in the concentration and discharge measurements, including sampling uncertainty as well as measurement uncertainty. Assuming that the measurement errors in Q_s, C_s, C_o, and C_n are independent and normally distributed, an estimate of the variance in Q_o, for example, may be calculated over time by

$$var(Q_o) = var(Q_s)var(R)$$

where

$$var(R) \simeq \frac{(C_s - C_n)^2}{(C_o - C_n)^2} \left[\left\{ \frac{var(C_s) + var(C_n)}{(C_s - C_n)} \right\} \right.$$
$$+ \left\{ \frac{var(C_o) + var(C_n)}{(C_o - C_n)} \right\}$$
$$\left. - \left\{ 2 \frac{var(C_n)}{(C_s - C_n)(C_s - C_n)} \right\} \right] \tag{7}$$

However, even given the expected uncertainties, there remains a considerable body of evidence that in many humid catchments the storm hydrograph has a significant rapid subsurface flow component. The mechanisms that might result in such rapid responses, such as groundwater ridging and macropore flows are discussed in detail by Beven (1989a) and Sklash (1990).

So why bother with hydrograph separation?

Analysis of hydrographs from simple rainstorms for a given catchment reveals some consistency in hydrograph shape, yet we know from long experience that the actual response to a particular storm will be a function of antecedent conditions and rainfall volume (and possibly intensities). If we carry out an analysis in which the effect of an antecedent flow is elimina-ted by a baseflow separation and constrained so that the volume of "storm runoff" is equal to some volume of "effective rainfall", then the first approxi-mation of a linear relationship might be expected to work well, given the observed consistency in shape. Such an analysis, however, avoids the difficult part of rainfall-runoff modelling. The difficult part of hydro-logical prediction is getting the proportion and timing of the rainfall that is "effective" in producing the observed discharge hydrograph correct. That there are problems in this type of analysis is evidenced by the difficulties of understanding patterns of derived effective rainfalls (not to say that other modelling strategies are not equally fraught with problems, see Beven, 1989b).

The major problem with the use of hydrograph separation is in the physical interpretation of components. Environmental tracer data suggest that many hydrographs may have significant proportions of old water, the outflow of which must be due to the storm rainfall inputs, but which must be the result of subsurface displacement mechanisms caused by rapid pressure wave propogation (at least within a Darcian framework). What is this old water? Stormflow or baseflow or both? Normally, of course, separations are carried out without the additional information available from tracers but are based on discharge data

alone. In this more usual case, therefore, I would suggest that no physical interpretation or naming of processes should be entertained. This is particularly so where the parallel component models resulting from time series analysis may give superficially similar results to tracer data. The temptation to equate the slow component with groundwater and the fast component with surface runoff and go on to do chemical mixing for water quality calculations must be resisted as revisiting the interpretational sins of the past.

In conclusion, the evidence of the environmental tracer data, albeit based on gross assumptions about mixing characteristics in a catchment, would persuasively suggest that all the discharge-based hydrograph separation techniques currently used in practice should be rejected as incompatible with any rigorous hydrological theory. We need not reject hydrograph separation in such cases entirely, however. There is one discharge-based technique that is both objective and theoretically defensible but, as far as I know, it is one that has been rarely used in flood hydrograph modelling. If the hydrologist really wishes to separate the marginal flow response due to a storm event, then the obvious procedure is to try to estimate the flow that would have occurred without that event, i.e. to extrapolate the preceding recession. The resulting "storm runoff" is just that - the best estimate of the runoff resulting from the storm rainfall, and we can make an equivalent search for a characteristic impulse response between them. No interpretation of the processes involved is inferred or need be made without additional sources of data. The problem, of course, is that the storm runoff separations resulting from an extrapolation of successive recession curves tend to be very long (infinitely long in the case of an exponential extrapolation), leading to problems in identifying the responses of multiple hydrographs, problems in identifying the IUH by ordinate matrix methods (although not by impulse-response function methods), and perhaps, though this is unproven, a greater likelihood of non-linearity in the relationship between storm runoff and the equivalent volume of "effective rainfall". As for an equivalently defensible technique of hyetograph separation, that will have to wait for another year (or a decade or two?).

Acknowledgements

Thanks to Renata Romanowicz for correcting my errors in the error analysis, to Peter Young for producing Figure 3 at short notice and to Charles Obled for reviewing the manuscript and for many stimulating discussions.

References

Barnes, B.S. 1940. Discussion of Analysis of Runoff Characteristics. *Trans. ASCE*, 105, 106.

Bedient, P.B. & Huber, W.C. 1988. *Hydrology and Flood Plain Analysis*, Addison-Wesley.

Beven, K.J. 1989a. Interflow. In H.J. Morel-Seytoux

(Ed.), *Unsaturated Flow in Hydrological Modelling*, Reidel, Dordrecht, 191-219.

Beven, K.J. 1989b. Changing ideas in hydrology: the case of physically-based models. *J. Hydrol.*,

Boorman, D.B. 1989. A new approach to unit hydrograph modelling. Unpublished PhD thesis, Lancaster University.

Dooge, J.C.I. 1973. Linear Theory of Hydrologic Systems. USDA Agric. Res. Serv., Tech. Bull. 1468, Washington.

Duband, D., Nablantis, I., Obled, Ch., Rodriguez, J.Y. & Tourasse, P. 1988. Unit hydrograph revisited through differencing and deconvolution on multi-event data sets: The FDTF approach. In: *Hydrology of Mountain Areas*, IAHS Publication No. 194.

Feldman, A.D., Ely, P.B. & Goldman, D.M. 1981. The new HEC-1 flood hydrograph package. In V.P. Singh (Ed), *Applied Modelling in Catchment Hydrology*, Water Resource Publications, Littlewood, CO, 121-144.

Germann, P.F. 1986. Rapid drainage response to precipitation, *Hydrological Processes*, 1, 3-13.

Guillot, P. & Duband, D. 1981. Une méthode de transfert pluie-débit par régression multiple. In *Hydrological Forecasting*, IAHS Publication No. 129, 177-186.

Hewlett, J.D. & Hibbert, A.R. 1967. Factors affecting the response of small watersheds to precipitation in humid areas. In W.E. Sopper & H.W. Lull (Eds), *Int. Symp on Forest Hydrology*, Pergammon Press, 275-290.

Horton, R.E. 1933. The role of infiltration in the hydrological cycle. *Trans. Am. Geophys. Un.*, 14, 446-460.

Horton, R.E. 1942. Some remarks on hydrologic terminology. *Trans. Am. Geophys. Un.*, 23, 479-482.

Hursh, C.R. & Brater, E.F. 1941. Separating storm-hydrographs from small drainage-areas in surface- and subsurface-flow. *Trans. Am. Geophys. Union*, 863-870.

Jakeman, A.J., Littlewood, I.G. & Whitehead, P.G. 1990. Computation of the instantaneous unit hydrograph and identifiable component flows with application to two small upland catchments, *J. Hydrol.*, 117, 275-300.

Linsley, R.K. & Ackerman, W.C. 1942. A method of predicting the runoff from rainfall. *Trans. ASCE*, 107, 825-835.

Linsley, R.K., Kohler, M.A. & Paulhus, J.L.H. 1988. *Hydrology for Engineers* (SI Metric Edn.), McGraw-Hill.

Nash, E. 1960. Unit Hydrographs with particular reference to British catchments. *Instn Civ. Eng. Proc.*, 17, 249.

O'Brien, A.L. 1980. The role of groundwater in stream discharge from two small wetland controlled basins in Eastern Massachusetts. *Groundwater*, 18, 359-365.

Rodriguez, J.Y., Sempere-Torres, D. & Obled, Ch. 1989. Nouvelles perspectives de developpement dans la modelisation des pluies efficaces par application de la methode DPFT. In *Surface Water Modelling - New Directions for Hydrologic Prediction*, IAHS Pubn. No. 181.

Sherman, L.K. 1932. Streamflow from rainfall by the unit-graph method. *Eng. News-Rec*, 108, 501-505.

Sklash, M.G. 1990. Environmental isotope studies of storm and snowmelt runoff generation. In M.G. Anderson & T.P. Burt, *Process Studies in Hillslope Hydrology*, 401-435.

Sklash, M.G., Stewart, M.K. & Pearce, A.J. 1986. Storm runoff generation in humid headwater catchments. 2. A case study of hillslope and low-order stream response. *Wat. Resour. Res.* 22, 1273-1282.

Vreeland, J.L. 1983. The role of shallow groundwater in the hydrogeochemical response of the White Oak Run catchment, Shenandoah National Park. Unpublished MSc thesis, University of Virginia.

Ward, R.C. & Robinson, M. *Principles of Hydrology* (3rd Edn), 1989.

Young, P.C. & Beven, K.J. 1991. Comments on "Computation of the instantaneous unit hydrograph and identifiable component flows with application to two small upland catchments" by A.J. Jakeman *et al.*, *J. Hydrol.*, in press.

Hydrograph separation into dominant quick and slow flow components

I.G. Littlewood & A.J. Jakeman

Abstract

A methodology for separating hydrographs into quick and slow response streamflow components, based on a transfer function representation of unit hydrograph theory, is applied to catchments which exhibit different baseflow characteristics. It is argued that the results are consistent with the traditional conceptualisation of streamflow generation, i.e. peaks in streamflow usually comprise mostly 'new' water from the rapid movement, essentially by runoff processes, of rainfall excess to the stream. Discussion of the hydrograph separations presented includes consideration of a fundamentally different view of streamflow generation, based on selected interpretations of field tracer studies, whereby streamflow peaks can comprise large proportions of 'old' or deep-layer-provenance water displaced by incoming 'new' (rain) water.

Introduction

Debate on the relative dominance of hydrological processes which operate during events to convert inputs of rainfall into outputs of streamflow has been gathering pace in recent years. This paper examines the relationship in broad terms between the more conventional view of storm streamflow generation, essentially by runoff processes, and the increasingly popular view that streamflow peaks are generated largely by displacement mechanisms. Here, the term 'runoff processes' means those mechanisms by which water flows to the stream over the surface, or via near-surface pathways, predominantly from saturated areas of the catchment. The term 'displacement mechanisms' refers to those processes by which 'old' water (i.e. water in the catchment before the causative rainfall in excess of antecedent baseflow) enters the stream during events.

Streamflow during events is a variable mixture of component flows of different 'ages' and provenances (i.e. from different depths within the catchment and from recent rainfall). The conventional conceptualisation of streamflow generation encourages the notion that peak streamflows are largely the result of runoff of 'new' rain water falling on saturated areas contiguous to or disjunct from the stream network. These saturated areas increase in size because of recent rainfall and seepage from upslope, then decrease in areal extent as the catchment drains after the rain ceases (the variable contributing area conceptual model). Some of the storm runoff comprises return flow which emerges onto the surface or into near-surface layers at the upslope boundary of the contiguous saturated area. Macropores in the soil (pipe networks in some upland catchments) may transmit water directly into the stream or into mires and can also provide effective hydraulic connections between the disjunct and contiguous saturated areas (Jones, 1979). A more comprehensive description of streamflow generation processes is given by Ward (1984).

The displacement mechanisms which operate at the same time during events have generally been considered to contribute a relatively small part of the streamflow at and near peak flows. The 'old' water component of peak streamflows is expected to be considerably smaller than the 'new' water component except, as discussed later in this paper, for very small peak flows. Many published accounts of field studies using chemical tracers and simple end-member mixing models, however, imply that the conceptualisation of streamflow generation essentially by runoff processes is seriously flawed.

Several investigators have interpreted field observations of 'conservative' tracers such as ^{2}H or ^{18}O (e.g. Sklash & Farvolden, 1979; Pearce et $al.$, 1986), or alkalinity (Robson & Neal, 1990), to indicate that peak streamflows comprise large amounts of 'old' water, or water from deep layers within the catchment, respectively. Typically, it has been concluded that peak streamflows comprise more than 70% 'old' water. Individual hydrographs, apparently, can be almost completely dominated by 'old' water; Pearce (1990) cites a case where the volumetric estimate of 'new' water under a hydrograph is only 3%.

If overwhelming proportions of hydrographs are 'old' water then the dominant type of mechanism involved must be one of displacement of pre-event water by 'new' rain water. Some writers have taken the results of individual tracer studies like those outlined above to be valid quite generally. According to Payne (1988), "The use of isotope techniques, for studying the components of runoff, has refuted the previous understanding that storm runoff consists of a major fraction of rainwater from the storm and a minor fraction of groundwater. In fact isotope studies have demonstrated that the contrary is the case". In a call for a new paradigm in hydrology, Beven (1987) presents "Exhibit A : studies of the isotopic content of the waters of storm hydrographs . . . have provided convincing evidence that traditional methods of 'baseflow separation' . . . are a nonsense".

To assist with an evaluation of these apparently opposing views of storm streamflow generation, this paper employs the methodology for rainfall-streamflow modelling and hydrograph separation of Jakeman et al. (1990). In the next section, the rainfall-streamflow model is described in outline (see Jakeman et al. (1990; 1991) for full details). Then, hydrograph separations into quick and slow flow components are presented for a small, low baseflow stream and a much larger, relatively high baseflow stream. These hydrograph separations are discussed in terms of their consistency with the possibility that 'old' (or deep-layer-provenance) water is dominant in streamflow at and near hydrograph peaks.

The rainfall-streamflow model

The model is based on unit hydrograph theory which describes the variation of streamflow x(t) over time t as a linear convolution between rainfall excess u(t) and a unit hydrograph. Rainfall excess is converted to streamflow by passing through a system of linear storages arranged either in series, or in parallel, or both. The configuration identified most commonly is two storages acting in parallel which, in discrete-time, can be represented by the second-order transfer function given by (1) below (Jakeman et al. 1991). One storage controls the quick flow component of streamflow (sub- or superscript q) and the other controls the slow flow component (s).

$$
\left.
\begin{aligned}
x_k &= x_k^q + x_k^s \\
x_k^q &= \beta_q u_k - \alpha_q x_{k-1}^q \\
x_k^s &= \beta_s u_k - \alpha_s x_{k-1}^s
\end{aligned}
\right\} \quad (1)
$$

The α and β parameters in (1) are estimated by an instrumental variable method (see Jakeman et al. (1990) for further details and Young (1984) for an introduction to these methods).

Rainfall excess u(t) at any time t is that part of rainfall r(t) which contributes to streamflow over the period in question and is assumed to be strongly dependent on antecedent rainfall. The approach is to account for variations in catchment wetness (i.e. the 'ripeness' of the catchment to produce streamflow at the time of rainfall) by maintaining a running index of exponentially weighted past rainfalls. Alternatively, this index can be considered to be a measure of the extent of a variable contributing area.

The catchment wetness index, s_k, is calculated by

$$
s_k = s_{k-1} + \tau_w^{-1} (r_k - s_{k-1}) \quad (2)
$$

where τ_w is a parameter which characterises the rate at which the catchment drains and dries out after rainfall ceases.

Rainfall excess is calculated by multiplying r_k by s_k at each time step and then scaling to ensure equality between the volumes of rainfall excess and streamflow over the model calibration period. Thus rainfall excess is given by

$$
u_k = \text{const.} \, r_k \, s_k \quad (3)
$$

where const. is the scaling factor.

Hydrograph separations

Nant y Gronwen (CI6)

Figures 1(a) and (b) show the model-fit and hydrograph separation (modelled streamflow) respectively for a 17-day period of hourly data for the Nant y Gronwen, one of the headwater streams of the Afon Tywi, Wales. The catchment drains about 0.7 km² of moorland pasture underlain by largely impermeable Ordovician shales, grits and mudstones and, on average, receives an annual rainfall of about 1800 mm. It is one of many small catchments instrumented for the Llyn Brianne Acid Waters Project (Edwards et al., 1990) for which it was designated 'catchment CI6'. Jakeman et al. (1990) give further details of the CI6 hourly rainfall record employed here for modelling.

Attention is directed to the numbered peaks in Figure 1 and to the corresponding proportions of slow flow listed in Table 1 (p. 3.14). Although peaks 2, 6, and 7 are modelled well (-7%, 7% and -3% from the observed peaks respectively), peaks 3, 4 and 5 fit less well (93%, 66% and -21% respectively). Peak 1 is a special case because it is close to the start of the modelled period, when slow flow is initialised at zero. More credence is given, therefore, to the hydrograph separations at peaks 2, 6 and 7 than those for the other numbered peaks. The proportion of slow flow at peaks decreases as the magnitude of the peaks increases; 32% at 84 ls⁻¹ , 20% at 91 ls⁻¹ and 16% at 151 ls⁻¹ for peaks 6, 7 and 2 respectively. This ranking is repeated for the less well modelled peaks; 40% at 21 ls⁻¹, 24% at 30 ls⁻¹ and 16% at 211 ls⁻¹ for peaks 4, 3 and 5 respectively. Although peaks 3 and 4 are

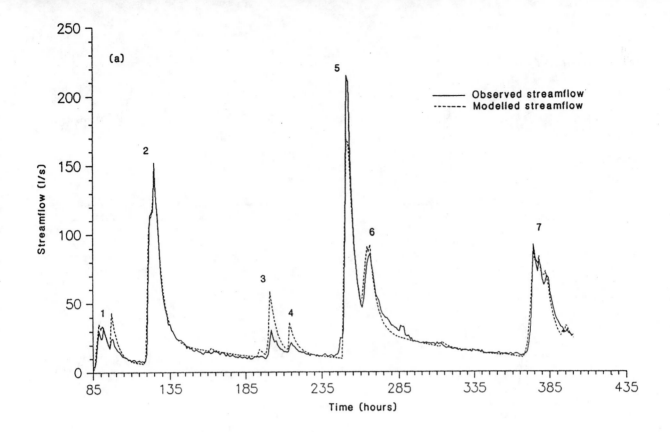

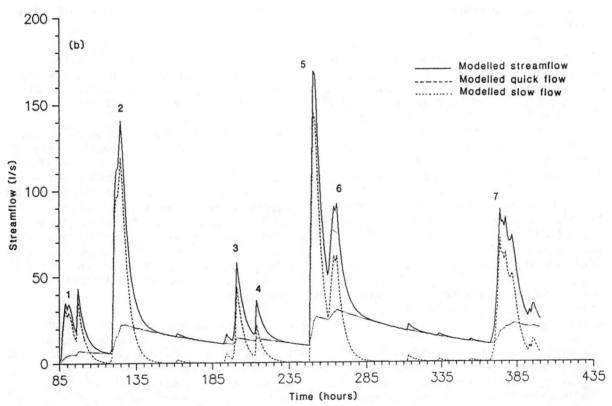

Figure 1   IHACRES model performance for the Nant y Gronwen, 1-18 September, 1987 (hourly data), (a) model fit, (b) hydrograph separation

not well matched by the modelled sequence it is clear that small peak streamflows can comprise quite large proportions of slow flow. Indeed, very small peaks are quite likely to comprise 80%, or more, slow flow.

Figures 2(a) and (b) show 15-minute interval variations of stage and electrical conductivity for the Nant y Gronwen (CI6) and the nearby Nant y Craflwyn (CI3) during January 1986. These data, and

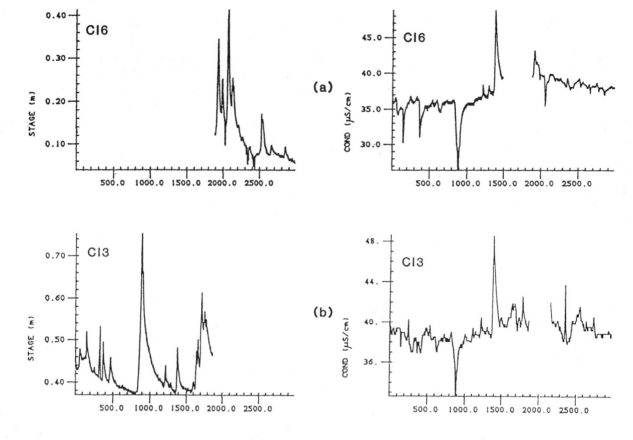

Figure 2 *Stage and electrical conductivity January 1986 (15-minute data), (a) Nant y Gronwen, (b) Nant y Craflwyn*

similar data for other Llyn Brianne catchments, have been presented and discussed in a previous investigation of the hydrological and hydrochemical responses of small streams in the upper Tywi valley (Littlewood, 1989). Catchment CI3 drains about 0.8 km² of moorland similar to CI6 (part of CI3 was ploughed, fertilized and re-seeded in the summer of 1986 for the Llyn Brianne Acid Waters Project - see Edwards *et al.*, 1990, for further details) and its centre is about 2 km from the centre of CI6. A cursory inspection of Figures 2(a) and (b) indicates that the conductivity responses of the two streams are, as might be expected, broadly similar. By inferring behaviour during periods of instrument failure in either catchment from behaviour in the other, close inspection of Figures 2(a) and (b) gives some insight to the basic nature of the response of small moorland streams in the Llyn Brianne catchment.

Littlewood (1989) demonstrates that usually (particularly in summer months) the electrical conductivity of most Llyn Brianne moorland streams decreases when streamflow increases in response to (relatively low conductivity) rainfall. It is argued that this observation alone is strong evidence to support the view that the extra streamflow during events is mostly water from recent rainfall. This streamflow–conductivity behaviour can be observed in Figure 2(a) where, for events before time step 1000, it can be seen that CI6 conductivity decreases to minima in

response to peaks in streamflow. As might be expected, the highest peak flow during that period, at about time step 900, is associated with the lowest of the conductivity minima for each stream.

Later in the sequence depicted in Figure 2, at about time step 1400 (i.e. during 15 January), it can be seen that, corresponding to a relatively small event (see CI3 at 1400), the conductivity of each stream increased dramatically. Littlewood (1989) argues that this conductivity response is due to a heavy atmospheric bulk deposition (wet plus dry) of sea-salts known to have occurred regionally on 14 and 15 January, and that this is further strong evidence to support the dominance of 'new' rain water in peak streamflows (even quite small peak CI3 and CI6 streamflows).

The following additional example demonstrates that the rainfall–streamflow modelling approach adopted here for CI6 can give good model-fits and reasonable hydrograph separations for much larger catchments and using different data intervals.

Teifi at Glan Teifi

Figures 3(a) and (b) show the model-fit and hydrograph separation respectively for a period of just over three years (daily data) for the Teifi at Glan Teifi, Wales. The catchment drains about 894 km² of mainly agricultural landscape on essentially

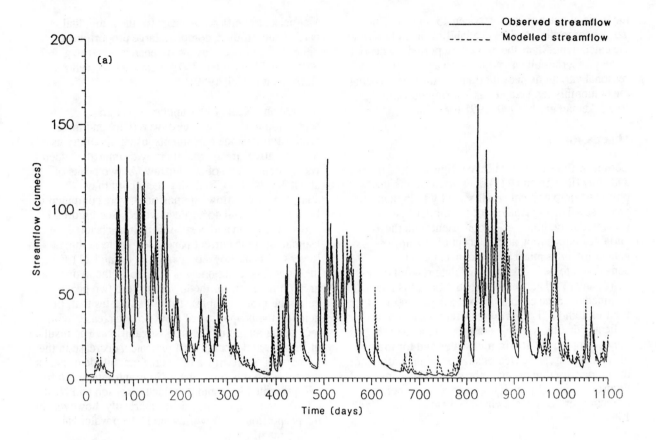

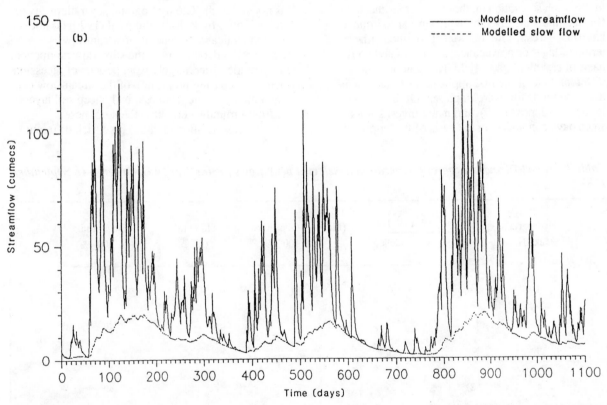

Figure 3 IHACRES model performance for the Teifi at Glan Teifi 26 July 1982 to 29 July 1985 (daily data), (a) model fit, (b) hydrograph separation

impermeable Ordovician and Silurian bedrock, and receives, on average, an annual rainfall of about 1340 mm. Daily mean streamflow data were obtained from the national Surface Water Archive maintained by the Institute of Hydrology. Daily areal rainfall was computed by the 'triangle method' (Jones, 1983) on the basis of catches from between 13 and 17 rain-gauges (according to data availability) in and close to the catchment. Since the modelling period was about three years, rainfall was adjusted to account for seasonal variations in evapotranspiration losses using mean monthly temperature as a surrogate variable (see Jakeman et al., 1990; 1991 for details).

Discussion

Certainly, the simple parallel configuration of quick and slow flow given by (1) does not describe the physical complexity of small-scale hydrological processes. The high quality of the model-fits presented here, however, is consistent with the variable contributing area concept of streamflow generation in as much as that concept can be considered to be invoked to calculate rainfall excess by (2) and (3). The fact that good model-fits are obtained over the calibration periods shown in Figures 1 and 3 (i.e. for quite different catchments) indicates that the variable contributing area concept may be applicable at different scales and for many different landscapes. Demonstration of the validity of the models used to estimate the streamflows in Figures 1 and 3 (by applying them to other periods of record) are given elsewhere (Jakeman et al., 1990; 1991).

It is interesting to compare the results of different hydrograph separation methods. Whereas the slow flow components given here are similar to intuitive baseflow, streamflow components defined either in terms of 'age' or provenance, and estimated on the basis of chemical tracer field data, can be quite different. One of the first applications of chemical tracer methods for hydrograph separation was by Pinder and Jones (1969), and many investigators since have concluded on the basis of this approach

that peak streamflows, at least for the individual catchments studied, comprise large proportions of either 'old' or deep-layer-provenance water (e.g. Sklash and Farvolden, 1979; Pearce et al., 1986; Robson and Neal, 1990).

Robson and Neal (1990) applied hydrograph separation to the Nant y Gronwen (CI6) and three other Llyn Brianne catchments, using alkalinity as a 'conservative' tracer, and thereby estimated a "deep water" component of streamflow. At two peaks of about 300 ls^{-1} for CI6 during the record they analysed, streamflow compositions were computed to be about 40% and 45% "deep water" (see Figures 1 and 4 in Robson and Neal, 1990). It has been estimated in the current paper (see Table 1) that at lower CI6 peak flows of about 151 ls^{-1} and 211 ls^{-1} the slow flow component is only 16% (the hydro-graph separation for the lower of these two peaks being the more reliable). Table 1 indicates that, in general, the proportion of slow flow decreases with increasing magnitude of peak streamflow. The results of Robson and Neal (1990) indicate a decrease in the proportion of "deep water" as the magnitude of peaks increases. In this sense the hydrograph separation for CI6 presented here and that due to Robson and Neal (1990) are similar. They differ markedly, however, in the proportions of slow flow and "deep water" at peak streamflows.

It is noted that the CI6 hydrograph separations given here and those by Robson and Neal (1990) do not refer to identical components of streamflow. However, the parameters of the slow flow component in (1) are identified largely from periods of recession when an increasing proportion of the streamflow can be assumed to come from relatively deep soil layers and from groundwater. Why, then, do these hydrograph separation methods give such different

Table 1   Model-fit and hydrograph separation at selected peak flows for the Nant y Gronwen 1-18 September, 1987

Hydrograph Peak No.	Peak flow ($l.s^{-1}$) Observed	Peak flow ($l.s^{-1}$) Modelled	(Mod. - Obs.)/Obs. (x 100 %)	Slow flow ($l.s^{-1}$)	Slow/Mod. (x 100 %)
1	30	33	10	5	15
2	151	140	- 7	22	16
3	30	58	93	14	24
4	21	35	66	14	40
5	211	166	- 21	26	16
6	84	90	7	29	32
7	91	88	- 3	18	20

results, even for the same catchment? Why have many published accounts of hydrograph separations by tracer methods indicated large components of 'old' or deep-layer-provenance water at peak streamflows? Clearly, these are questions which should be addressed as a matter of priority.

A step common to many tracer studies (including that of Robson and Neal) is prescription of the simple end-member mixing model given by (4).

$$\frac{Q_2}{Q_s} = \frac{C_s - C_1}{C_2 - C_1} \tag{4}$$

where $Q_s = Q_1 + Q_2$

and Q_s is streamflow
Q_1 is flow component 1 of Q_s
Q_2 is flow component 2 of Q_s
C_s is concentration of Q_s
C_1 is concentration of component 1 source
C_2 is concentration of component 2 source.

The validity of any prescribed model depends on the degree to which necessary conditions are satisfied. In the case of (4) it is necessary that there exist just two clearly identifiable sources of water which individually are well mixed and have concentrations C_1 and C_2 respectively. Rainfall concentration is used for one of the flow components and, usually, antecedent streamflow concentration is assumed representative of the other component. For (4) to be usefully accurate, the difference between C_1 and C_2 for the event has to be large enough to cause a change in C_s much greater than the background variation in C_s; (4) can be inaccurate if $(C_2 - C_1)$ is small with respect to C_1. Small errors in C_2 and/or C_1 then lead to large errors in Q_2/Q_s. It is evident from field observations that the conditions necessary for the validity of (4), and for its usefulness, are rarely, if ever, satisfied (e.g. concentration in rainfall varies during events). The two-component end-member mixing model given by (4) is, therefore, not strictly valid for hydrograph separation - a view endorsed by Turner and Macpherson (1990) and others (e.g. Anderson and Burt, 1982; Lawler, 1987).

Concluding remarks

Hydrograph separation into quick and slow flow components by the method demonstrated in this paper cannot, in isolation, provide any conclusive information about the variable composition of streamflow in terms of 'age' or provenance. Nevertheless, the results for CI6, in combination with the distinctly variable nature of recorded CI6 conductivity responses, indicate that hydrograph peaks (at least in the Llyn Brianne area) are due mainly to the rapid movement of recent rain water, not water which was resident in the catchment before the causative rainfall. The quick flow component undoubtedly comprises some displaced water but many published estimates of the 'old' water fraction

of streamflow at and near peaks, based on field tracer studies, appear to be unreasonably high.

A sound scientific basis for accurate hydrograph separation remains to be developed and there is, therefore, a need for caution when interpreting all field observations, particularly those from tracer studies using the simple end-member mixing model given by (4). The authors do not agree with the views of some writers and investigators, based on the use of (4) for hydrograph separation, that there has been what amounts to a Copernican revolution in the way we should conceptualise streamflow generation. There remains much to be discovered about the mixing dynamics of streamflow components, and tracer studies clearly have an important part to play in research with that aim. One way towards a better quantitative understanding of the dynamics of streamflow composition would be to attempt to develop a hybrid approach for hydrograph separation involving rainfall-runoff modelling and field tracer observations.

References

Anderson, M.G. & Burt, T.P. 1982. The contribution of throughflow to storm runoff : An evaluation of a chemical mixing model. *Earth Surf. Processes*, 7, 565-574.

Beven, K.J. 1987. Towards a new paradigm in hydrology. In: Water for the future : Hydrology in perspective, IAHS Publication No. 164, 393-403.

Edwards, R.W., Gee, A.S. & Stoner, J.H. (eds) 1990. *Acid Waters in Wales*. Kluwer Academic Publishers, Dordrecht, The Netherlands.

Jakeman, A.J., Littlewood, I.G. & Whitehead, P.G. 1990. Computation of the instantaneous unit hydrograph and identifiable component flows with application to two small upland catchments. *J. Hydrol.*, 117, 275-300.

Jakeman, A.J., Littlewood, I.G. & Symons, H.D. 1991. Features and applications of IHACRES : A PC program for Identification of unit Hydrographs And Component flows from Rainfall, Evapotranspiration and Streamflow data. *Proc. 13th World IMACS Congress on Computation and Applied Mathematics*, July 1991, Dublin.

Jones, J.A.A. 1979. Extending the Hewlett model of stream runoff generation. *Area*, 11(2), 110-114.

Jones, S.B. 1983. The estimation of catchment average point rainfall profiles. *I.H. Report No. 87*.

Lawler, H.A. 1987. Sampling for isotopic responses in surface waters. *Earth Surf. Processes*, 12, 551-559.

Littlewood, I.G. 1989. The dynamics of acid runoff from moorland and afforested catchments draining into Llyn Brianne, Wales. Unpublished thesis, University of Wales.

Payne, B.R. 1988. The status of isotope hydrology today. *J. Hydrol.*, 100, 207-237.

Pearce, A.J., Stewart, M.K. & Sklash, M.G. 1986.

Storm runoff generation in humid headwater catchments. 1. Where does the water come from? *Wat. Resour. Res.* 22, 1273-1282.

Pearce, A.J., 1990. Streamflow generation processes : An austral view. *Wat. Resour. Res.* 26(12), 3037-3047.

Pinder, G.F. & Jones, J.F. 1969. Determination of the ground-water component of peak discharge from the chemistry of runoff. *Wat. Resour. Res.* 5(2), 438-445.

Robson, A.J. & Neal, C. 1990. Hydrograph separation using chemical techniques : an application to catchments in Mid-Wales. *J. Hydrol.* 116, 345-363.

Sklash, M.G. & Farvolden, R. N. 1979. The role of groundwater in storm runoff. *J. Hydrol.* 43, 45-65.

Turner, J.V. & Macpherson, D.K. 1990. Mechanisms affecting streamflow and stream water quality : An approach via stable isotope, hydrogeochemical, and time series analysis. *Wat. Resour. Res.* 26(12), 3005-3019.

Ward, R.C. 1984. On the response to precipitation of headwater streams in humid areas. *J. Hydrol.* 74, 171-189.

Young, P.C. 1984. *Recursive Estimation and Time-Series Analysis - An Introduction.* Spinger-Verlag, New York.

Chemical signals in an upland catchment in mid-Wales - some implications for water movement

A. Robson & C. Neal

Abstract

In this paper, information is brought together for the Hafren catchment, mid-Wales, as an example of how analysis of chemical signals in small upland streams can provide extensive information on how water moves through the catchment. Chloride, isotope and conductivity signals in the Hafren stream give a very damped response relative to rainfall inputs, indicating that little rainfall directly contributes to stream flow. Despite this, the chemistry of the streamwaters is strongly associated with flow showing that flow pathways have important effects on stream water composition. Baseflow and stormflow chemistries are explained in terms of variable contributions from soil waters and deeper waters. Hydrograph separation between these chemically distinct water types is made which shows that the non-hillslope waters make up a high proportion of streamflow, even during storm events.

A physically-based semi-distributed model, TOPMODEL, is used to provide estimates of water flowing from saturated contributing areas (quick flow) and components of subsurface flow (slow flow) identified by depth for the Hafren catchment. The modelling results are compared with those obtained from chemical considerations. They suggest that both the quick and slow flow components simulated by TOPMODEL have a well-mixed composition.

Introduction

For upland catchments, questions of where water moves, how fast it travels, and for how long and where it is stored are still the subject of much debate. Hydrograph separation techniques have played an important role in trying to address these problems. In a hydrograph separation, stream waters are separated into a number of components which are defined in either hydrological or chemical terms. By separating stream waters into components, the system is broken up into smaller, more manageable, sub-units which can then be studied in detail. However, different approaches to hydrograph separation can give rise to radically different component types, both in terms of volume and composition. For example, the results from isotope studies give a very different partitioning to the separations derived from many hydrological rainfall-runoff models. Comparison and linkage of the components resulting from different techniques is required if catchment processes are to be better understood.

Hydrograph separation

Hydrograph separation techniques may be grouped into two broad categories: hydrological and hydrochemical.

(1) Hydrological

Hydrological separations use methods which rely on hydrological data to derive flow sub-division. At minimum, rainfall and runoff data are required. More sophisticated modelling techniques make use of information on the hydrological characteristics of the catchments. Many hydrological models, though not explicitly methods of hydrograph separation, use the partitioning of flow into components as the core of the model and are, therefore, included in this category.

Historically, unit hydrograph based models separated flow into surface runoff and baseflow components (Sherman, 1942). This was based on the conception that the main body of the hydrograph resulted from incoming rainwater moving quickly to the stream as Hortonian overland flow (Horton, 1933). Later, Hewlett and Hibbert (1967) proposed a more rigorous method for separation into 'quick' and 'delayed' runoff; the separation was graphical, based on numerical rules and equations. More recent examples of hydrological models using two or more components to explain flow include physically based models, such as TOPMODEL (Beven and Wood, 1983), lumped parameter models, such as HYRROM (Blackie and Eeles, 1985) and black box models such as the time series model IHACRES (Jakeman *et al*, 1990).

Although there are large differences between these models, some similarities exist. A common characteristic of the models is the difference in the speed of movement of the component flows. For the case in which there are two components, the terminology 'slow', corresponding to a baseflow/ subsurface-flow component and 'quick', corresponding to surface-runoff/quick flow, is used. The definition of 'slow' and 'quick' rests ultimately with the mathematical representation used in each model. This means that the components in one model will not necessarily correspond with those from a different hydrological model. Caution is required in assessing the implications of the differences which arise.

(2) Hydrochemical

This class of hydrograph separations employs methods which use artificial or natural chemical tracers to subdivide flow. Tracer concentrations in the components and in the stream are measured and a simple mixing equation is used to calculate the proportions of each water type reaching the stream.

Isotope studies often take advantage of the natural isotopic variations in rain water to identify 'new' and 'old' components (e.g. Sklash and Farvolden, 1979). Here 'new' is defined to be the rain water falling during the storm, 'old' is defined as water already present in the catchment at the start of a storm. For separation to be possible, the isotopic compositions of 'old' and 'new' components need to be distinguishable.

Another approach to hydrograph separation has been to make use of continuously monitored stream chemistry variations which occur in response to flow changes. For this, a conservative chemical tracer is used to separate stream waters into two chemically distinct endmembers (Neal *et al*, 1991); a 'soil' (or acidic) component and a 'deep' (or well-buffered) component. The technique is, in essence, very similar to that used in new/old separations but the frequency of data points and the choice of the components is quite different. Indeed in this approach it is usually assumed that the chemical contribution of the 'new' component, to the stream, is not significant on an individual event basis.

Models which have been built on a hydrological framework but which incorporate chemical reactions and stream chemistry, bridge the gap between the above categories. Of particular relevance are the Birkenes (Christophersen *et al*, 1982) and PULSE (Bergstrom *et al*, 1985) models. Earlier versions of both models were found to reproduce major stream chemistry variations in the stream. However, when the models were tested on isotopes the hydrological representation was found to be inadequate and had to be modified (Christophersen *et al*, 1985; Lindstrom and Rodhe, 1987). Increased storage and more thorough mixing of waters was necessary. This is a good example of how scientific development can be accelerated by the linking of different approaches. It also illustrates the importance of understanding how components identified hydrologically (quick/slow) relate to chemical components (old/new or soil/deep).

Site description

The Hafren catchment (area 347 ha; altitude range 350-690 m), located at the south-eastern edge of Plynlimon Fawr, forms part of the headwaters of the River Severn in central Wales. Lower portions of the area have been planted with conifers (mainly Sitka spruce - *Pinus sitchensis*) in various phases between 1947 and 1964. Upper portions of the catchments drain acidic semi-natural moorland and peats. The soils range from peats, podzols and brown earths, to gleys. They overlie either greywacke, mudstone, sandstone, and grit of Silurian to Ordovician age or boulder clay and colluvium derived from the bedrock. Rainfall levels average about 2400 mm y^{-1} with losses by evapotranspiration of between 400 and 600 mm y^{-1}. The typical hydrograph response of the catchment is rapid and 'spiky'.

Chemical data

Chemical and hydrological information for the Hafren stream waters exists in a number of forms. These include weekly spot sampled data (analysed for major and minor elements), isotope data, and continuously monitored stream flow, pH and conductivity data. Chemical data on rainwater and soil water composition has also been collected, mainly on a weekly basis.

A strong flow dependency is seen at the weekly scale for most of the spot-sampled chemical determinands in the stream (Neal *et al.*, 1990). These determinands group into two main categories - those where concentration drops at high flows (e.g. calcium, alkalinity), and those where concentration increases at high flows (e.g. hydrogen ion, aluminium). This same flow dependency is seen, but in more detail, for the continuously monitored pH and conductivity data (Figure 1) and also for the acid neutralisation capacity (ANC). The ANC is defined to be the difference between the 'strong' cations and the 'strong' anions in solution and is estimated from pH using a non-linear relationship calibrated on spot-sampled data (Neal *et al.*, 1991).

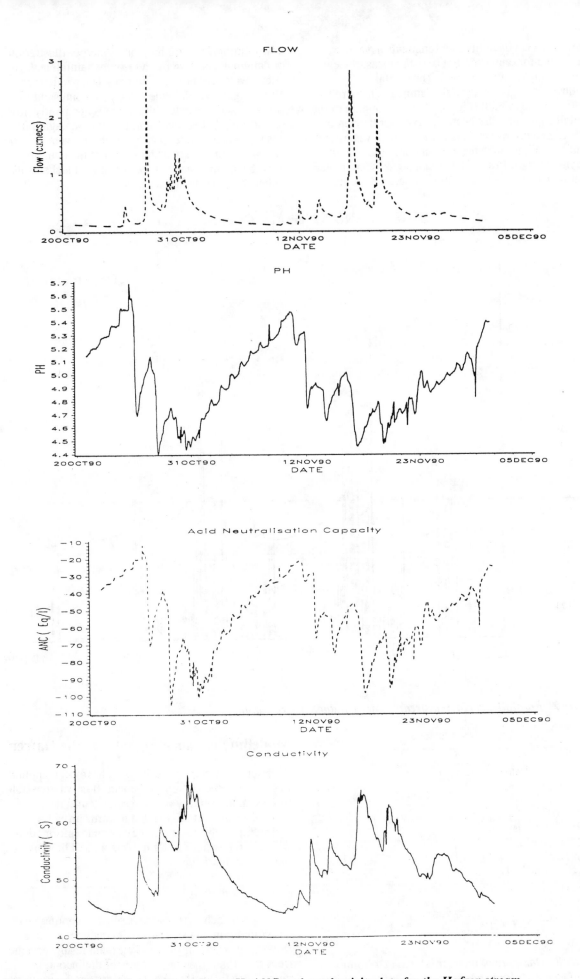

Figure 1 Continuously monitored flow, pH, ANC and conductivity data for the Hafren stream

3.19

Continuous conductivity measurements have also been made for rainwater, but only the measurements taken during rainfall are used. The rainfall conductivity signal is strongly damped in the stream relative to the rainfall (Figure 2). This damping of the rainfall signal has also been observed for the nearby Cyff catchment where the chloride signal was traced from rainfall, through the soils and into the stream (Reynolds et al, 1988). The strong signal seen in the rainfall was progressively damped out as it moved down through the soil horizons. Another illustration of damping is shown by [18]O isotope rainfall and streamwater data for the Hafren (Neal and Rosier, 1990; Figure 3). Here the catchment damps out the signal to such an extent that there is apparently little relationship between rainfall and stream. Again this has important implications for water movement. The isotope is conservative and therefore the damping must be taking place via water storage mechanisms rather than chemical reactions.

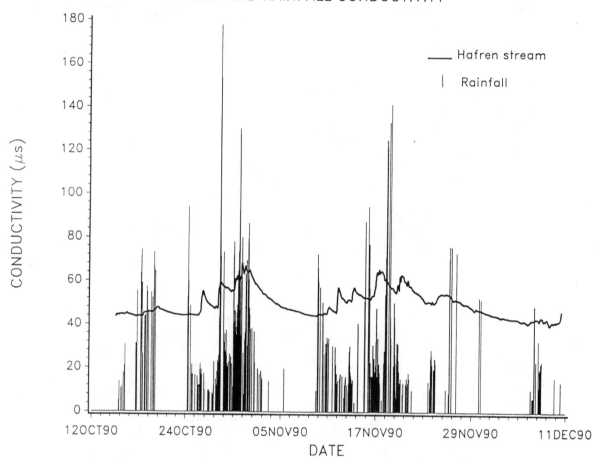

Figure 2   *Rainfall and Hafren stream water conductivity variations*

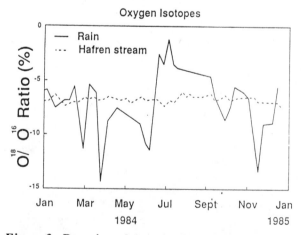

Figure 3   **Damping of the rainfall oxygen isotope signal in the Hafren stream**

Modelling chemical signals for the Hafren

A variety of modelling techniques have been applied to data from the Hafren catchment. It is only possible to present a summary of the results here. The techniques are not all directed towards providing a hydrograph separation but they provide information which is relevant to water movement and helpful in making comparisons.

Time series models

Time series techniques were applied to continuously monitored rain and stream water conductivity data (Robson et al.(a), in press). Two main results emerge from this. First, the conductivity of the incoming rainfall has little effect on the stream conductivity on

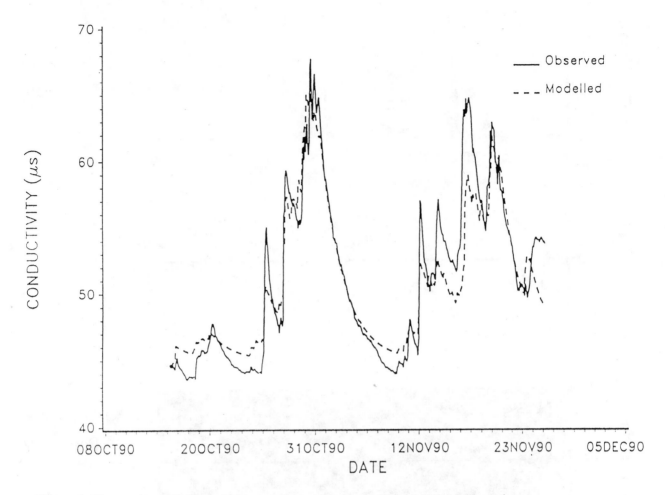

Figure 4   Time series modelling of stream conductivity data using rainfall volume as input

an event scale. Second, the rainfall volume is a good predictor of stream conductivity when simple time series models are used (Figure 4). Thus, for conductivity, it is the quantity rather than the quality of the rainfall which determines the quality of the stream water. This implies that the chemical impact of the 'new' water component is small.

Mixing models

Mixing model techniques have been used to provide hydrograph separation of stream waters into chemically distinct water types (Neal *et al*, 1991; Christophersen *et al*, 1990; Hooper *et al*, 1990). As has already been demonstrated, the chemistry of the Hafren stream is closely tied to flow. At low flows, the waters are well-buffered, low in H^+ and Al and high in Ca^{2+}, Mg^{2+} and HCO_3^-.

At high flows, the waters become more acidic and aluminium-rich whilst base metal concentrations decrease. These variations are explained in terms of the flow dependent contributions of two endmembers: (1) the'deep' waters, which have been generated through reaction with the bedrock (Reynolds *et al*, 1986), and (2) the acidic upper soil waters, which contribute when the water table is high.

The mixing approach, used here, makes a number of simplifying assumptions - that there are just two endmembers, that they mix conservatively and that their composition remains constant over time. The composition of the rainwater has also been neglected. This is, in part, justified by the results from the time series models as they show that the rainfall composition has little effect on the stream.

In order to carry out the hydrograph separation, it is necessary to select a chemically conservative tracer which distinguishes well between the two endmembers. For this, the ANC has been used as it is conserved with respect to the processes taking place as water moves from the catchment into the stream (e.g. degassing, loss of organics and $Al(OH)_3$ precipitation/solution reactions). 'Deep' waters have not been directly measured. Instead, their chemical composition has been inferred from the baseflow chemistry of the stream. The ANC of the soil water endmember is determined from the mean soil water composition. The calculated contribution of each endmember is only approximate since there are uncertainties over the chemical composition of the endmembers. Nevertheless, allowing for the errors which may result, there is a significant contribution from the deep-water endmember at all times (Figure 5).

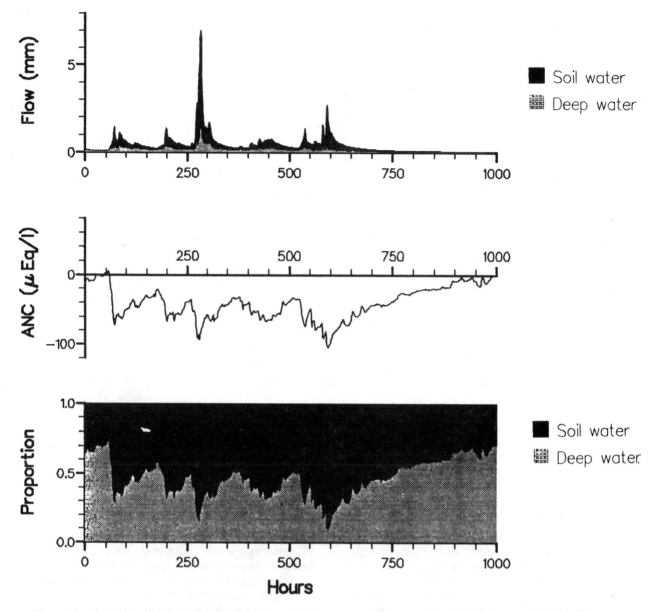

Figure 5   Hydrograph separation of stream waters into proportions of soil- and deep-water (a) total flow showing soil-water (black) and deep-water (grey) components (b) ANC (c) proportions of soil- and deep-water

Hydrological modelling (TOPMODEL)

TOPMODEL is semi-distributed physically-based model (Beven and Wood, 1983, Beven and Kirkby, 1979). Given a series of rainfall inputs, the resultant flows from the catchment are estimated. The modelled flow is composed of two components: water generated by rainfall landing on saturated contributing areas (quick flow) and water flowing from subsurface zones (slow flow). The extent of the saturated contributing area is dependent on the mean depth to the water table within the catchment and varies, in areal extent, during the course of a storm event. To examine whether the hydrological description of water movement used in TOPMODEL is compatible with the chemical signals seen in the stream, TOPMODEL has been modified to enable the subsurface endmember to be divided into components identified by depth of origin (Robson *et al* (b), in press). Figure 6 shows the proportions of

flow derived from the saturated contributing areas and from the different layers of the soil profile. These components can be linked with the 'soil' and 'deep' waters identified in the mixing models. Water flowing through the upper soils is assigned a soil water ANC and water flowing at depth is assigned a deep-water ANC. It is also necessary to assign a chemistry to the quick component of flow identified within TOPMODEL. For this three possibilities are considered: (1) the quick flow has a rainwater ANC, (2) the quick flow has a soil water composition and (3) the quick flow has a mixed composition, i.e. it is displacing a mixture of old water from within the catchment. Having assigned compositions to each component, TOPMODEL is used to predict the expected stream-water ANC and the results are compared with the observed stream chemistry. Examination of Figure 6 shows that if either of the first two options for the 'quick' composition were used, a noisy chemical response would result (reflecting the 'spiky' contribution of the quick component). In contrast, no corresponding sharp responses are observed in the stream-water chemistry. However, with the third option, TOPMODEL can give a predicted chemical response similar to the measured response. This is demonstrated in Figure 7, where a chemical composition has been assigned to the TOPMODEL layers and used to predict stream chemistry. The true chemistry of the stream is also shown and compares well.

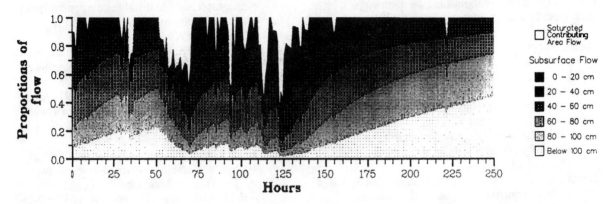

Figure 6   TOPMODEL components of subsurface flow: the period corresponds to hours 450 - 700 of Figures 5 and 7

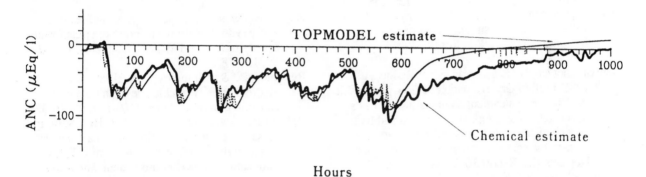

Figure 7   Comparison of stream ANC and ANC predicted by TOPMODEL. The dotted TOPMODEL line shows the effect of assuming a soil-water composition for the quick component. The solid TOPMODEL line shows the effect of assuming a mixed composition for the quick component. The thick solid line shows the observed stream-flow chemistry.

Discussion

The damping of rainfall isotope, chloride and conductivity signals in the stream water indicates that, for average sized events, the contribution of rainwater to the stream is small. This result is in agreement with isotope separations carried out on other catchments where the volume of new water was found to be relatively small (Sklash and Farvolden, 1979). Thus, for the Hafren, for moderate or small events, the 'new' component may be neglected and the 'old' component can be taken as the combined contribution of either 'soil' and 'deep' waters, or 'quick' and 'slow' components. During extreme events it may not be valid to neglect the 'new' component, this will need to be verified once more continuous data becomes available. Comparison of 'soil' and 'deep' components with the 'quick' and 'slow' components from the hydrological model, TOPMODEL, show that these components cannot be directly equated. However, by subdividing the slow component of TOPMODEL so that a depth varying

chemistry can be applied, TOPMODEL can give good estimates of stream ANC variations. Furthermore, the results imply a chemically mixed and variable composition for both the quick and slow components. Since the quick and slow flow components are highly model dependent, this conclusion need not apply to all models. However, the results provide an example where quick flow is neither 'new' nor 'soil' water.

The results underline the value of using chemical data in conjunction with hydrological information when studying flow paths. In particular, short-term chemical data open up many avenues to the modeller which are worthy of investigation. Resolution of the chemical signal at the hourly scale enables detailed short-term dynamics to be modelled. The complexity of the system is also emphasized by such data. Examples include the hysteresis observed between flow and stream ANC, and the short drop in stream conductivity occasionally seen at the onset of the hydrograph rise.

The above study has implications for many hydrological models. Whilst such models adequately predict flow, this cannot in itself be used as a proof that the structure within the model is valid. Only by using either chemical data or more detailed hydrological data in conjunction with these models can scientific testing of hypotheses about the flow pathways, which such models seek to represent, take place.

References

Blackie, J.R., & Eeles, C.W.O. 1985. Lumped catchment models. In Anderson, M.G., & Burt, T.P. (eds) *Hydrological Forecasting*, Wiley 313-345.

Bergstrom, S., Carlsson, B., Sandberg, G. & Maxe, L. 1985. Integrated modelling of runoff, alkalinity and pH on a daily basis. *Nordic Hydrol.*, 16, 89-104

Beven, K.J, & Kirkby, M.J. 1979. A physically based variable contributing area model of basin hydrology. *Hydrol. Sci. Bull.* 24(1), 43-69.

Beven, K.J., & Wood, E.J., 1983. Catchment geomorphology and the dynamics of runoff contributing areas. *J. Hydrol.* 65, 139-158.

Christophersoen, N., Seip, H.M., & Wright, R.F., 1982. A model for streamwater chemistry at Birkenes, Norway. *Wat. Resour. Res.* 18, 977-996.

Christophersen, N., Kjaernsrod, S., & Rodhe, A. 1985. Preliminary evaluation of flow patterns in the Birkenes catchment using natural ^{18}O as a tracer. IHP Workshop, Hydrological and hydrogeochemical mechanisms and model applications to the acidification of ecological systems, Uppsala, IHP Report 10, 29-40.

Christophersen, N., Neal, C., & Hooper, R.P., 1990. Modelling streamwater chemistry as a mixture of soil water endmembers, a step towards second generation acidification models. *J. Hydrol.*, 116, 307-321.

Hewlett, J.D. & Hibbert, A.R., 1967. Factors affecting the response of small watersheds to precipitation in humid areas. In: Sopper, W.E. & Lull, H.W. (eds), *Forest Hydrology*, Pergamon, Oxford, 275-290.

Hooper, R.P., Christophersen, N., & Peters, J., 1990. Endmember mixing analysis (EMMA): an analytical framework for the interpretation of streamwater chemistry. *J. Hydrol.* 116, 321-345.

Horton, R.E., 1933. The role of infiltration in the hydrological cycle, *Trans. Amer. Geophys. Union* 14, 446-60.

Jakeman, A.J, Littlewood, I.G., & Whitehead, P.G. 1990. Computation of the instantaneous unit hydrograph and identifiable component flows with application to two small upland catchments. *J.Hydrol.* 117, 275-300

Lindstrom, G. & Rodhe, A., 1987. Modelling water exchange and transit times in till basins using oxygen-18. *Nordic Hydrology* 17, 325-334

Neal, C., Robson, A.J., & Smith, C.J. 1991. Acid Neutralisation Capacity variations for Hafren forest streams: Inferences for hydrological processes. *J. Hydrol.* 121, 85-101

Neal, C. & Rosier, P. 1990. Chemical studies of chloride and stable oxygen isotopes on two conifer afforested and moorland catchment sites in the British uplands. *J. Hydrol.* 115, 269-283.

Neal, C., Smith, C.J., Walls, J., Billingham, P., Hill, S., & Neal, M., 1990. Hydrogeochemical variations in Hafren forest streams, mid-Wales. *J. Hydrol.* 116, 185-200.

Reynolds, B., Neal, C., Hornung, M. & Stevens, P.A., 1986. Baseflow buffering of stream water acidity in five mid-Wales catchments. *J. Hydrol.* 87, 167-185.

Reynolds, B., & Pommeroy, A.B., 1988. Hydrochemistry of chloride in an upland catchment in mid-Wales. *J. Hydrol.* 99, 19-32.

Robson, A.J., Neal, C., Smith, C.J. & Hill, S. (a; in press). Short term variations in stream water conductivity at a forested site in mid-Wales - implications for water movement. *Sci. of the Total Environ.*

Robson, A.J., Beven, K. & Neal, C. (b; in press). Towards identifying sources of subsurface flow: a comparison of components identified by a physically based runoff model and those determined by chemical mixing techniques. *Hydrological Processes.*

Sherman, L.K. & Musgrave, G.W., 1942. Infiltration. In O.E. Meinzer (ed), *Hydrology*, Dover Publications, New York, 244-58.

Sklash, M.G. & Farvolden, R.N., 1979. The role of groundwater in storm runoff. *J. Hydrol.* 43, 45-65.

Flow separation of water movement through a large soil core using bromide and fluorobenzoate tracers

D.E. Henderson, K.J. Beven & A.D. Reeves

Abstract

This paper is concerned with the separation of surface runoff from a large undisturbed soil column into rainfall, 'return flow' and old water components using tracers. The experiments combined simulated rainfall and pumped 'return flow' at a range of flow rates. The use of the tracers and the different combinations of flow rates made it possible to quantify the contribution of different sources of water to the hydrographs produced during the experiments and to see how these are affected by the relative application rates used.

Introduction

In contemporary conceptual models of water flow through structured field soils the importance of structural voids such as cracks, root channels and animal burrows is now well accepted and documented. Water flow through such channels can be very rapid, effectively by-passing most of the soil volume. This has important consequences for catchment response to precipitation. The process of rapid by-pass flow mechanisms in catchment response is still not fully understood. In a study at the hillslope scale Wheater et al. (1989) suggested that 'the strong evidence of macropore flows adds further support to the importance of this as yet poorly understood process'. At the same scale Anderson and Burt (1982) have suggested that old water discharge is related to translatory or displacement flow in the saturated zone, especially in the saturated wedge at the base of hillslopes. Sklash and Farvolden, (1979) and Kennedy et al.(1986) have observed that this discharge of old water into main channels can occur quite quickly after the start of a storm. Hino and Hasebe (1986) separated hydrographs into overland flow, interflow and groundwater flow. They concluded that the groundwater component could be separated into a slow response groundwater flow and a quick response groundwater flow. They explained the latter as the quick subsurface flow response to rapid infiltration through the vadose zone.

It seems then that the rapid flow of new water through the unsaturated zone through macropore systems may act to rapidly increase the extent of the saturated zone leading to the discharge of old water. This is especially so in catchments characterised by thin soils and steep slopes where a saturated wedge of old water often exists at the base of hillslopes (Anderson and Burt, 1982). Moore (1989) reiterates the saturated wedge extension model of Anderson and Burt and has suggested that both new infiltrating water and old water mobilised from the vadose zone move into the phreatic zone resulting in an increase in subsurface discharge. Additionally Moore suggests that overland flow over surface saturated areas was not the dominant flow process but that the rapid movement of water through macropore systems in combination with the proposed ridging mechanism described by Sklash and Farvolden (1979), Abdul and Gillham (1984) and Novakowski and Gillham (1988) was responsible for the extension of the saturated zone and the subsequent discharge of old water.

Experimental methods

The soil core used in the experiments was taken from an area of deciduous woodland on the campus of Lancaster University. The soil was a brown earth with a distinct loamy organic A horizon overlying a more clayey B horizon. The sides of the soil core were sealed using fibreglass and resin. The core was 35 cm deep and 30.5 cm in diameter.

In the laboratory the core was mounted on a porous plate with an intervening layer of sand to ensure a good contact between the plate and the core. Rainfall was simulated through an array of 13 0.2 mm hypodermic needles 5 cm apart in a moving frame 30 cm above the core. Return flow was pumped up into the base of the core using a peristaltic pump The experiment included four sections in total, each section characterised by a combination of rainfall and return flow application rates. Discharge was collected from the top surface of the column. Before the start of each section the core was drained for 48 hours. Rainfall and return flow were then applied simultaneously for a period of 7 hours. At the end of this period the rainfall was stopped while the return flow continued, lasting for a length of time necessary to pump in one pore volume of tracer-tagged water. Three tracers were used to label water inputs to the soil cores. These were potassium bromide, o–(trifluoromethyl)-benzoic acid (o-TFMBA) and 2,6-difluorobenzoic acid (2,6-DFBA). The latter two organic anions were recommended for use in soil water studies by Bowman (1984). Using bromide as an accepted standard against which to compare the others Bowman found that they exhibited no significant adsorption and showed similar distributions in soil after flow tests. All tracers were analysed using high performance liquid chromatography (see Reeves and Beven 1990).

Table 1 Tracer types and concentrations used in each section

Section	Rainfall Tracer	Tracer Concentration (ppm)	Return Flow Tracer	Tracer Concentration (ppm)
A	Bromide	100	2,6-DFBA	30
B	Bromide	100	o-TFMBA	20
C	Bromide	100	2,6-DFBA	30
D	Bromide	100	2,6-DFBA	30

Table 2 Rainfall and return flow parameters for each section

Section	Rainfall Rate (mm.hr.$^{-1}$)	Return Flow Rate (mm.hr.$^{-1}$)	Return Flow Darcian Flux Rate (cm.hr.$^{-1}$)	Return Flow Estimated Mean Pore Velocity (cm.hr.$^{-1}$)
A	15.29	40.72	1.297	2.880
B	3.90	40.95	1.304	2.898
C	17.17	9.57	0.305	0.678
D	3.28	10.04	0.320	0.711

Table 1 shows the tracers used in each section of the experiment; Table 2 gives details of flow rates and velocities for each section.

The Darcian flux velocity (v) is calculated using

$$v = Q/A$$

where Q is the rate of discharge and A is the cross-sectional area of the column. The estimated mean pore velocity (v') is calculated using

$$v' = v/\theta$$

and the estimated pore volume of 11.5 l. The water content can be taken as constant and saturated (θ=0.45) for steady flow conditions.

Use of multiple tracers for flow separation

By using different tracer chemicals for different flow sources it is theoretically possible to quantify the relative importance of each source to the discharge hydrograph. It is also possible to assess the nature of flow pathways in operation and also the degree of mixing occuring between the different flow sources. A fundamental assumption made about the system being considered is that the initial concentration of a tracer being used is zero within the soil before the input of the tracer. In most if not all cases this is not possible due to background concentrations of the tracers naturally present in the soil. Therefore, before the use of any tracer the concentration of that tracer in the effluent water must be at background level. The concentration of tracers entering the column either as rainfall or return flow will be of a known concentration significantly greater than that of the existing soil water. Thus the concentration of tracers within any significant volume of water in the soil column likely to interact with any new tracer solutions will be unlikely to have any appreciable effect on the outcome. The component parts of each of the hydrographs from the experiment were identified using the following technique. The discharge from the soil at any time t in terms of the separate flow sources involved can be represented as

$$Q = Q_R + Q_G + Q_{old}$$

where: Q = total discharge at any time t,
Q_R = rainfall discharge,
Q_G = groundwater (return flow) discharge,
Q_{old} = old water discharge.

For the rainfall component

$$\frac{Q_R}{Q} = \left(\frac{C}{C_o}\right)_{br}$$

and for the return flow component

$$\frac{Q_G}{Q} = \left(\frac{C}{C_o}\right)_{tr}$$

where C is the measured concentration of a tracer at time t and C_o is the input concentration of the tracer. The subscripts br and tr refer to bromide tracer and the two return flow tracers respectively. Combining these equations the ratio of old water flux to the total water flux is given by

$$\frac{Q_{old}}{Q} = 1 - \left(\frac{C}{C_o}\right)_{br} + \left(\frac{C}{C_o}\right)_{tr}$$

Results and discussion

Figures 1 to 4 show the results of the application of the flow separation technique to the tracer data for sections A to D respectively. First inspection shows the initial rapid breakthrough of water at the surface outflow. Breakthrough times are much in advance of those predicted by the calculated Darcy velocities and mean pore velocities. This indicates the operation of by-pass flow mechanisms.

Patterns of flow separation show that the higher flow rate sources are more dominant in the total flow during the earlier discharge times. For example, when the return flow rate is significantly higher than the rainfall rate as in section B (Figure 2), the portion of the surface discharge that is attributable to return flow is correspondingly high (of the order of 50% of the total discharge). However, when flows are more comparable as in sections A and D (Figures 1 and 4), the equivalent parts of the separated hydrographs are more comparable in size. The rainfall discharge is initially slightly larger in part due to its proximity to the point of discharge collection.

The way in which the hydrographs are, in the first instance, composed of rainfall and/or return flow water in proportions controlled by the different flow rates of these two flows within each section suggests this is the direct result of by-pass flow through the structural voids in the soil. In each section old water discharge is preceded by rainfall and return flow discharge. Rapidly infiltrating water from both above and below exceeds pedal infiltration capacity and so flows rapidly through the column utilising only a small fraction of the total porosity. While the maximum total discharge is roughly constant for a period of 7 hours, matching the duration of the rainfall period, the proportion of old water discharge gradually diminishes. This is due to the increasing proportion of new return flow water being discharged

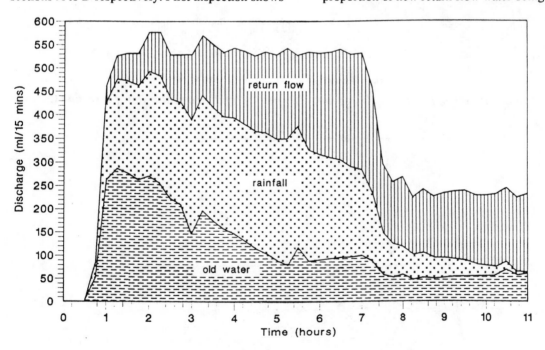

Figure 1 Flow separation of surface discharge into old water, rainfall and return flow for section A

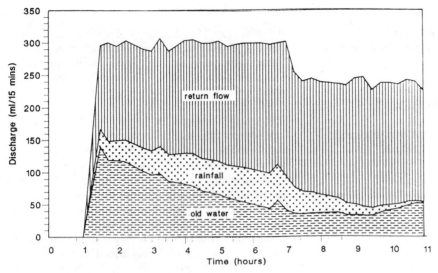

Figure 2   Flow separation of surface discharge into old water, rainfall and return flow for section B

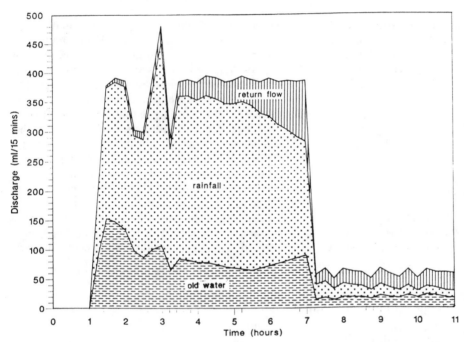

Figure 3   Flow separation of surface discharge into old water, rainfall and return flow for section C

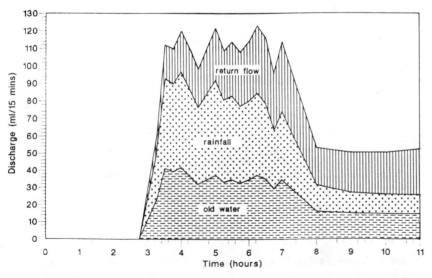

Figure 4   Flow separation of surface discharge into old water, rainfall and return flow for section D

from the soil. This suggests a mechanism of gradual displacement of old water from the soil as the return flow moves through an increasing volume of the soil pore space. The discharge of old water declines as a gradually smaller pore space is flushed by the incoming return flow. Slowly an increasing number of pores discharge return flow as the number discharging old water decreases. In terms of the mobile/immobile model of soil water movement (De Smedt and Wierenga, 1979; 1984), this suggests an increasingly large mobile phase as a gradually increasing porosity is involved in the flushing of old water from the soil.

Only in section B (Figure 2), where the rainfall input rate is 3.9 mmh[-1] compared with the return flow rate of 40.95 mmh[-1], is the rainfall discharge very small compared with the return flow discharge. In response to the high input rate the return flow appeared almost immediately in the discharge travelling rapidly through the soil secondary structure. In each of the other three sections the initial discharge is a combination of rainfall and old water with only a comparatively small volume of return flow water. During subsequent sections of the hydrographs the volume of rainfall runoff remains fairly constant while the volume of return flow in the discharge increases at a fairly constant rate directly at the expense of the old water volume. This is particularly clearly shown in Figure 1 (section A). Also shown in Figure 1 and in Figure 3 (section C) is the tendency for the rainfall portion to be diminished 1 to 2 hours before the end of the rainfall input while old water discharge is seen to become constant or even increase at the expense of rainfall. This may be a result of a delayed flush of old water from relatively small pores within the soil into the top few centimetres of soil.

The pattern is most clearly seen in section C with a rainfall rate of 17.17 mmh[-1] and a return flow rate of 9.57 mmh[-1]. The hydrograph for section B shows no such patterns at this stage while for section D there is a gradual decline in the volume of rainfall in the total discharge after the initial high start. In the remaining part of the hydrographs following the cessation of rainfall and the sole continuation of return flow, rainfall derived water is still discharged from the soil. This shows the amount of rainfall that has entered into the soil during the 7 hour rainfall period and is then removed due to the action of upward flowing return flow. In section B the volume of rainfall derived discharge is not reduced to zero until 11 hours after the start of the experiment (4 hours after rainfall ended). The continued discharge of rainfall water towards the end of the sections is most noticeable in section C. This illustrates the way in which the high rainfall rate has led to a deeper rainfall penetration and the low return flow rate has delayed the return of rainfall to the surface.

By-pass flow effective porosities

Section A used flow rates of 15.29 mmh[-1] for the rainfall and 40.72 mmh[-1] for the return flow (bromide and 2,6-DFBA respectively). This resulted in the very rapid discharge of bromide-tagged water and the later, although still relatively quick, emergence of 2,6-DFBA-tagged water at the surface outflow. Table 3 shows the total amount of water and the amount of return flow pumped into the column prior to discharge for each section. This shows the different pore-space volumes filled by rainfall and return flow before discharge from the surface of thecolumn. In terms of total water input prior to discharge, the effective porosity varies between 1032 ml and 1477 ml while the pore space volume utilised by return flow varies between 222 ml and 952 ml.

The section with the largest effective return flow volume before discharge (smallest by-passing effect) is B, with low rainfall and high return flow rates, and the smallest effective volume (largest by-passing effect) is in section C, with the opposite conditions of high rainfall and low return flow. The return flow effective porosity is less for the section with the high rainfall rate and low return flow rate and greater for the section with the low rainfall rate and high return flow rate. This illustrates the dispersion of the return flow through a larger pore space at the higher return flow rate.

Conclusions

These experiments have illustrated how soil macropores influence the flow characteristics of the soil at certain flow rates whether this is downward percolation or upward return flow (see Beven and Germann, 1982). Despite the obvious importance of by-pass flow mechanisms the experiments also show the mobility of old water in the vadose zone during combined rainfall and return flow. Old water discharge is seen to occur following the initial by-pass flow effects as water initially enters and travels rapidly through the soil secondary structure. This was confirmed by flow visualization after dye input and sectioning of the core at the end of the experiments.

The results for the experiments compare favourably with separated hydrographs of Hooper and Shoemaker (1986) in the initial stages of the hydrographs. These also showed significant old water discharge at the same time as flow through the secondary soil structure. However, in the catchment scale separated hydrographs of Hooper and Shoemaker, the old water component is much more apparent and consistent throughout the discharge periods. This illustrates the differences between the processes at the different scales and the importance of buffering and old water displacement in the phreatic zone at the catchment scale.

The patterns of the flow separated hydrographs do show both the high velocity macropore flows necessary for quick channel hydrograph response to storms and the mobilisation of old water in the vadose zone and as such seem to agree with evidence from larger scale channel hydrograph separations

Table 3 *Delays to the start of discharge and the volumes of input before the start of discharge for each section (percentage of estimated total porosity in parentheses)*

Section	Time to start of discharge (mins.)	Volume added prior to the start of discharge (ml)	Time to start of return flow discharge (mins.)	Volume of return flow added prior to the start of return flow discharge (ml)
A	30	1032.2 (9.4)	30	473.6 (4.3)
B	60	1237.7 (11.3)	60	952.7 (8.7)
C	60	1477.0 (13.4)	60	222.7 (2.0)
D	165	1301.3 (11.8)	165	642.4 (5.8)

already reported. This mobilisation of old water in the vadose zone is also in agreement with the findings of Moore (1989). This then supports the model of rapid subsurface water movement with old water mobilised from the vadose zone resulting in the rapid extension of the saturated wedge leading to rapid runoff.

Acknowledgements

This work was supported by European Commission contract no. EV4V 0091 and the NIREX Ltd. NSARP research programme.

References

Abdul, A.S. & Gillham, R.W. 1984. Laboratory studies of the effects of the capillary fringe on streamflow generation. *J. Hydrol.*, 20, 691-698.

Anderson, M.G. & Burt, T.P. 1982. The contribution of throughflow to storm runoff: An evaluation of a chemical mixing model. *Earth Surf. Proc. & Land.*, 7, 565-574.

Beven, K.J. & Germann, P.F. 1982. Macropores and water flow in soil. *Wat. Resour. Res.*, 18, 1311-1325.

Bowman, R.S. 1984. Evaluation of some new tracers for soil water studies. *Soil Sci. Soc. Amer. J.*, 48, 987-992.

De Smedt, F. & Wierenga, P.J. 1979. Mass transfer in porous media with immobile water. *J. Hydrol.*, 41, 59-67.

De Smedt, F. & Wierenga, P.J. 1984. Solute transfer through columns of glass beads. *Wat. Resour.*

Res., 20, 225-232.

Hino, M. & Hasebe, M. 1986. Separation of a storm hydrograph into runoff components by both filter-separation AR method and environmental isotope tracers. *J. Hydrol.*, 85, 251-264,

Hooper, R.P. & Shoemaker, C.A. 1986. A comparison of chemical and isotopic hydrograph separation. *Wat. Resour. Res.*, 22, 1444-1454.

Kennedy V.C., Kendall, C., Zellweger, G.W., Wyerman, T.A. & Avanzino, R.J. 1986. Determination of the components of stormflow using water chemistry and environmental isotopes. *J. Hydrol.*, 84, 107-140.

Moore, R.D. 1989. Tracing runoff sources with Deuterium and Oxygen-18 during spring melt in a headwater catchment, Southern Laurentians, Quebec. *J. Hydrol.*, 112, 135-148.

Novakowski, K.S. & Gillham, R.W. 1988. Field investigations of the nature of water-table response to precipitation in shallow water-table environments. *J. Hydrol.*, 97, 23-32.

Reeves, A.D. & Beven, K.J. 1990. The Use of Multiple Ionic Tracers in the Study of Soil Water Flows: Analytical Procedures. Centre for Research on Environmental Systems Technical Report no. CRES/TR/9006/05.

Sklash, M.G. & Farvolden, R.N. 1979. The role of groundwater in storm runoff. *J. Hydrol.*, 43, 45-65.

Wheater, H.S., Langon, S.J., Brown, A. & Beck, M.B. 1989. Hillslope processes - observations from the Allt a Mharcaidh catchment, Scotland. *Proc. 2nd BHS National Hydrology Symposium*, University of Sheffield, 1989.

The separation of Alpine glacial meltwater hydrographs into quickflow and delayed flow components

M. Tranter, G.H. Brown & R. Raiswell

Abstract

Alpine glacial meltwaters exhibit a characteristic inverse association between discharge and conductivity throughout pronounced diurnal discharge cycles which occur during the ablation season. Earlier attempts to separate glacial meltwater hydrographs into dilute and concentrated components (a simple two component, conservative mixing model based on conductivity measurements) relied on pragmatic choices of conductivity values for the composition of each component, which was assumed to have a constant composition throughout the ablation season. More recent attempts are based on meltwater chemistry, which allows the composition of each component to vary and for the non-conservative mixing behaviour of the base cations and bicarbonate ions.

Introduction

Alpine glacial meltwaters exhibit inverse associations between discharge and total dissolved solids (or conductivity) over diurnal discharge cycles throughout much of the ablation season (Collins, 1978). Each day, maximum concentrations of solute are found in meltwaters at low discharge and minimum concentrations are found at maximum discharge (see Figure 1). The simplest model to describe these associations considers that the meltwaters issuing from the glacier portal, the bulk meltwaters, consist of two components (Collins, 1978), although more complex models exist (e.g. Oerter et al, 1978).

Here, we consider hydrograph separation based on the two component mixing model. The first component, quickflow, consists of waters which have a rapid transit through the hydroglacial system, largely in ice-walled conduits and channels (Collins, 1978; Sharp et al, in prep). Quickflow is relatively

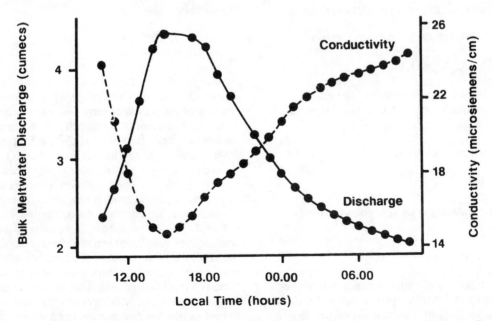

Figure 1 *An example of the inverse relationship between discharge and conductivity during a diurnal discharge cycle. The hydrograph derives from the Haut Glacier d'Arolla (Brown & Tranter, 1990).*

dilute because the suspended load is small and rock-water contact times are relatively short. Hence, the potential for solute acquisition is limited to rapid reactions such as surface exchange (Lerman, 1979). By contrast, the second component, delayed flow, is composed of waters which have had a relatively slow transit through the distributed system located at the glacier bed and have been in contact with till, the glacier bed or with debris-rich basal ice (Collins, 1978; Sharp et al, in prep). Delayed flow is relatively concentrated because rock-water contact times are long, allowing solute acquisition by reactions such as sulphide oxidation and carbonate dissolution from recently comminuted glacial flour (Tranter et al, in prep). Bulk meltwaters form by the mixing of these two components in the channel system (Sharp et al, in prep).

Earlier attempts to achieve a meaningful hydrograph separation were performed by assigning conductivity values to each of the components (Collins, 1978; 1979). The conductivity of quickflow was set to the minimum recorded conductivity of the bulk meltwaters or that of representative supraglacial streams, while the conductivity of delayed flow was set to the maximum recorded conductivity. This pragmatic method has two main weaknesses. It assumes that neither component exhibits any temporal variation in chemical composition and that no post-mixing chemical evolution of meltwaters occurs. However, it is likely that each component will demonstrate some temporal variation during the course of the ablation season (e.g. due to the development of new hydro-glacial flowpaths) and that post mixing chemical evolution (i.e. non-conservative behaviour) will occur, particularly for base cations and bicarbonate, when relatively reactive sediment is transported into and through the mixing environment (Raiswell & Thomas, 1984; Tranter et al, 1989).

Hydrograph separation of the bulk melt - waters into quickflow and delayed flow

Two-component, conservative mixing requires that

$$Q_b C_b^i = Q_q C_q^i + Q_d C_d^i \qquad (1)$$

where Q represents the discharge of the bulk meltwater (b), quickflow (q) and delayed flow (d), and C denotes the concentration of species i.

Continuity of flow requires that

$$Q_b = Q_q + Q_d \qquad (2)$$

Combining equations (1) and (2) gives the following expression:

$$Q_q = Q_b (C_d^i - C_b^i) / (C_d^i - C_q^i) \qquad (3)$$

Equation 3 illustrates that four parameters must be known to perform a hydrograph separation. Of these, only two, Q_b and C_b^i, are routinely measured. Hence, the other two parameters, C_q^i and C_d^i, need to be

evaluated by independent means. The usual method is to equate C_q^i and C_d^i with the minimum and maximum conductivity values recorded during the sampling season (Collins, 1978; 1979). As noted earlier, this pragmatic approach has a major weakness because the composition of either or both components may vary throughout the season. The following method is based on the variability of sulphate in bulk meltwaters (Tranter & Raiswell, in press), which is the most conservative of the major ions in Alpine glacial meltwaters (Sharp et al, in prep).

Figure 2 shows that there is a strong linear association between sulphate and discharge during diurnal discharge cycles, and that this type of association may be found at a number of different glaciers (Brown & Tranter, 1990; Tranter & Raiswell, in press). The linear association can be utilised to find the first of the two unknowns, C_d^{SO4} (Tranter & Raiswell, in press).

Since there is a linear association between C_b^{SO4} and Q_b,

$$C_b^{SO4} = mQ_b + k \qquad (4)$$

where m and k are constants derived from the regression equation of C_d^{SO4} versus Q_b. Substituting equation 4 into equation 3 and rearranging gives

$$\frac{Q_q}{Q_b} = \frac{-mQ_b + C_d^{SO4} - k}{(C_d^{SO4} - C_q^{SO4})} \qquad (5)$$

We assume conservative mixing for sulphate and therefore that C_d^{SO4} and C_q^{SO4} are constants. Inspection of equation 5 reveals that the bulk discharge, Qb, is a simple, linear measure of the mass fraction of quickflow in the bulk meltwater (Q_q/Q_b). The value of C_d^{SO4} is defined when the mass fraction of quickflow is zero. Given this condition, from equation 5,

$$^*Q_b = \frac{C_d^{SO4} - k}{m} \qquad (6)$$

where $^*Q_b$ is the bulk discharge where the mass fraction of quickflow is zero. Since m is a negative value, C_d^{SO4} cannot be greater than k, because $^*Q_b$ cannot be a negative value. If C_d^{SO4} is less than k, $^*Q_b$ is positive. At discharges lower than $^*Q_b$, the delayed flow must become more concentrated to satisfy equation 6. This condition is not permissible given that we are assuming that the end-member compositions are constant. An alternative explanation is that if C_d^{SO4} is less than k, there must be a constant discharge of subglacial water of fixed composition underlying a more variable discharge of subglacial waters with a similar composition. In other words, there is a third component. This is also not consistent with a simple two component mixing model. Hence, to best satisfy the requirements of a simple two component mixing model, C_d^{SO4} must equal k.

The evaluation of the second unknown, C^{SO4}_q, derives from the assumption that this value is zero or near zero during much of the ablation season. There are two lines of evidence to support this view. Firstly, the sulphate concentration of supra-glacial meltwaters is usually near zero (Tranter & Raiswell, in press; Brown *et al*, in prep). Table 1 gives examples of the composition of supra-glacial meltwaters flowing

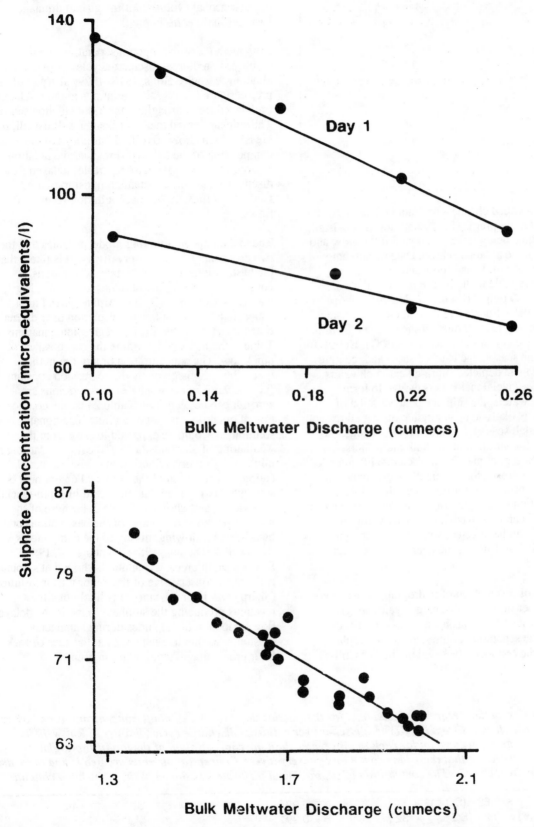

Figure 2 Examples of the linear association between sulphate concentrations and bulk meltwater discharge. The upper scatter plot derives from Les Bossons glacier (Tranter & Raiswell, in press), while the lower derives from Haut Glacier d'Arolla (Brown et al, in prep). All associations are statistically significant at the 1% level.

Table 1 *The composition of supra-glacial meltwaters collected from Haut Glacier d'Arolla (Brown et al, in prep)*

Species	Range of concentration Units are µeq l⁻¹
Ca^{2+}	4.4 - 15
Mg^{2+}	0.4 - 2.4
Na^+	0.7 - 6.2
K^+	0.0 - 5.0
HCO_3^-	<40
SO_4^{2-}	1.7 - 7.7
NO_3^-	0.7 - 2.3
Cl^-	0.0 - 2.5
pH	6.0 - 8.1

within ice-walled channels on Haut Glacier d'Arolla (Brown *et al*, in prep). This assumption is consistent with sulphate being largely removed from snow and ice early in the ablation season. Data on sulphate concentrations in Alpine snow and ice are only sparsely available in the literature, but values are typically < 20 µeq l⁻¹ (Psenner & Nickus, 1986; Delmas, 1989). Successive diurnal melting of snow and ice rapidly leaches most of the sulphate from the snow and ice crystals (Davies *et al*, 1987). Hence, for much of the season, the leached snow and ice gives rise to sulphate depleted supra-glacial meltwaters. Since supra-glacial meltwaters evolve to form quickflow waters, the sulphate concentration of quickflow is likely to be negligible during all except the early melt season. Secondly, on occasions, the sulphate concentration of the bulk meltwaters approaches zero at maximum discharge (Tranter & Raiswell, in press). Since quickflow dominates at maximum discharge, it follows that the sulphate concentration of the quickflow must too be near zero. Equation 3 can be solved, and hence hydrograph separation can be effected, since both unknown terms on the right hand side of the equation have been determined.

Examples of this method of hydrograph separation for a number of diurnal discharge cycles are given in Figure 3, where C_q^{SO4} has been set to zero. Figure 4 presents the separation of the same hydrographs based on the conductivity-based method of Collins

(1978). As can be seen, the different methods of hydrograph separation give rise to large differences in the proportion of quickflow and delayed flow, which is most apparent for the June hydrographs. These differences are significant in the interpretation of the seasonal evolution of the glacial drainage system (Sharp *et al*, in prep).

Both methods of hydrograph separation can be employed on diurnal discharge cycles throughout the ablation season (Collins, 1978; 1979; Sharp *et al*, in prep). Figure 5 shows the variations in the discharge of delayed flow throughout the 1989 ablation season. The sulphate-based method (Tranter & Raiswell, in press), which allows five-fold variations in the composition of the delayed flow over the ablation season, generally gives rise to greater delayed flow discharges than the constant composition-based method (Collins, 1978), except during recession flows.

The two component mixing model assumes that the two components mix conservatively. It is likely that the base cations and bicarbonate exhibit non-conservative mixing. Most major ions (Ca^{2+}, Mg^{2+}, Na^+, K^+, HCO_3^- and SO_4^{2-}) in Alpine glacial melt-waters exhibit strong linear correlation over diurnal timescales (see Table 2). The regression equations of Table 2 enable us to determine the composition of quickflow. The concentration of any ion in the quickflow (C_q^i) is given by the regression constant (i.e. the value when sulphate concentrations are zero). It can be seen from Table 2 that the composition of quickflow is that of a dilute bicarbonate solution, as would be expected to arise from the weathering of aluminosilicate, silicate and carbonate minerals by relatively pure water. The estimated cation concentration of the englacial component is somewhat larger than that measured in supra-glacial meltwaters, also shown in Table 2, because of the non-conservative behaviour of the base cations and bicarbonate following mixing of the components (Raiswell & Thomas, 1984; Tranter *et al*, 1989; Sharp *et al*, in prep). Calculations show that sulphate is the most conservative of the major ions in solution (Sharp *et al*, in prep), since it is likely that the reactions producing the sulphate found in the delayed flow, oxidation of sulphides during subglacial erosion, are complete near to or at the sites of rock flour production (Tranter *et al*, in prep).

Table 2 *An example of regression equations for the relationship between sulphate concentrations and other ions in bulk meltwaters from the Gornergletscher over a diurnal discharge cycle (Tranter & Raiswell, in press). The regression constant for each ion is greater than the concentration of the ion in supra-glacial waters, demonstrating that these ions do not mix conservatively. Concentration units are µeq l⁻¹ and there are 8 data pairs in each case. The composition of supra-glacial meltwaters is shown in the right-hand column.*

$(Ca^{2+}) = 0.68 \ (SO_4^{2-}) + 86$	R = 0.997	Ca^{2+}	14 - 44
$(Mg^{2+}) = 0.28 \ (SO_4^{2-}) + 32$	R = 0.991	Mg^{2+}	0 - 17
$(K^+) = 0.032 \ (SO_4^{2-}) + 5.6$	R = 0.946	K^+	0 - 4
$(Na^+) = 0.027 \ (SO_4^{2-}) + 2.3$	R = 0.960	Na^+	0 - 3
$(HCO_3^-) = 0.24 \ (SO_4^{2-}) + 170$	R = 0.95	HCO_3^-	36 - 72

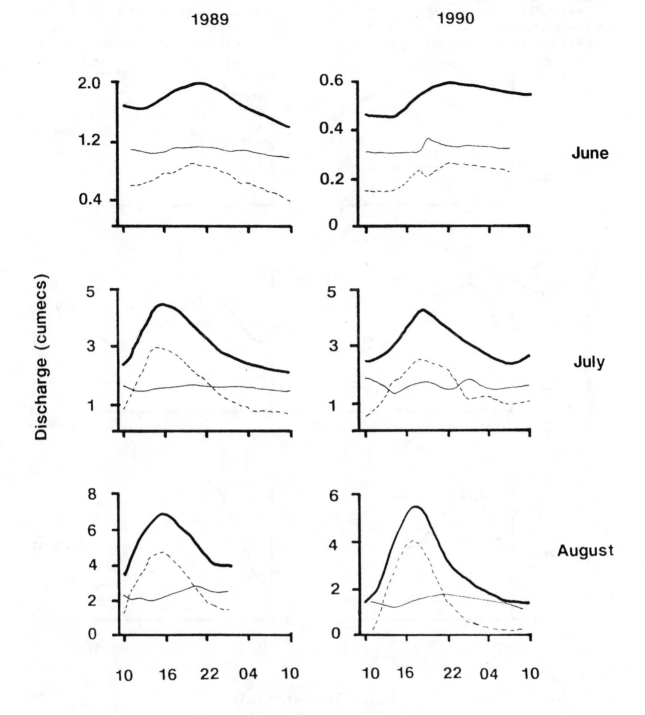

1989 **1990**

Discharge (cumecs)

June

July

August

Local Time (hours)

Figure 3   Examples of the separation of the bulk meltwater hydrograph (upper solid line) into quickflow (dashed line) and delayed flow (lower solid line), using the method of Tranter & Raiswell (in press). The hydrographs are derived from Haut Glacier d'Arolla (Brown et al, in prep).

Conclusions

The simple, two-component, conservative mixing equation (see equation 3) of bulk Alpine glacial meltwaters can be determined uniquely for diurnal discharge cycles, given a knowledge of bulk meltwater sulphate concentrations and their variations with discharge. This method of hydrograph separation allows for variability in the composition of both components throughout the melt season, and allows for non-conservative mixing of species other than sulphate, which is the most conservative major ion in bulk meltwaters.

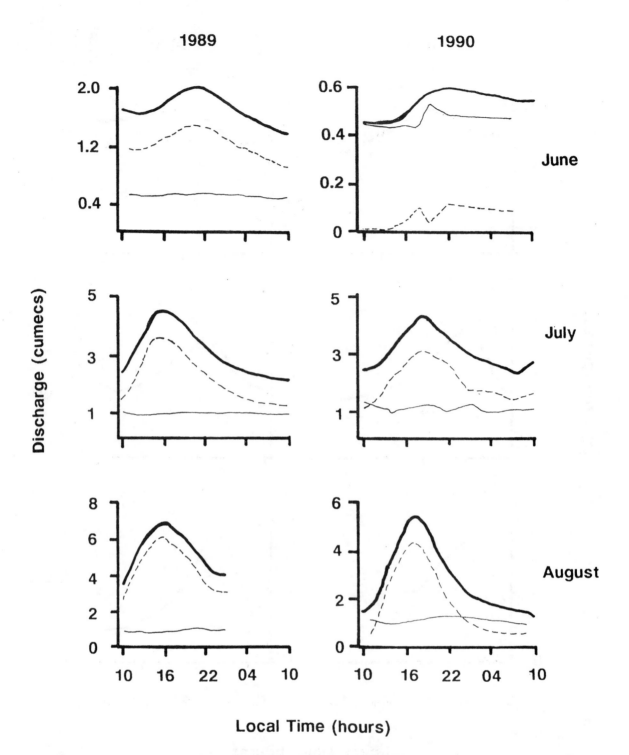

Figure 4 *Examples of the separation of the bulk meltwater hydrograph (upper solid line) into quickflow (dashed line) and delayed flow (lower solid line), using the method of Collins (1978). The hydrographs are derived from Haut Glacier d'Arolla (Brown et al, in prep).*

References

Brown, G.H. & Tranter, M. 1990. Hydrograph and chemograph separation of bulk meltwaters draining the Upper Arolla glacier, Valais, Switzerland. IAHS Publications 193, 429-437.

Brown, G.H., Tranter, M., Clarke, M.J., Gurnell, A.M. & Hill, C.T. in prep. The variation of the major ions throughout the ablation season in bulk meltwaters draining the Upper Arolla glacier, Valais, Switzerland.

Collins, D.N. 1978. Hydrology of an Alpine glacier as indicated by the chemical composition of meltwater. *Zeit. Glets. Glaz., Bd.* 13, 219-238.

Collins, D.N. 1979. Quantitative determination of the subglacial hydrology of two Alpine glaciers. *J. Glac.* 23, 347-362.

Davies, T.D., Brindlecombe, P., Tranter, M.,

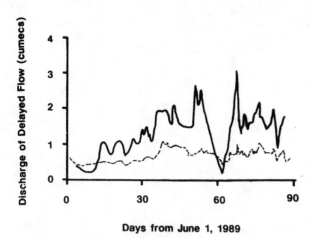

Days from June 1, 1989

Figure 5 A comparison of the sulphate-based method of hydrograph separation:solid line (Tranter & Raiswell, in press) with the constant composition-based method of Collins (1978): broken line. The discharge of delayed flow throughout the 1989 ablation season at Haut Glacier d'Arolla is depicted (Sharp et al, in prep.).

Tsiouris, S., Vincent, C.E., Abrahams, P. & Blackwood, I. 1987. The removal of soluble ions from melting snowpacks. In: *Seasonal Snowcovers: Physics, Chemistry, Hydrology*, Les Arcs, July 1986 (eds H.G. Jones and W.J. Orville-Thomas, pub., D. Reidel, Derdrecht), NATO ASI Series C, Vol. 211, 337-392.

Delmas, V. 1989. Chimie de la neige et de la fonte printaniere au Casset (Alps du sud). Influences des poussieres minerales. Unpublished doctoral thesis, Laboratoire de glaciologie et geophysique de l'environnement, Grenoble.

Lerman, A. 1979. *Geochemical Processes: Water and Sediment Environments*. Wiley-Interscience.

Oerter, H., Behrens, H., Hibsch, G., Rauert, W. & Stickler, W. 1978. Combined environmental isotope and electrical conductivity investigations at the runoff of Vernagtferner (Oetztal Alps, Austria). In *Int. Symp. Computation and Prediction of Runoff from Glaciers and Glacierised Areas*, Tblisi, USSR, 1978, Akademiia Nank SSSR. Institut Geografii, Materialy Gliatsiologicheskikh Issledovanii Khronika, Obsuzhdeniia 39, 157-161 and 86-91.

Psenner, R. Nickus, U. 1987. Snow chemistry of a glacier in the central eastern Alps (Hintereis-ferner, Tyrol, Austria). *Zeit. Glets. Glaz.*, Bd 22, Heft 1 (1986), S1-18.

Raiswell, R. & Thomas, A.G. 1984. Solute acquisi-tion in glacial melt waters. I. Fjallsjokull (south-east Iceland): bulk meltwaters with closed-system characteristics. *J. Glac.* 30, 35-43.

Sharp, M., Tranter, M., Brown, G.H., Nienow, P. & Willis, I.C. in prep. Hydrological behaviour of the Haut Glacier d'Arolla, Valais, Switzerland, as inferred from the hydrochemistry of glacial meltwaters.

Tranter, M., Brown, G.H., Raiswell, R. & Sharp, M. in prep. On solute acquisition by glacial meltwaters. Submitted to *J. Glac.*

Tranter, M. & Raiswell, R. in press. The composition of the englacial and subglacial components in bulk meltwaters draining the Gornergletscher. *J. Glac.* 125.

Tranter, M., Raiswell, R. & Mills, R.A. 1989. Chemical weathering reactions in Alpine glacial meltwaters. In: *Proc. 6th Int. Sym. Water-Rock Interaction*, Malvern, 1989, ed D. L. Miles, Balkema, 687-690.

Session 4

Unusual Hydrological Events

A hydrological review of the volatile climatic conditions experienced over the period 1988-90

T. J. Marsh & S. J. Bryant

Abstract

A long-term rainfall deficiency, extending back to the spring of 1988 in some parts of Great Britain, was the foundation for a number of notably severe regional droughts. The drought episodes were, however, punctuated by several exceptionally wet interludes, including a six-week spell early in 1990 when rivers were in spate throughout the United Kingdom and runoff and recharge rates were unprecedented. Over the last three years evaporation rates have also been close to record levels and sustained high soil moisture deficits (SMDs) have been a feature of the English lowlands. This paper examines national and regional rainfall, runoff and recharge patterns over the period 1988-90 and considers the recent volatility within a historical context. Data are presented to serve as a benchmark against which future changes and trends may be assessed. Attention is directed to the difficulties of distinguishing changes due to climatic variabilities from those arising from artificial disturbances to flow regimes and recharge patterns.

Introduction

In a number of regions of the United Kingdom the range of recorded variation in river flows and groundwater levels has been extended over the last three years. 1990, in particular, exhibited extreme spatial and temporal variations in rainfall which in turn brought widespread flooding and severe drought conditions over extensive areas. This very full expression of the capricious nature of the British climate coincided initially with the run-up to water privatisation and extended over a period of burgeoning public and scientific debate regarding the implications of climate change for flow regimes and water resources. Understandably therefore the flooding and, especially, the sustained drought episodes stimulated substantial public interest and unprecedented media attention. Certainly the warm conditions, dry soils and enhanced seasonality in runoff and aquifer recharge which has been a feature of the 1988-90 period, appear consistent with an emerging scientific consensus regarding likely climate change scenarios (Anon, 1991). The uncertainties associated with such scenarios remain very large however and informed speculation, let alone firm prediction, is hampered by the limited understanding of how global warming - for which the evidence is increasingly compelling - will affect hydrological systems in the UK. Nonetheless, the hydrological impact of the unusual weather patterns experienced over the last three years may be expected to provide valuable insights regarding our vulnerability to climatic change.

The UK is very heterogeneous in terms of its climate, geology, land-use and patterns of water utilisation. Many of these factors influence the relationship between rainfall and rates of runoff and recharge. Given also their wide natural range of variability, the detection of any, initially faint, climate change signal represents a major scientific challenge. Whilst lengthy rainfall series provide an invaluable perspective against which to compare the recent unusual conditions, it is the principal hydrological variables - runoff and recharge - which sustain rivers and replenish surface and groundwater reservoirs. The manner in which hydrometric data are collected, quality controlled and exploited will play a central role both in the detection of trends and regime changes and to stimulate further scientific investigation.

Rainfall - a historical perspective

On average, rainfall is well distributed throughout the year in the UK although a tendency towards a late-autumn/early-winter maximum may be recognised especially in western Britain. The strong seasonality in runoff and recharge rates is largely a consequence of the cyclic nature of evaporative losses - typically

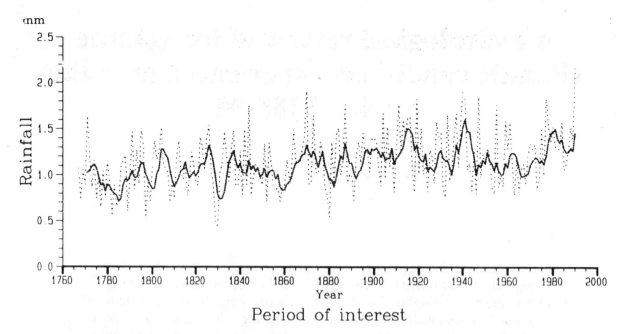

Period of interest

* WIGLEY, T.M.L., LOUGH, J.M. and JONES, P.D. (1984) Spatial patterns of precipitation in England and Wales and a revised homogenous England and Wales precipitation series. Journal of Climatology. Vol. 4, p.1-25.

Figure 1 Ratio of winter to summer half-year for the England and Wales rainfall series (Wigley et al., 1984)*

70 per cent of the annual total occurs between April and September. Any tendency towards a more distinct partitioning of rainfall between the winter and summer half-years would have important water resources implications.

During much of the 19th century, the average ratio between rainfall over the winter and summer half-years was close to unity for England and Wales (see Figure 1). This ratio increased significantly in the twentieth century - reaching 1.3:1 in the 1980s (Anon, 1990), which was the wettest decade on record for Britain as a whole. In 1989/90 the October-March rainfall exceeded twice that for the ensuing April-September period for the first time in a rainfall series extending back to 1766. The trend in this ratio is partially explained by increased winter rainfalls especially in the more maritime regions of Britain. For Scotland, where exceptional rainfall totals have characterised the western highlands in particular, eight of the twelve wettest winters - in a series extending back to 1869 - have occurred since 1978. A further climatological feature of the 1980s was a tendency for the normal west-to-east rainfall gradient to be accentuated; regional contrasts in precipitation became even more pronounced towards the end of the decade.

The 1989 drought

The seeds of the 1989 drought were sown early in the previous year. Although over England and Wales as a whole 1988 was marginally wetter than average, the rainfall was very unevenly distributed throughout the year especially in lowland England; some districts recorded a quarter of their annual total in January. As a consequence, rivers were in spate and groundwater

levels stood at a 10-15 year high in many areas (Anon, 1990). Subsequently, a significant rainfall deficiency developed in southern Britain which increased in magnitude from mid-autumn and constituted a severe drought by early February 1989.

Some relief was afforded by abundant early spring rainfall in 1989; it was especially beneficial in boosting much depleted groundwater stocks. However, May was hot and dry and - as evaporation rates climbed through the very warm summer - the drought re-intensified. Initially, most of the problems experienced by the water industry were associated with heavy peak demands and an overstretched supply network. The continuation of the dry conditions into the autumn switched attention to the adequacy of the resources themselves. Hosepipe bans were widespread and at a few localities (e.g. in Cornwall) standpipes were deployed, but not used. One of the most significant manifestations of the intensifying drought was the virtual absence of the anticipated increase in river flows and in groundwater levels as evaporative demands declined in the autumn. Over wide areas, the limited autumn rainfall produced a relatively stable pattern of river flows at a time when a strong seasonal upturn would normally be expected. The prospect of a second successive dry winter - especially in parts of southern Britain - was viewed with some foreboding.

Throughout much of lowland England the drought continued to increase in severity through into the early winter. One measure of the drought's intensity was the discharge in the River Itchen (see Figure 2) - an important trout river in Hampshire sustained principally from groundwater outflow. Flow rates declined steadily through much of 1989 and, from the

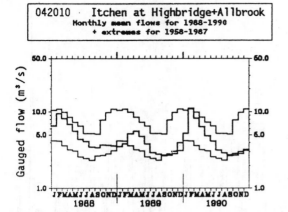
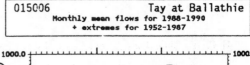
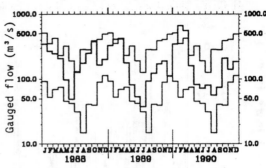

Figure 2 Monthly mean river flow hydrographs for 1988-1990

summer, were artificially augmented using water pumped directly from the Chalk. After adjusting to account for the immediate effect of this augmentation, flow rates in mid-December were the lowest ever recorded at the Highbridge gauging station (commissioned in 1958) having fallen below those registered in September 1976. The nearby Lavant stream, which is exclusively spring-fed, recorded no flow throughout the entire year - its longest dry spell since 1972/73. By mid-December, groundwater levels were also exceptionally low in most regions, extremely so in some eastern and southern areas. Throughout most major aquifers, water-tables stood close to, or below, the seasonal minimum. At the Dalton Holme observation borehole which penetrates the Chalk of the Yorkshire Wolds, levels had declined to significantly below the lowest previously recorded in a 102-year record (Figure 3). In a few areas of eastern England no significant groundwater replenishment had occurred for over 20 months.

The floods

The anticyclonic conditions, which dominated weather patterns over the United Kingdom during the early part of December, then changed to allow the passage of a sequence of vigorous depressions which brought widespread and heavy rainfall to southern Britain. In some parts of lowland England, this

extremely wet spell produced rainfall totals roughly equivalent to a quarter of the rainfall over the rest of the year. Droughts of any significant severity are seldom terminated by a fortnight's rainfall but December 1989 certainly witnessed a major change in the drought's complexion. Following the rapid elimination of SMDs in mid-month, limited flooding was experienced in the Severn and Thames Valleys over the Christmas period.

Very unsettled weather conditions continued into 1990. The improvement in the water resources outlook gathered momentum through January and reached a climax in February which, in both meteorological and hydrological terms, was a remarkable month. Many new hydrological records were established. Great Britain recorded its wettest February in a series extending back to 1869 and the winter (December-February) rainfall total was the highest since 1914/15 (Marsh & Monkhouse, 1990). With soils saturated in most regions many rivers were vulnerable to further precipitation and the abundant late-January/early-February rainfall caused very widespread and persistent floodplain inundation.

Monthly mean river flows for February exceeded previous maxima (for any month) over wide areas. The extent of the flooding was without recent parallel (although peak flows were normally well below historical maximum); rivers were in spate from

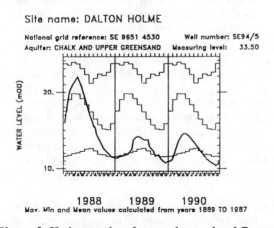
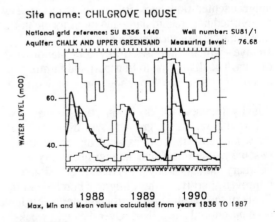

Figure 3 Hydrographs of groundwater level fluctuations for 1988-1990

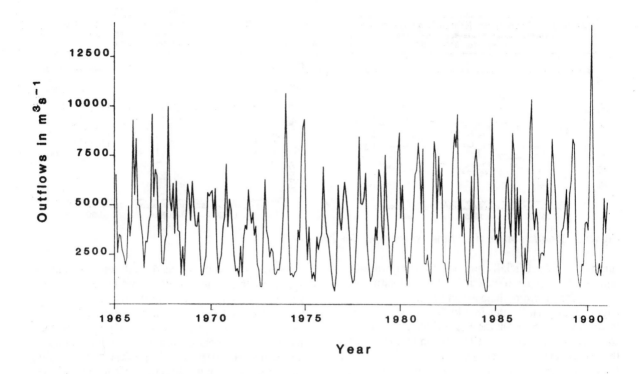

Figure 4 Monthly total outflows from Great Britain for 1965-1990

Cornwall to Wester Ross. Figure 4 illustrates monthly total outflows from Great Britain over the period 1965-90 based on 33 representative catchments - which provide a broad geographical coverage and have combined average rainfall and runoff totals close to the mean for Great Britain. The outstanding nature of the February outflow is readily apparent; total runoff from the mainland was the highest for any month for at least 25 years and probably considerably longer.

Flows in the Thames remained above 300 m³s⁻¹ - at Kingston - for the longest period since 1947 and the Itchen remained at, or above, bankfull throughout February. Spate conditions were maintained on the Severn from the 23 January to the 18 February. In Scotland, water levels in Loch Lomond easily exceeded their previous maximum in a 45-year record and, with snowmelt a major contributory factor, many gauging stations registered unprecedented flow rates. Runoff for the River Tay established new record daily and monthly mean flows (see Figure 2) for the entire national river flow archive - which comprises over 25,000 station years of data. The disruption to transport and farming activities was severe throughout much of Scotland.

Equally dramatic, if less obvious, transformations occurred in relation to groundwater resources over the winter. Infiltration rates were unprecedented in some parts of the Chalk aquifer in January and February and, generally, the groundwater situation improved sharply. At the Chilgrove borehole in the Chalk of the South Downs, groundwater levels have been monitored since 1836. Over the eight weeks ending in mid-February 1990, levels rose by 38

metres - an extraordinary recovery and one for which there is no close precedent; in early-December 1989 the water-table had stood within a few centimetres of the lowest ever recorded (Figure 3). Large increases in groundwater levels characterised boreholes throughout much of southern Britain but close to the eastern seaboard, where winter rainfall had been less abundant, recoveries were more sluggish and limited in magnitude.

The drought returns

In March 1990 the prospect of a return to widespread drought conditions seemed remote indeed. However, England and Wales experienced its driest spring for 100 years and the warm sunny weather encouraged very high evaporation rates. Rivers were in steep recession and water-tables fell rapidly from the February peaks. The hot and dry conditions continued into the autumn. For England and Wales as a whole, the March to September 1990 period was the driest on record and an intense seven-month drought extended across much of southern Britain. Over longer durations large regional and temporal variations in drought intensity could be recognised (Table 1). By the late summer, river flows in parts of East Anglia were comparable with the minima established during the 1976 drought. Runoff rates were less depressed throughout most of western and northern Britain (see Table 2); consequently total outflows, for the summer, at the nationwide scale were not greatly below average (see Figure 4).

Warm and sunny weather throughout the extended summer stimulated increased demand for water and, as in 1989, triggered measures to restrict usage -

Table 1 Rainfall in mm and as percentage of the long-term average with return period estimates

		MAR-SEP 90	Est Return Period, years	JAN-SEP 90	Est Return Period, years	OCT 89-SEP 90	Est Return Period, years	NOV 88-SEP 90	Est Return Period, years
England and	mm	288		563		856		1474	
Wales	% LTA	59	100-150	88	5	94	<2	85	20
NRA REGIONS									
North West	mm	457		847		1176		2107	
	% LTA	69	30-40	99	2-5	97	2-5	91	5-10
Northumbria	mm	323		570		751		1304	
	% LTA	66	30-50	90	2-5	85	5-10	77	60-90
Severn Trent	mm	241		456		725		1254	
	% LTA	55	100-150	82	5-10	94	2-5	85	10-20
Yorkshire	mm	277		507		727		1274	
	% LTA	60	40-60	84	2-5	87	2-5	80	30-40
Anglia	mm	194		321		496		919	
	% LTA	56	150-200	72	20-30	81	10-15	79	40-60
Thames	mm	187		393		636		1082	
	% LTA	48	>200	78	10	90	2-5	81	30-40
Southern	mm	209		466		737		1184	
	% LTA	51	>200	86	5	93	2-5	78	40-50
Wessex	mm	243		525		849		1390	
	% LTA	53	100-120	88	2-5	98	<2	84	10-20
South West	mm	383		816		1260		2051	
	% LTA	65	30-40	100	≤2	106	2-5	90	5-10
Welsh	mm	420		875		1363		2299	
	% LTA	61	100-120	95	2-5	102	≤2	91	5-10
Scotland	mm	866		1410		1753		3156	
	% LTA	117	5-10	143	>>200	123	40-60	116	40-60
RIVER PURIFICATION BOARDS									
Highland	mm	1124		1882		2328		4203	
	% LTA	140	90-100	161	>>200	135	>>200	129	>>200
North-East	mm	497		754		924		1623	
	% LTA	89	2-5	105	2-5	90	2-5	83	40-50
Tay	mm	584		1110		1383		2485	
	% LTA	87	2-5	126	10-20	101	2-5	104	2-5
Forth	mm	550		994		1224		2208	
	% LTA	89	5	125	15-20	110	2-5	104	2-5
Tweed	mm	413		758		934		1658	
	% LTA	74	20-30	105	2-5	93	2-5	86	10-20
Solway	mm	625		1164		1487		2688	
	% LTA	83	5-10	118	5-10	104	2-5	99	2
Clyde	mm	1032		1689		2113		3795	
	% LTA	121	5	150	>>200	127	30-40	121	40-50

Return period assessments are based on tables provided by the Meteorological Office*. These assume a start in a specified month; return periods for a start in any month may be expected to be an order of magnitude less. "Wet" return periods underlined. The tables reflect rainfall totals over the period 1911-70 only and the estimate assumes a sensibly stable climate.

* Tabony, R C, 1977, The variability of long duration rainfall over Great Britain, Scientific Paper No. 37, Meteorological Office (HMSO)

Table 2 Runoff as mm and as a percentage of the period of record average for September 1990 and for selected periods

Station name	Grid Reference	Sep 1990		4/90 to 9/90		1/90 to 9/90		10/89 to 9/90		11/88 to 9/90	
		mm %LT	rank /yrs	mm %LT	rank /yrs	mm %LT	rank /yrs	mm %LT	rank /yrs	mm %LT	rank /yrs
Tay at Ballathie	NO147367	41 58	10 /38	295 82	8 /38	1176 158	38 /38	1446 129	37 /38	2620 123	37 /37
Derwent at Buttercrambe	SE731587	5 38	1 /17	48 43	1 /17	128 52	2 /17	161 48	1 /17	336 51	1 /16
Trent at Colwick	SK620399	9 53	2 /32	66 53	2 /32	207 80	3 /32	292 81	6 /32	546 78	2 /31
Lud at Louth	TF337879	8 70	4 /23	61 51	4 /22	115 52	4 /22	138 51	3 /22	282 54	2 /21
Bedford Ouse at Bedford	TL055495	3 60	20 /58	30 53	12 /58	156 98	29 /58	221 102	30 /57	408 95	25 /56
Thames at Kingston (natr.)	TQ177698	5 56	11 /108	50 63	19 /108	182 100	53 /108	236 96	47 /107	398 83	28 /106
Coln at Bibury	SP122062	10 70	2 /27	111 72	4 /27	338 107	15 /27	402 102	10 /27	646 83	6 /26
Great Stour at Horton	TR116554	7 50	1 /26	60 57	2 /24	155 72	4 /24	197 66	4 /23	356 61	1 /21
Itchen at Highbridge+Allbrook	SU467213	20 76	3 /32	177 85	5 /32	351 98	14 32	423 91	7 /32	732 81	2 /31
Brue at Lovington	ST590318	4 26	1 /26	42 37	2 /26	270 91	8 /26	390 90	6 /26	676 80	2 /25
Severn at Bewdley	SO782762	6 27	6 /70	51 40	1 /70	297 98	31 /69	432 96	30 /69	736 85	11 /68
Cynon at Abercynon	ST079956	19 28	5 /32	150 46	2 /32	944 122	27 /32	1480 119	28 /32	2320 98	14 /30
Eden at Sheepmount	NY390571	22 50	6 /20	132 64	2 /20	603 134	20 /20	768 111	13 /19	1322 103	9 /17
Clyde at Daldowie	NS672616	35 60	10 /27	203 89	11 /27	770 159	27 /27	937 124	25 /27	1622 113	22 /26

Notes   (i)   Values based on gauged flow data unless flagged (natr.), when naturalised data have been used.
(ii) Values are ranked so that lowest runoff as rank 1;
(iii) %LT means percentage of long term average from the start of the record to 1989. For the long periods (at the right of this table), the end date for the long term is 1990.

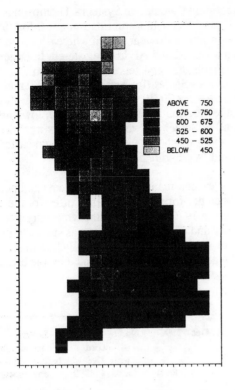

(a) Potential evaporation (for grass) in mm for 1990

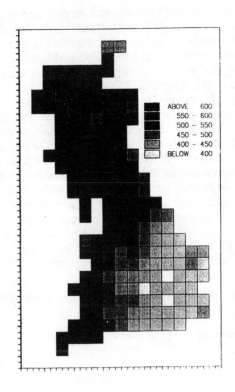

(b) Actual evaporation (for grass) in mm for 1990

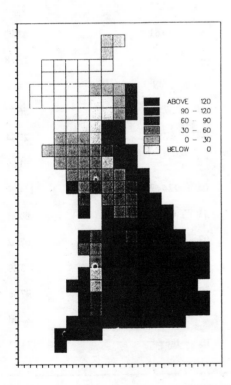

(c) Soil moisture deficits (for grass) in mm for 1990

Figure 5 Maps showing MORECS data for Great Britain

Table 3   Ranked potential and actual evaporation totals (mm) 1961-90 for Whittering, Cambridgeshire

Potential Evaporation	Year	Actual Evaporation	Year
540	1968	317	1976
543	1978	402	1990
549	1981	421	1972
553	1987	445	1964
555	1972	452	1961
563	1963	462	1979
568	1971	462	1978
569	1969	463	1970
573	1977	464	1962
578	1966	466	1984
579	1965	467	1977
580	1979	473	1983
580	1980	480	1963
581	1988	483	1971
582	1966	483	1981
586	1986	485	1975
587	1985	488	1965
590	1983	489	1969
591	1973	495	1989
606	1984	508	1980
619	1986	512	1985
621	1964	512	1973
621	1974	513	1982
626	1967	516	1988
636	1961	517	1968
638	1970	518	1974
646	1975	518	1987
682	1976	523	1967
689	1989	540	1986
725	1990	543	1966

chiefly involving the introduction of hose-pipe bans. Whilst the drought's impact was most evident during the summer, its hydrological character reflected the warm conditions - and the associated high evaporation rates - throughout the year. Annual potential evaporation (PE) totals were very high throughout Great Britain and, in parts of the lowlands, the record totals registered in 1989 (Lees *et al.*, 1990) were eclipsed - 1990 PE losses exceeded 700 mm over wide areas (Figure 5a). The inhibiting influence of high SMDs imposed a rather contrary pattern on actual evaporative (AE) losses which were below average throughout the English lowlands but at record, or near record, levels in the more maritime regions (Figure 5b). Table 3 provides evidence of the inordinate shortfalls of annual AE totals relative to PE for both 1989 and 1990 for an individual MORECS (Meteorological Office Rainfall and

Evaporation Calculation System - Thompson *et al.*, 1981) grid square in Cambridgeshire. PE for 1990 is the highest in a 30-year record whereas only in 1976 was a lower annual AE loss registered. In large part this reflects the persistence of very dry soil conditions - SMDs (for grass) exceeded 80 mm in some areas for 20-30 weeks in 1990, almost twice the average duration in parts of the English lowlands. At the end of September very large SMDs were obtained throughout much of central, southern and eastern England (see Figure 5c).

By November, many spring-fed streams and ponds had been dry for several months - often for the first time since 1976. As in 1989, the temporary loss of amenity and of aquatic habitats was substantial; in parts of southern England especially, the impact on headwater streams was exacerbated by the effects of

Table 4   Groundwater levels for December 1990

Borehole	Grid Reference	Aquifer	First year of record	Av. Dec level	Dec 1990 Day	Dec 1990 level	No. of years of record with Dec levels ≤ 1990	Lowest recorded level before 1990 for any month
Dalton Holme	SE96514530	C & U.G.	1889	15.74	31	10.98	1	10.73
L. Brocklesby	TA13710888	"	1926	11.99	27	4.86	0	4.56
Washpit Farm	TF81381960	"	1950	43.48	04	41.31	1	41.24
The Holt	TL16921965	"	1964	86.89	06	85.81	3	83.90
Fairfields	TM24616109	"	1974	23.07	06	22.16	0	22.18
Rockley	SU16557174	"	1933	133.73	31	dry	5	dry
L. Bucket Farm	TR12254690	"	1971	64.05	31	57.63	0	56.77
Compton House	SU77551490	"	1894	39.65	28	27.96	1	27.64
West Dean	TV52909920	"	1940	1.97	28	1.39	15	1.01
Limekiln Way	ST37630667	"	1969	124.91	05	124.69	6	124.09
Ashton Farm	SY66208810	"	1977	66.88	11	63.20	0	63.23
West Woodyates	SU01601960	"	1942	85.82	03	68.90	1	67.62
New Red Lion	TF08853034	L.L.	1964	12.70	31	5.49	0	3.29
Ampney Crucis	SP05950190	M.J.	1958	101.97	10	97.38	0	97.86
Bussels 7A	SX95289872	PTS	1972	23.74	19	23.46	7	22.90
Alstonfield	SK12925547	C.B.	1974	192.33	18	186.64	5	174.22

Groundwater levels are in metres above Ordnance Datum

C & U.G.	Chalk and Upper Greensand
L.L.	Lincolnshire Limestone
PTS	Permo-Triassic Sandstones
M.J.	Middle Jurassic Limestone
C.B.	Carboniferous Limestone

groundwater abstraction. Echoing late-1988 and 1989, hydrological conditions had thus become fragile again in parts of lowland England; in water resources terms the outlook was least encouraging where the 1990 drought overlay a substantial long-term rainfall deficiency (see Table 1). Broadly speaking such areas coincided with those parts of the country principally dependent on groundwater for public water supplies and the need for above average winter rainfall was particularly acute in a zone extending from Kent to Lincolnshire.

Widespread blizzards in the second week of December 1990 heralded a further change in weather conditions. A series of active depressions on a mild south-westerly airstream brought substantial rainfall to all areas and, generally, produced a transformation in river flows reminiscent of, but less dramatic than, that witnessed a year earlier. Overall, the water resources outlook had improved appreciably by year-end and aquatic habitats began to take on a more familiar appearance. However, by their nature, groundwater droughts tend to be very much more persistent than droughts defined on the basis of rainfall alone. With SMDs still appreciable in the lowlands around the end of the year, recoveries in many eastern aquifers had barely begun and levels remained remarkably low for early winter; many Chalk wells established new winter minima in December (see Table 4).

Discussion

Rainfall for Great Britain over the 1988-90 period was marginally above the 1941-70 average. Its distribution in time and space was however remarkable and served to re-emphasise the variable nature of the UK climate after a period during which the water resources outlook was generally encouraging. The persistent and, for certain periods, intense drought conditions experienced over large areas of lowland Britain - where population, industry and intensive agriculture are concentrated - highlighted its continuing vulnerability to sustained periods of rainfall deficiency. The exaggeration in the North-West to South-East rainfall gradient, which has characterised much of the period since early 1988, is a particular concern given the continuing increase in water demand in the South-East.

A countervailing influence - for England and Wales as a whole - could be the higher winter precipitation totals envisaged by some climate change scenarios (Hulme and Jones, 1989). However the benefits are expected to be greatest in the wetter regions of the UK and, certainly, recent evidence provides little support for any increase in winter precipitation in the eastern lowlands. In addition, 1990 provided a timely reminder that even an exceptionally wet winter (December-February) cannot allay all fears regarding

the water resources outlook for the ensuing summer and autumn. If the inordinate seasonality in rainfall represented by the temporal distribution over 1989/90 was to become more typical, the monthly distribution of rainfall through the winter would assume a crucial importance. For a given amount of winter rainfall, most benefit would accrue from abundant precipitation in the February-April period providing a late boost to runoff and recharge rates before evaporation rates accelerate through the late spring. Enhanced seasonal contrasts allied to warm dry summers extending into the autumn, imply high to very high SMDs which may not be satisfied until well into the following year. Thus the window of opportunity for infiltration to replenish groundwater resources, in the east especially, may become very restricted with serious consequences if, in the event, the late-winter and early spring are relatively dry.

Acknowledgements

Much of the material upon which this paper is based was assembled as part of a hydrological monitoring programme maintained by IH and the British Geological Survey on behalf of the Department of the Environment. Hydrometric data are supplied princi-pally by the regional divisions of the National Rivers Authority in England and Wales and the River Purification Boards in Scotland; meteorological data are provided by the Meteorological Office.

*Figure 2 is from Wigley et al., 1984.

References

Anon. 1991. The potential effects of climate change in the United Kingdom. First report of the UK Climate Change Impacts Review Group (Dept. of the Environment). HMSO.

Anon. 1990. *1989 Yearbook*, Hydrological data UK series. Institute of Hydrology, Wallingford.

Hulme, M. and Jones, P.D. 1989. Climate change scenarios for the UK. Climatic Research Unit, University of East Anglia. Report to the Institute of Hydrology.

Lees, M.L., Bryant, S.J. and Marsh, T.J. 1990. The 1988/89 drought – a hydrological review. *1989 Yearbook*. Institute of Hydrology, 27-44.

Marsh, T.J. and Monkhouse, R.A. 1990. Hydrological aspects of the development and rapid decay of the 1989 drought. *Weather*, 45, 8, 290-299.

Thompson, N., Barrie, I.A. and Ayles, M. 1981. The Meteorological Office rainfall and evaporation calculation system: MORECS. Hydrological Memorandum No. 45, Met. Office. (HMSO).

Wigley, T.M.L., Lough, J.M. & Jones, P.D. 1984. Spatial patterns of precipitation in England and Wales and a revised homogeneous England and Wales precipitation series. *J. Climatol.*, 4, 1-25.

The Calderdale storm revisited: an assessment of the evidence

M. C. Acreman & V. K. Collinge

Abstract

There is no doubt that the rainfall of 19 May 1989 in Calderdale and the surrounding area was locally very intense. However, data from raingauges and weather radar can be interpreted as giving conflicting estimates of the maximum point rainfall. This paper reassesses the available evidence, including structural damage, the geomorphological response and information concerning other extreme rainfalls which have occurred in the area, in order to reconcile these differences. It concludes that the maximum gauged rainfall of 193 mm is not inconsistent with the other information available for this storm.

Introduction

Nothing provokes controversy quite like a potential record-breaking event and the storm which occurred in and around Calderdale, West Yorkshire, on 19 May 1989 reinforces this notion. There is no doubt that the rainfall was locally very intense. Eyewitness accounts of torrential rain, widespread flooding and destruction of sewers and culverts all bear witness to this fact. However, the precise total depth of precipitation which fell at one particular location, Walshaw Dean Lodge, is a matter for conjecture. The raingauge adjacent to the Lodge was reported to have been filled by the storm, equivalent to around 193 mm of rainfall, in only about two hours. This would not only constitute a record depth of rainfall for that duration in the UK, but would exceed the currently recommended probable maximum precipitation (PMP) for the area. In apparent contrast, data from the weather radar imply that the average total rainfall depth for the 4 km² around the gauge was only 43.6 mm (falling in about one and a half hours).

General details of the event were described by Acreman (1989c) and a comprehensive analysis of the weather radar data was published by Collinge et al.(1990). Controversy over the total rainfall at Walshaw Dean Lodge was discussed in the *New Civil Engineer* and *Weather*, in which in-splash was suggested to explain the difference between the radar and raingauge estimates.

This paper examines: the results of raingauge in-splash studies; the weather radar data; structural damage and the geomorphological response to the storm; and information on other historical extreme rainfalls in the area, in order to reconcile this difference.

In-splash to raingauges

The raingauge at Walshaw Dean Lodge is surrounded by a turf wall, within which dead grass and other debris indicated that water had ponded to a depth of around 50 mm. Damage to the wall was such that the water would not have reached a level sufficient to drown the gauge, but may have resulted in some in-splashing, thus leading to an over-estimate of the total rainfall. However, it is also possible that there was some loss of catch due to hail. Recent experiments at the University of Lancaster have provided preliminary estimates of the volume of water which might in-splash to a gauge. However, the results (unpublished) indicate that even with ponding within the turf wall of 100 mm and drops of 2.9 mm diameter, in-splash only amounted to 1.8%.

Weather radar data

Fortunately, the storm was located close to the weather radar at Hameldon Hill in Lancashire. According to data from this instrument, the storm started almost at the radar site and ended at a distance of about 45 km (Figure 1) some six hours later. Data were available as instantaneous rainfall rates over 2 km x 2 km pixels, measured every five minutes. Conversion of the radar signal to rainfall rates was by use of

$$Z = 200 \, R^{1.6} \tag{1}$$

where Z is the returned signal strength (mm⁶m⁻³) and R is the rainfall rate (mm h⁻¹). The on-line system for calibrating the radar data (adjusting the radar-derived rainfall rates from equation (1) by reference to telemetering raingauges) only came into effect 4 ¾ hours after the start of the storm. Data from that time

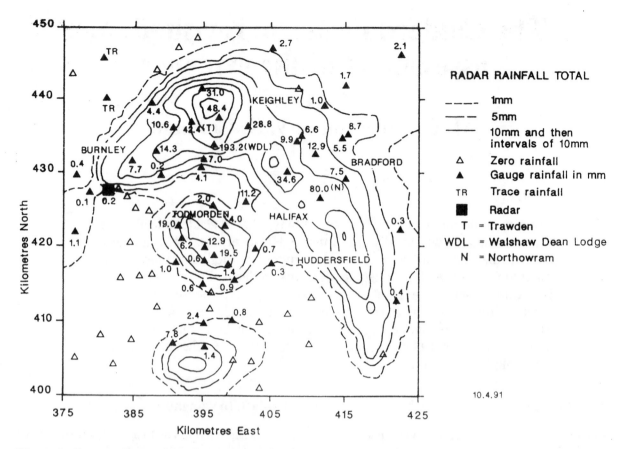

Figure 1   Storm rainfall totals (equals daily rainfall totals) from radar (contours) and raingauge

onwards have been decalibrated (i.e. that adjustment has been removed) for this analysis to avoid the complication that the adjustment can change every 15 minutes and varies within the area of the radar field.

The radar certainly gave an accurate indication of the area and timing of heavy rainfall, with good correspondence to the areas of flood damage, but the agreement with raingauge data was less convincing. Since the only rain in the area during the rainfall day was during the storm, daily rainfall totals can be compared with radar storm totals, obtained by integrating over time measured rainfall rates in the pixels corresponding to each gauge.

Twenty-two gauge totals were obtained, ranging from the controversial 193 mm at Walshaw Dean Lodge, to 5.5 mm. Some lower values were ignored, because of the distorting effects of low level evaporation. Comparison was made by the well-known Assessment Factor (AF), where

$$AF = R_r/R_g \qquad (2)$$

where R_r is the radar rainfall, R_g is the gauge rainfall. Values of the radar rainfall and corresponding AF values given below are slightly larger (though not significantly so) than those in Collinge *et al* (1990) as a result of re-analysis to reduce rounding errors. Values of AF range from 0.23 to 3.18. A logarithmic transformation of AF values gave a mean value

equivalent to 1.32. It is noteworthy that, if the value of 200 in equation (1) was replaced by 300, which the system is intended to do under showery conditions (Collier 1989), the mean AF value would be 1·03. Figure 2 illustrates the 15 minute data from Trawden, the only recording raingauge to receive significant rainfall during the storm, and demonstrates the rapid fluctuations in R_r and R_g, and hence in their ratio. But it is the large raingauge reading at Walshaw Dean Lodge (193 mm) and the much

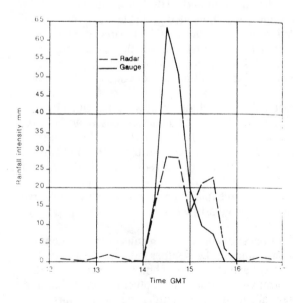

Figure 2   Radar and raingauge data for Trawden

4.12

smaller radar storm total (43.6 mm) which have caused so much interest. There are several factors which could contribute towards the large difference between these two observations.

(i) The raingauge reading may be an overestimate due to in-splash (discussed above).

(ii) The average over the rainfall over the 2 km x 2 km pixel may be lower than the point gauge measurement.

(iii) Down draught conditions, which occur in the mature stage of convective cells as a result of the falling rain drops, increase the fall speed of the drop relative to a stationery surface so that the value of Z for a given R (equation 1) would be less than for the same rainfall rate in still air (Collier, 1989). Austin (1987) calculates that in a downdraught of 8 ms^{-1} the reflectivity will be about 3dB less than in still air. Updraughts have the reverse effect.

(iv) Under severe reflectivity gradients (in space or time) the radar will tend to underestimate the target reflectivity. Rogers (1971) concluded that a signal reduction of 3dB is possible under moderate gradients and 6dB under severe gradients. Acceptance of the Walshaw Dean Lodge reading of 193 mm means a very severe rainfall gradient to the south and south west. The nearest raingauge is Gorple Reservoir S S, 2.5 km to the south west (Figure 3), which recorded 7.0 mm, a gradient of 74 mm km^{-1}.

(v) Radar signals suffer from attenuation (loss of strength) as they pass through intervening rain between the radar and the point of measurement. Corrections for this are made in the signal processing using the Gunn and East formula (Collier, 1989). If rainfall rates are underestimated by the radar due to factors (iii) and (iv) above, attenuation will also be underestimated, which creates further under-estimation of the true rainfall rate.

One factor which could lead to an increased radar signal is the presence of hail. It is known from an eye witness that only a small amount of hail fell at Walshaw Dean Lodge at the start of the storm, and this suggests that hail was not a significant factor in the radar observations at that site.

Clearly a wide range of assumptions can be made, but calculations have been made to illustrate how the gauge total of 193 mm can be reconciled with the radar value of 43.6 based on the following:
1. a small in-splash equal to loss of catch due to hail bouncing out of gauge;
2. 193 mm fell in 1.75 hours = 110.4 mm h^{-1}; and
3. an average rainfall over the pixel 10% less than the point rainfall = 99.4 mm h^{-1}.

Adjustment to the radar signal as given by equation (1) with R= 99.4 mm h^{-1} have been made, and rainfall rates obtained as follows:

	(a)	(b)
Signal error due to reflectivity gradient and downdraught	6dB	7dB
Radar rainfall rate (mm h^{-1})	41.9	36.3
Radar rainfall rate after attenuation adjustment (mm h^{-1})	35.3	30.0
Radar rainfall total (mm)	61.8	52.5*

*cf actual = 43.6 mm

The same calculation was applied to the pixel immediately to the west of that covering Walshaw Dean Lodge (Figure 3), which covers much of the 4.8 km^2 catchment of Greave Clough for which Acreman (1989a) estimated the peak flow at 34 m^{3}s^{-1}, and the rainfall to be in the range of 75-120 mm. Using the upper figure of 120 mm and the assumption of a 7dB signal loss (alternative (b) above) this becomes 22.1 mm h^{-1}, equivalent to 38.7 mm. This can be compared with the 38.3 mm actual radar measurement (Figure 3).

Clearly, these calculations must be kept in perspective. They do, however, illustrate how it is possible, using assumptions consistent with the available literature, to explain the large difference between the gauge value of 193 mm and the radar total for the pixel of 43.6 mm.

Structural damage and geomorphological response

Calderdale Borough Council (1989) provided ample evidence of the serious urban damage caused by the storm. The bed of several streams draining through Halifax were severely eroded in places, gabions and river retaining walls were damaged and parts of several mill foundations, over 100 years old, were undermined. Sewers also suffered heavy structural damage and flooding of many residential and commercial properties occurred on the west side of the town. Flows in the Luddenden Brook (in a small village to the west of Halifax) exceeded the capacity of culverts, causing collapse of one section and flooding of the road and houses in the centre of the village. This evidence implies that the return period of the storm may have been in excess of several hundred years, but not necessarily that it was a record-breaking event.

Response to the flood in the rural environment also provides inconclusive evidence. Greave Clough (a stream to the west of Walshaw Dean) suffered erosion of its banks and bed, in places scoured to bedrock, and areas of peat bog on the surrounding hilltops had 'burst'. Immediately below the raingauge at Walshaw Dean Lodge a landslide of some 1,000 m^3 was generated. In contrast, the area between the Lodge and Greave Clough was remarkably free of damage, although evidence of overland flow was widespread, which the cover of grass tussocks was clearly able to withstand.

4.13

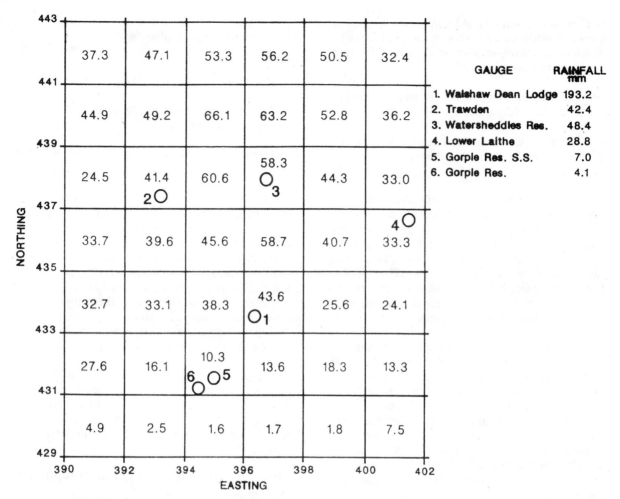

Figure 3 Radar storm totals for pixels in the vicinity of Walshaw Dean Lodge, together with raingauge locations and storm totals

Erosion rates and thresholds for landslide initiation depend on many factors including climatic regime, regolith and geomorphological history. Results of studies of other major localised flood events demonstrate that geomorphological evidence alone can be unreliable as an indicator of the hydrological magnitude of the event or its rarity. For example, the peak flow on the Caldwell Burn, in the Scottish borders, during the flood of June 1979, was estimated as 189 m^3s^{-1} (Metcalfe, 1979) from a catchment of only 5.8 km^2. This ranks as one of the highest runoff rates (40 $m^3s^{-1}km^{-2}$) recorded in the UK (Acreman, 1990), but it resulted in very little sediment transport due to the thin regolith which limited sediment availability. In contrast the severe thunderstorm over the Hermitage Water catchment, some 25 km to the east, in which rainfall probably exceeded 65 mm in 75 minutes, resulted in severe erosion of hillslopes and fluvial sediments (Acreman, 1991).

Other historical extreme rainfalls

It is instructive to examine other extreme rainfall events of a similar duration which have occurred in the vicinity of Calderdale (Figure 4). Brief details of three such events are given below, though of course there were others of lesser magnitude, e.g. Embsay Moor.

Hewenden Reservoir 11 June 1956

A violent thunderstorm with torrential rain occurred a few miles west of Bradford. British Rainfall 1956 records 6.09 inches (154.7 mm) in 105 minutes. This was later rejected in the *Flood Studies Report* (NERC, 1975) on the grounds that "... this very intense rainfall with a dew point of only 12°C is not accepted on the scientific evidence available from investigations of storms". This statement was based on calculations using a dew point of 12°C and a typical storm efficiency, which gave a precipitation total of only 102 mm.

No investigation of this storm was published at the time, but recent extensive searching has produced some valuable information and data. A letter written by the gauge owner quotes the above gauge reading and storm duration. Reports and newspaper cuttings provide strong evidence that the storm was centred over Black Moor, a small area (elevation 340 m AOD) about 2 km west of Hewenden Reservoir. Daily weather reports from the Meteorological Office provide dew point measurements for 1800 GMT (about the time of the storm) at Manchester (13.9°C) and Lindholme, near Doncaster (17.2°C). Weather maps show that the latter value would be more representative of the atmospheric conditions in the

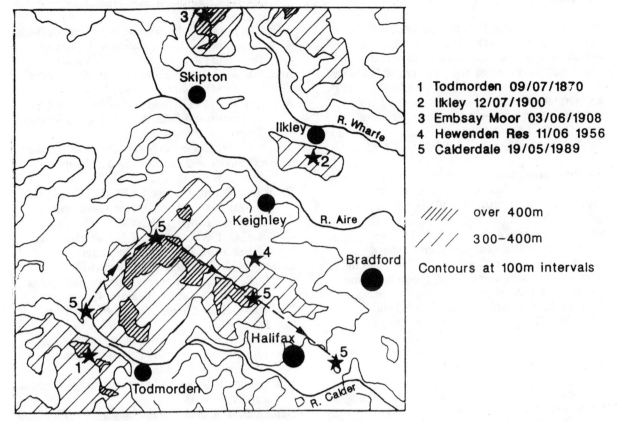

Figure 4 Location of extreme rainfall events (1870-1990) in the vicinity of Calderdale, which have all occurred over high ground

1 Todmorden 09/07/1870
2 Ilkley 12/07/1900
3 Embsay Moor 03/06/1908
4 Hewenden Res 11/06 1956
5 Calderdale 19/05/1989

///// over 400m

/// 300-400m

Contours at 100m intervals

Bradford area. This is much higher than the 12°C quoted by NERC (1975); no evidence to support the latter estimated value can be found.

The foregoing details suggest that the observation at Hewenden Reservoir was reliable and that over Black Moor the rainfall was in excess of 155 mm.

Ilkley, 12 July 1900

This storm is well documented, mainly in Mill (1900). Wilson (1900) records that a terrific thunderstorm raged over a part of the West Riding of Yorkshire, beginning in the west about noon and extending gradually eastward. Twenty raingauge readings in excess of 2.40 inches (61 mm) are quoted by Mill, the highest being 5.40 inches (137.2 mm) on the south side of the town of Ilkley. An isohyetal map and depth area data have been produced (Mill, 1900; Glasspoole, 1929).

The observer who recorded the highest rainfall considered his gauge to be "somewhat shaded" and thought a value of 6 inches (152 mm) would be more representative. There is good observer evidence that the storm centre was on Rombald's Moor, which separates the valleys of the Wharfe (in which Ilkley lies) on the north side and the Aire on the south side (Figure 4). It rises to a height of 400 m AOD. These various pieces of evidence indicate a fall well in excess of 150 mm at some point on Rombalds Moor.

The duration of the storm is more difficult to determine but is estimated at 3 hours.

Todmorden 9 July 1870

For an event so long ago, data are naturally sketchy, though eyewitness accounts are detailed and graphic. The area concerned, Heald Moor and Carn Craggs Moor, lies about 5 km north west of Todmorden on the Lancashire/Yorkshire border. These moors rise to a height of 430 m AOD. The thunderstorm that developed in the early afternoon was clearly of quite extraordinary ferocity causing severe flooding, damage and loss of life in the vicinity of three mountain streams which drain an area of about 4.5 km² on the northern side of the moor into the headwaters of the river Calder. There are eyewitness references to water spouts, and to "one continuous sheet of water extending all along the hill top and so dense that they could not see through it". The duration of this storm seems to have been about two hours.

According to Manley (1962) "... records ... undoubtedly point to a local fall of upwards of nine inches of rain". Some simple calculations made by a resident in the area (Meteorological Office, 1870) are clearly the source of this figure. The evidence hardly justifies such a positive statement, but certainly leaves little doubt about the extreme rate of fall over a two-hour period.

Conclusions

The storm of 19 May 1989 in Calderdale and the surrounding area was clearly an extreme event, though the estimated maximum point rainfall of 193 mm in less than two hours will probably always be controversial. Details of structural damage and the geomorphological response to the resulting floods provides ample evidence of a severe storm, but can not be used reliably to quantify its precise magnitude, duration or rarity.

For three further storms which have occurred within the last 120 years there is evidence, ranging from strong to circumstantial, of rainfall equal to or in excess of 162 mm (the PMP for the area). They all lie within an upland region about 1000 km², an exceptional number of severe storms to have occurred in such a small area. In all four cases the storm centre was over moorland, typically around 400 m AOD, lying between valleys. This strongly suggests that orographic uplift triggered the instability. There is also firm evidence in all four cases that the exceptionally high rainfall was confined to a small area and PMP may have been exceeded on more than one occasion.

At first sight data from raingauges and weather radar for the May 1989 storm appear contradictory. However, after making allowances for the various factors which can influence the rainfall estimated from the radar, it can be shown that the maximum point rainfall of 193 mm is not inconsistent with the radar data.

References

Acreman, M.C. 1989a. The rainfall and flooding on 19 May 1989 in Calderdale, West Yorkshire. Internal Report Institute of Hydrology, Wallingford.

Acreman, M.C. 1989b. Extreme historical UK floods and maximum flood estimation. *J. Instn of Water and Environ. Manage.*, 3, 404-412.

Acreman, M.C. 1989c. Extreme rainfall in Calderdale, 19 May 1989. *Weather*, 44, 438-446.

Acreman, M.C. 1991. The flood of 25 July 1983 on the Hermitage Water, Roxburghshire. *Scottish Geographical Magazine* (in press).

Austin, P. 1987. Relation between measured radar reflectivity and surface rainfall. *Monthly Weather Review*, 115, 1053-1070.

Calderdale Borough Council 1989. Flooding event - 19 May 1989. Internal report, Calderdale Borough Council, Halifax.

Collier, C.G. 1989. *Applications of weather radar systems*. Ellis Horwood, Chichester.

Collinge, V.K., Archibald, E.J., Brown, K.R. & Lord, M.E. 1990. Radar observations of the Halifax storm, 19 May 1989. *Weather*, 45, 354-365.

Manley, G. 1962. *Climate and the British Scene*. Fontana.

Metcalfe, M. 1979. The flood at Berryscaur, June 13th 1979. Undergraduate dissertation, University of St Andrews.

Meteorological Office 1870. *British Rainfall*. HMSO, London, 96-105.

Natural Environment Research Council 1975. *Flood Studies Report*. NERC, London. Volume II Meteorological Studies.

Rogers, R. 1971. The effects of target reflectivity on weather radar measurements. *Quarterly Journal of the Royal Meteorological Society*, 97, 154-167.

Wilson, A. 1900. The cloudburst on Rombald's Moor. *Symons Meteorological Magazine*, 35, 97-99.

Heavy rainfall in northeast England in August 1990 and some implications for calibration of rainfall radar

D. Archer & D. Wheeler

Abstract

In northeast England, the weather of August 1990 is remembered not only for the record-breaking heatwave of the first week, but also for the severe rainstorm of the 24th. On that day, although many locations had no rainfall at all, some daily totals were amongst the highest recorded in the region and short period intensities were even more remarkable. The synoptic conditions for the storm are examined. Its areal extent is illustrated by daily gauge totals and radar, and its severity by reference to daily and recording gauges. Detailed local structure of the storm rainfall is examined using four closely spaced recording gauges operating at a 2-minute time interval, and implications for calibration of radar in such events is discussed.

Synoptic situation

On 24th August, Britain lay beneath a col with high pressure centres to east and southwest, a typical synoptic condition for thundery activity in Britain. The preceding three days had been extremely warm and in the morning preceding the storm, temperatures reached 23.9°C, and midday dew point depressions of 3°C indicated an area of high humidity embracing much of northeast England. On the coast at Sunderland, thick fog reducing visibility to less than 200m indicated that at least on the coast, low level air was already saturated before onset of the rain. Winds were generally light in an indeterminate pressure field. Although southeasterly sea breezes developed along the coast and were recorded at Sunderland from 0900 GMT until the commence-ment of rainfall just after 1300 GMT, there is no evidence of their occurrence further inland at Durham or Leeming.

The upper air charts show a ridge at 5°E with a generally weak southwesterly air flow at all levels up to the tropopause. The nearest radiosonde ascent from Aughton in Merseyside (Figure 1) clearly reveals the instability of the atmosphere at all levels. The environment curve shows the fall of temperature with height and an isothermal layer just below 600mb. The drier and cooler air above 600mb adds to the potential instability and little uplift was necessary for this potential to be realised.

The predominant lifting mechanism was undoubtedly convection. Along the coast, where the first storm cells developed, on lower Wearside at 1300 GMT,

uplift may have been assisted or even initiated along the sea breeze front. By 1400 GMT, separate centres had begun to develop further west on the lower slopes of the Pennines, Durham lowlands and North Yorkshire. These centres showed a tendency to propagate slowly northeastward following the movement of the upper winds in the manner described, for example, by Newton and Frankhauser (1975). Rainfall was heaviest and most widespread overland from 1700 to 1900 GMT and thereafter drifted out over the North Sea and decreased in intensity. A localised cell developed late over north Northumberland after 1800 GMT.

Areal extent

The distribution of rain on 24th August reflects the typical irregularity associated with convectional activity. Figure 2 shows the rainfall pattern as constructed from daily raingauges. The largest centre covers an area from the middle Tyne and Derwent valleys to the coast at Sunderland with the highest totals over 70 mm near the western margin. Further south, rainfall over much of the Vale of York exceeded 10 mm but totals in two cells exceeded 50 mm and the highest daily rainfall of 100.8 mm was recorded at Thornton Steward near Leyburn. Remarkably, 86.7 mm was measured in the gauge at Brignall near Barnard Castle whilst surrounding gauges registered nil.

The irregular cover of rainfall stations leaves open the possibility that small local foci of intense rainfall could have passed unobserved through the daily raingauge network. It was considered that rainfall

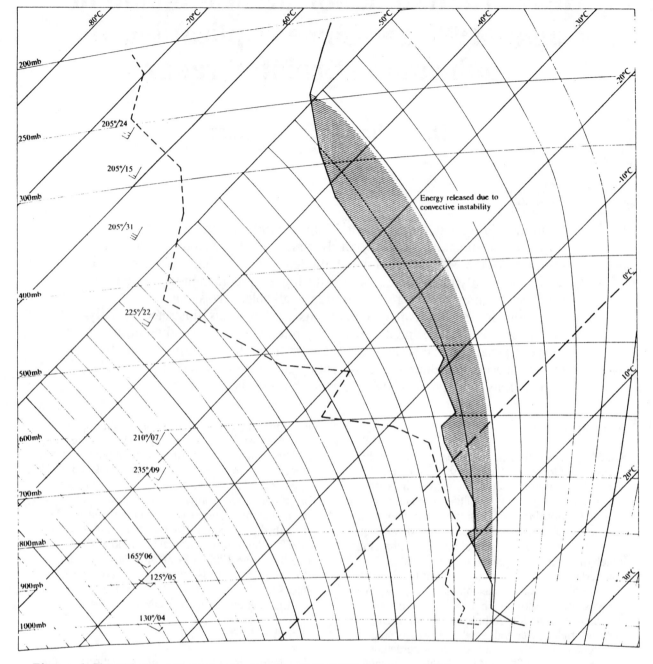

Figure 1 Simplified tephigram for Aughton for 1200 GMT, 24 August 1990

radar data might provide a more comprehensive guide to rainfall distribution even though the storm area is largely outside the 75 km inner quantitative ring based on Hameldon Hill. The radar rainfall map (Figure 3) was constructed by summing 15-minute rainfall totals over the storm period for each 5 x 5 km square. The 15-minute totals were estimated by assuming the instantaneous uncalibrated measurements of rainfall intensity on a 43 level display scheme to apply over the 15-minute interval between observations.

The two maps show good areal coincidence in the main storm centres and, remarkably, the radar map shows no major or minor foci not already defined by daily gauges. There is even a coincidence in the

three isolated cells in south Durham and North Yorkshire, though this no doubt by fortunate placing of gauges. The radar map appears to give better definition within the main Derwent-Tyne cell and also suggests the centre of the area of intense rainfall in the Vale of York to be located further north than shown by gauges. A centre near Alnwick in Northumberland illustrated as isolated by the raingauge network is shown by radar to be continuous with the larger coastal centre nearby.

The uncalibrated radar totals are well in excess of the gauge totals and increase with increasing radial distance from the radar origin. This presumably reflects the growing radar beam elevation intersecting more intense precipitation within cumulonimbus clouds.

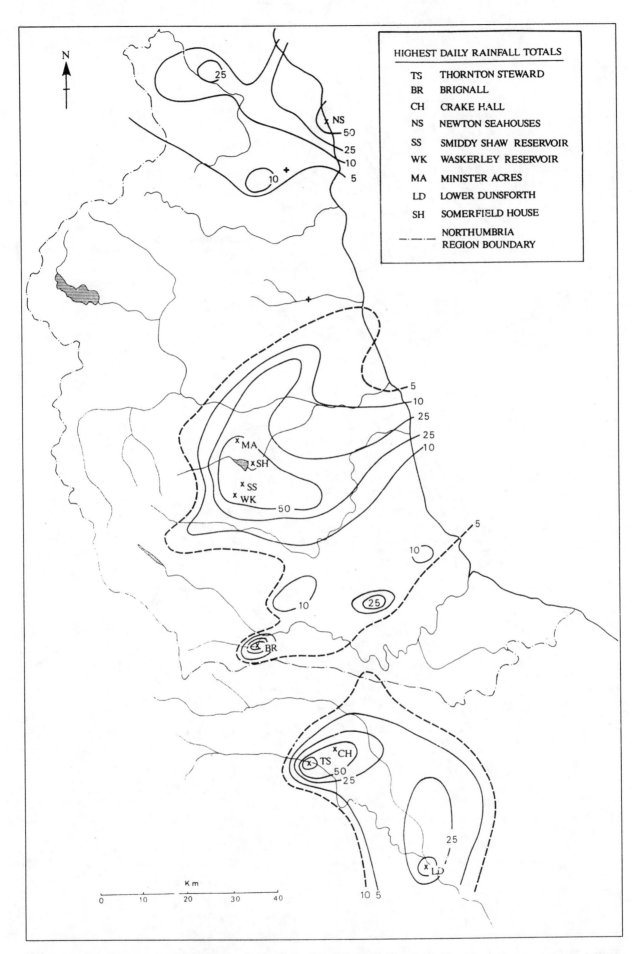

HIGHEST DAILY RAINFALL TOTALS

TS   THORNTON STEWARD
BR   BRIGNALL
CH   CRAKE HALL
NS   NEWTON SEAHOUSES
SS   SMIDDY SHAW RESERVOIR
WK   WASKERLEY RESERVOIR
MA   MINISTER ACRES
LD   LOWER DUNSFORTH
SH   SOMERFIELD HOUSE
- - -   NORTHUMBRIA REGION BOUNDARY

K m
0   10   20   30   40

Figure 2   Rainfall (mm) for 24 August 1990, constructed from daily raingauges

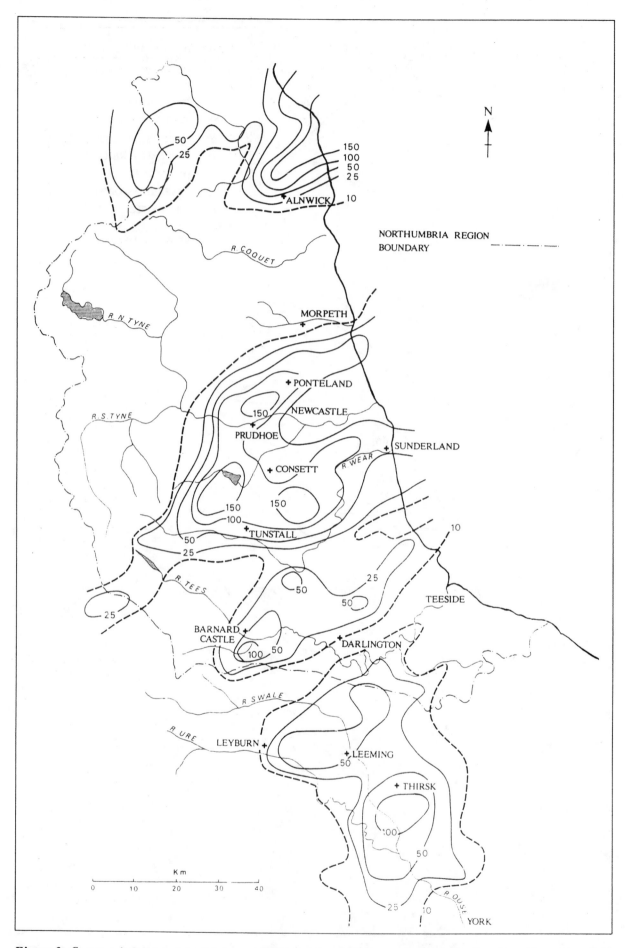

Figure 3 Storm rainfall (mm) for 24 August 1990, constructed from rainfall radar data from Hameldon Hill

The coincidence of radar and gauge distributions suggests that radar data even outside the 75 km inner ring can contribute to retrospective analysis of convective storms. This particular event led to widespread surcharging and overflow of storm sewage systems, and the radar rainfall distribution provided some guidelines in discriminating those areas where the storm intensity may have exceeded design capacity.

Similarly, there appears to be potential for real time application of outer ring rainfall radar to flood warning in defining rainfall areas even if calibration is uncertain.

Rainfall severity

Northeast England is not known for the severity of either its storm or daily rainfall. In a national study, Bleasdale (1963) identified 142 occasions when 127 mm or more and over 450 occasions when 102 mm or more rainfall occurred in the day for the years 1893 to 1960. Only 1 and 8 of these respectively were in the Northumbria region, and most of these resulted from persisting rain over the greater part of the day.

It is not surprising therefore, that some of the daily totals recorded on 24th August (Table 1) were the highest or amongst the highest on the station record, although in some instances the record lengths are short. Daily rainfall for Waskerley was second highest in a 95-year record after 11th September 1976 (81.2 mm). The comparatively modest daily total of 46.6 mm for Sunderland was the third greatest in a record since 1859. It was exceeded only by the rainfalls of 27th October 1900 (83.3 mm) and 12 August 1890 (69.8 mm).

There is one tantalising August total of 233 mm from a monthly raingauge at Feldon Burn near Smiddy Shaw reservoir (Fig 2: grid reference NY 999 461). Given totals at neighbouring gauges for the month excluding 24th of 29.6 to 37.5 mm, the implied total for 24th August at Feldon Burn was between 195 and 203 mm. There is no evidence that the gauge had been over-topped or misread, and whilst tampering with this remote moorland gauge is possible, one must also leave open the possibility of the true occurrence of this amount. A similar such total was reported in Calderdale in May 1989 (Acreman 1989).

Rodda (1966) showed that 100-year return period daily rainfalls are generally in the range 50 to 75 mm and show little tendency to differ over most of low-land England. Several of the listed totals exceed these limits.

Over shorter durations, the severity of the rainfall was more unusual. In some instances, gauge readers carefully noted the duration of the storm. Thus the observer at Brignall reported that 86.7 mm of the daily total fell between 1700 and 1840 GMT (rain was actually measured at 1910), and at Smiddy Shaw

reservoir, the rain lasted two hours from 1700 to 1900 GMT. Return periods for these durations and amounts have been assessed by Flood Studies methods (NERC, 1975) as 1850 years and 990 years respectively.

Table 1   Highest daily rainfall totals recorded in Northeast England on 24th August 1990

Station	Grid Reference	Rainfall (mm)
Thornton Steward	SE 184 886	100.8
Brignall	NZ 070 122	86.9
Crake Hall	SE 238 903	82.5
Newton Seahouses	NU 242 343	79.5
Smiddy Shaw Resr	NZ 039 462	78.3
Waskerley Resr	NZ 022 444	76.2
Ministeracres	NZ 025 556	70.4
Lower Dunsforth	SE 435 643	61.8
Somerfield house	NZ 059 510	59.7
Derwent Bridge	NZ 032 513	56.2

More precise information may be derived for shorter durations within the storm from several recording gauges, fortunately placed with respect to the storm centres. Characteristics of these gauges are shown in Table 2. The most intense rainfall for a series of specified durations within the storm has been derived for each of these stations and equivalent rainfall return periods calculated and shown in Tables 3A and 3B. These show that, for very short durations, the intensity was not particularly unusual, but with the exception of Leeming, the return period increases and reaches a maximum for durations between 1 and 3 hours with the highest return periods approaching 200 years.

Table 2   Recording gauges measuring significant storm totals on 24th August, 1990

Station	Gauge Type	Grid Reference	Recording Interval	Total Rainfall
Lower Dunsforth	TB	SE 425 643	1	61.8
Prudhoe STW	TB	NZ 090 637	2	47.4
Sunderland Poly	TS	NZ 392 657	Chart	46.6
Leeming RAF	TS	SE 305 890	Chart	44.3
Prudhoe W. Ave	TB	NZ 087 628	2	42.0
Prudhoe Low Cl.	TB	NZ 103 631	2	41.2
Tunstall Reservoir	TB	NZ 120 348	15	39.6
Prudhoe Highfield	TB	NZ 096 626	2	36.6
Ponteland	TB	NZ 147 712	15	33.2

TB = Tipping bucket   TS = Tilting syphon

Local structure of storm rainfall

The gauges at Prudhoe with a 2-minute recording interval provide particularly useful information on space and time variations. The gauges were installed

Table 3A *Return periods (years) for specified durations and measured amounts (mm) for stations with coarser time definition*

Duration	Station							
	Ponteland		Sunderland Poly		Tunstall Reservoir		Leeming RAF	
	Amt	RP	Amt	RP	Amt	RP	Amt	RP
Mins								
15	14.3	11	10.0	3.9	10.2	4.7	23.9	117
30	16.4	6.9	18.1	11	15.6	7.8	36.2	216
Hrs								
1	26.9	20	31.2	50	24.4	17	36.6	82
2	31.7	17	32.1	20	37.2	43	36.7	35

Table 3B *Return periods (years) for specified durations and measured amounts (mm) for stations with 1- or 2-minute time definition*

Duration	Prudhoe STW		Prudhoe W.Avenue		Prudhoe Highfield		Prudhoe Low Close		Lower Dunsforth	
	Amt	RP	Amt	RP	Amt	RP	Amt	RP	Amt	RP
Mins										
1	–	–	–	–	–	–	–	–	2.0	3.8
2	4.2	15	3.2	4.4	3.0	3.6	3.4	5.5	4.0	5.6
4	8.0	43	5.8	7.8	4.6	3.5	6.0	8.9	7.0	10
6	10.4	43	8.4	13	7.4	7.4	9.0	18	10.0	16
8	12.6	51	11.0	23	8.8	8.0	10.2	15	13.0	28
10	14.4	50	13.4	33	9.6	6.8	12.0	17	15.0	29
12	15.8	52	15.2	42	10.0	5.9	13.8	23	17.8	49
15	–	–	–	–	–	–	–	–	21.0	64
16	18.0	52	16.4	30	11.2	5.7	15.2	19	–	–
20	19.8	55	18.0	33	13.4	8.2	17.6	28	25.4	91
30	24.4	62	23.2	50	16.4	9.0	21.2	29	28.4	73
40	27.0	65	23.8	34	17.8	8.8	22.0	22	32.2	87
50	36.8	175	29.0	61	19.0	8.5	25.2	29	35.0	91
Hrs										
1.0	40.2	184	34.8	97	27.2	30	31.0	58	38.8	104
1.5	43.6	154	39.0	94	23.4	47	37.4	77	40.0	77
2.0	44.2	106	39.4	63	33.8	30	38.6	57	42.4	68
2.5	45.8	97	42.2	67	35.2	28	40.6	56	50.8	121
3.0	47.2	87	42.8	56	36.6	26	41.2	46	57.0	164
3.5	47.4	71	43.0	45	36.6	20	41.2	36	58.2	149

by Total Flow Surveys as part of a programme of sewer monitoring and WASSP analysis. The gauges have a maximum separation of 1.6 km but with a considerable range of elevation, from 10 m OD at the sewage treatment works adjacent to the River Tyne, to 140 m OD at Highfield. The location of these and neighbouring daily gauges is shown in Figure 4 with daily rainfall totals which illustrate the marked variation in storm rainfall over comparatively short distances.

The progress of the storm at Prudhoe as illustrated in Figure 5 shows several notable features.

1.　There were rapid fluctuations in intensity through the storm period which could well have been more marked had measurements been instantaneous rather than 2-minute totals as recorded.

2.　The fluctuations occurred as pulses, each lasting 10 to 15 minutes. The first two pulses showed some overlap, but the third pulse was separated by a period of lighter rain lasting about 12 minutes.

3.　The pulses occurred nearly at the same time at all four gauges. The maximum separation in time between peak pulse intensities was 4 minutes with the later times being recorded at Low Close, the station furthest east. However, the intensities recorded for a particular 2-minute period frequently differed between gauges by a factor greater than 2 especially on the arrival or decay of the pulse.

4.22

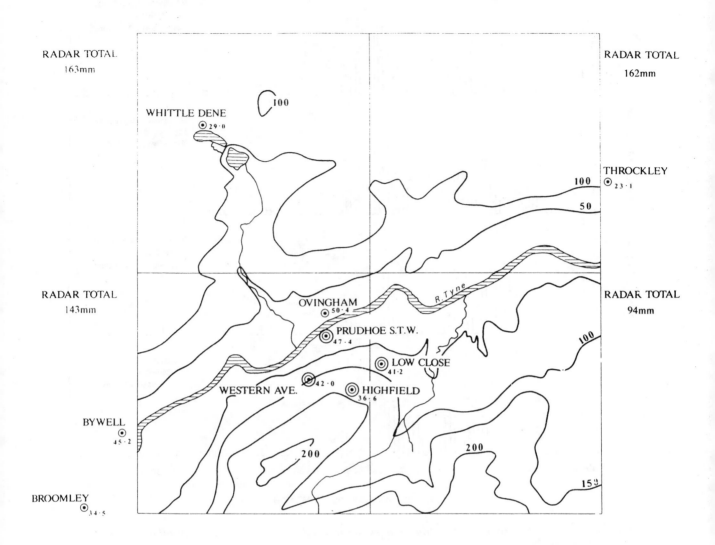

Figure 4   Raingauges in the Prudhoe area showing daily totals on 24 August 1990. Radar grid squares (5 x 5 km) are superimposed showing uncalibrated radar storm rainfall totals

Some implications for rainfall-radar calibration

The calibration of radar using recording raingauges is an essential component in all rainfall radar systems. Such calibration is necessary because of the variability in the relationship between radar reflectivity and the rate of rainfall at ground level. Browning (1981) for example, lists several sources of this variability stressing the dominant effects of drop size distribution variations, enhancement of the signal from melting snow (the bright band) and changes in intensity between the level of the radar beam and the ground, due to raindrop growth or evaporation.

However, in addition to errors from these sources, there are potential errors arising from the representativeness of the instantaneous radar measurements of rainfall intensity over the measurement interval and

the representativeness of the calibration gauge over the radar grid square. Errors from these sources may be small in the typically limited spatial and temporal variations of frontal precipitation, but make a large contribution to the additional errors typical of isolated shower conditions (Collier 1977).

An assessment of the potential errors arising from extrapolation over the measurement interval of 5 or 15 minutes may be made by determining the effects on total storm rainfall of starting times at successive 2-minute intervals, using the 2-minute intensity of the Prudhoe gauges both individually and as a group to represent the instantaneous intensity measured by radar.

Thus, by sampling intensity at a 15-minute interval at Prudhoe STW, the assessed total storm rainfall varies from 31.5 mm starting at 1805 GMT to 63.0 mm

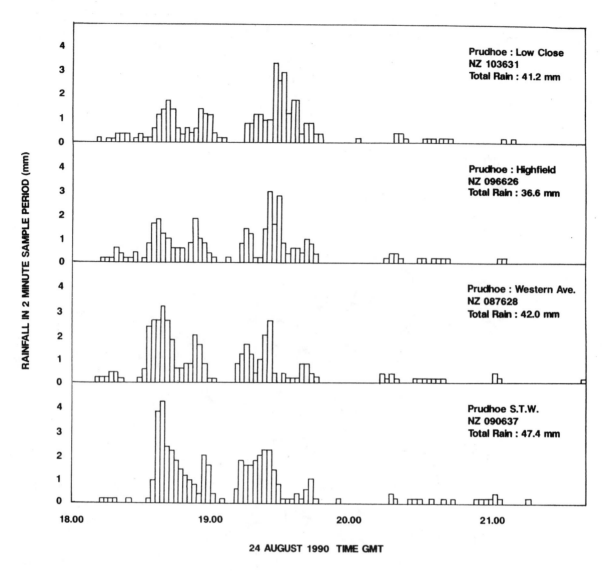

Figure 5 *Progress of storm rainfall at four gauges in the Prudhoe area, showing rainfall amounts over 2-minute intervals*

starting at 1815 GMT. Similarly at the three other gauges, the assessed minima and maxima are:

Western Avenue	36.0 mm	64.4 mm
Highfield	22.5 mm	48.0 mm
Low Close	34.5 mm	57.0 mm

Taking the mean of the four gauges to represent the average conditions over a 2 x 2 km radar square, the variation remains high – from 31.1 mm to 53.5 mm. These large variations result from a sampling interval approximately the same as the pulse duration and the fact that peak pulse intensities occur at nearly the same time over all gauges.

Calibration procedures in the UK (Moore 1989) use an assessment factor defined as the ratio of the radar to the gauge estimate of rainfall over a 15-minute period. By application of mean assessment factors to the square in which rainfall is measured, the total is adjusted to that measured by the gauge. However, application of an assessment factor containing this component to the full rainfall field represented by the

gauges will result in a systematic error in the areal rainfall. Reduction of the sampling interval from 15 to 5 minutes significantly reduces the range in assessed total storm rainfall, and in the case of the group of four gauges, the range is from 40.6 mm to 43.5 mm.

A second problem is the extent to which an individual gauge measuring rainfall at a point represents the average conditions over a 4 or 25 km² area. It is interesting that the radar totals for 5 x 5 km squares in the Prudhoe area (Fig 4) show no relationship in rank order to the gauges within or adjacent to them. Figure 4 also shows the spread of total rainfall over a more limited distance in Prudhoe. The variation is even greater for shorter periods within the storm. It can be seen that whilst the first pulse was of greatest intensity at Prudhoe STW and Western Avenue, the third pulse was heaviest at Highfield and Low Close. Such variations in amount may lead to much greater variations in the assessment of severity. Return periods for some durations vary between Prudhoe STW and Highfield by a factor of 10 (Table 3B).

Thus assessment factors based on a gauge unrepresentative of the square in which it stands may transmit systematic errors to the surrounding rainfall field, this error being significantly greater for a 5 x 5 km grid than for a 2 x 2 km grid.

Discussion and conclusions

The Northumbria region of the National Rivers Authority is the only region wholly outside the 75 km quantitative range of an existing or proposed radar. It also has no real time access to the outer ring radar although such information extends nearly to its northern boundary.

However, the region has a comparatively small number of properties vulnerable to river flooding and most of these are on downstream reaches of main rivers where monitoring of upstream river levels can provide timely and reliable warnings.

One of the potential benefits to the region of a rainfall radar would be to provide flood warning coverage to a number of small urban catchments for which none now exists. Catchments such as the Cotting Burn in Morpeth, Northumberland, with short concentration times are susceptible to flooding from intense short duration storms such as occurred in August 1990. Comparison of radar and gauge rainfall distributions in Figures 2 and 3 suggest that, outside the 75 km inner ring, radar data can give a good general guide to storm rainfall distribution even for intense convectional storms. However, apart from the normal radar calibration problems, errors arising from effects of temporal and spatial variation in rainfall in calibration would make forecasting unreliable on small catchments based on such outer ring rainfall data.

The occurrence of such variations as at Prudhoe on 24th August 1991, does not give confidence that flood forecasts and warnings could be issued with confidence even using inner ring radar. Certainly a maximum 5-minute time sampling interval is required, but a spatial resolution much better than 2 x 2 km may well be necessary.

Acknowledgements

The authors thank Rit Walton and Jeff White of Total Flow Surveys who provided access to recording rainfall data at Prudhoe.

References

Acreman, M.C. 1989. Extreme rainfall in Calderdale 19 May 1989. *Weather* 44, 438-446.

Bleasdale, A. 1963. The distribution of exceptionally heavy falls of rain in the United Kingdom, 1863-1960. *J. Inst. Water Engineers* 17, 45-55.

Browning, K.A. 1981. A total system approach to a weather radar network. Proc. IAMAP Symposium Hamburg, 115-122.

Collier, C.G. 1977. Radar measurements of precipitation. Proc. WMO Technical Conf. on Instr. and Methods of Observation. Hamburg. WMO No 480, 202-207.

Moore, R.J. 1989. Radar measurement of precipitation for hydrological application. Proc. Conf. on Weather Radar and the Water Industry, Wallingford, 17-28.

Natural Environment Research Council 1975. Flood Studies Report. NERC.

Newton, C.W. & Frankhauser, J.C. 1975. Movement and propagation of multicellular convective storms. *Pure and Applied Geophysics*, 113, 747-764.

Rodda, J.C. 1966. A study of magnitude, frequency and distribution of intense rainfall in the United Kingdom. *British Rainfall 1966*. HMSO.

Rainfall profiles for design events of long duration

E. J. Stewart & N. S. Reynard

Abstract

The problem of defining realistic design rainfall profiles for durations from three to 12 days is addressed. Details of a study of sequences of heavy rainfall events in north-west Scotland are given, the results of which are applicable to large, reservoired catchments. A series of design profiles for long durations is presented and compared with the profiles currently in use in the Highlands of Scotland.

Introduction

An understanding of the temporal variability of storm rainfall is fundamental to the application of techniques for design flood estimation. Current practice relies on the definition of design storm profiles which seek to characterize the typical variability of rainfall intensity during an event. The paper focuses on the problem of deriving representative rainfall profiles for long durations relevant to spillway flood design on relatively large, reservoired catchments. Previous studies are reviewed and a method of design profile derivation is selected which appears to have particular advantages when dealing with long durations. This technique is used to derive a set of design profiles for the study area of north-west Scotland and the results are compared with current design procedures.

Background to the study

Context

A rainfall profile is the distribution of rainfall depth with time during an event. Variability in profile shape can be related to rainfall type; for example, sharply peaked profiles of short durations are often associated with convective rainfall, while flatter profiles of longer duration may be produced by frontal rainfall. The movement of weather systems also affects the nature of the temporal profile of rainfall at a point or over an area.

In the context of hydrological design, a temporal profile is used to distribute the design rainfall depth of a given duration through time. The time distribution then forms the input to a rainfall-runoff model which converts the design rainfall to a design flood hydrograph. Whilst it is desirable for a design profile to reflect the temporal variability typical of fixed-duration rainfall extremes, it does not follow that any individual storm event will exhibit such a pattern.

The rainfall process is very variable and in most cases it is impossible to predict the exact nature of the temporal distribution of rainfall at any location. Therefore, to provide satisfactory design inputs, the temporal variability of rainfall must be analysed statistically using historical records.

Current design practice

In the UK, current practice in hydrological design relies on the method given in the Flood Studies Report (Natural Environment Research Council, 1975). Volume II of the Flood Studies Report (FSR) presents a series of unimodal, symmetrical rainfall profiles which are recommended for application to design storm durations of up to several days. Separate sets of profiles for increasing degrees of peakedness are given for summer and winter. The design profiles are presented as a series of cumulative percentage graphs related to the storm peak. Variations in profile with return period and duration are assumed to be insignificant in relation to the variations between individual storms in a particular classification.

The FSR profiles are recommended for application throughout the UK, although it is recognized that typical profiles in upland areas are less peaky. Particular problems are encountered when dealing with complex multi-reservoired catchments such as those in the Highlands of Scotland, where critical durations can be as long as seven to ten days (Johnson et al., 1981). Such long critical durations reflect the sensitivity of large, reservoired catchments to a rapid succession of storms which can cause reservoir level to build up over several days. In this case, it is clearly inappropriate to assume a symmetrical storm profile. Instead, the Institution of Civil Engineers (1978) recommends the adoption of the temporal pattern of the severest sequence of storms of the required duration that has been observed locally. This has been put into practice in the Highlands of Scotland (Johnson et al., 1981), where the complexity of the reservoir systems makes it appropriate to consider a number of profiles rather than a single design profile. The profiles of nine historic storms chosen subjectively from local rain-gauge records are assumed to have equal probability of occurrence. The profiles are based on storms of either 48-hour or 8-day duration. Floods are routed using all nine profiles and the median peak reservoir level is taken to be a compromise design.

From the foregoing it is clear that although *ad hoc* solutions have been found, no objective alternative to the symmetrical FSR profile exists for design durations of greater than three days. A technique for deriving design profiles which is appropriate to long durations is therefore required.

Review of previous studies

A large number of methods of design profile derivation are used throughout the world, each country tending to adopt a particular technique or set of profiles as standard. Generally, it is possible to distinguish three types of methods: those derived from averages of observed profiles, those involving the fitting of models to observed hyetographs, and more flexible, empirical methods.

A widely used approach to design profile definition was developed by Huff (1967) and is based on the derivation of dimensionless mass curves, i.e. cumulative plots of depth against time. Huff grouped storms together according to the quartile in which rainfall was heaviest and produced an average curve for each quartile. A similar approach was used in the FSR, although in this case storms were centred on the most intense period of rainfall and the resultant design profiles were chosen to be symmetrical.

A number of studies have used a particular model to approximate the form of observed rainfall profiles. One of the earliest was carried out by Keifer & Chu (1957), who used a pair of power functions character-ised by a single parameter to describe the design hyetograph. However, its value is not necessarily constant for different durations and locations (Yen & Chow, 1980) and the method can produce unrealistic profiles. Other workers have assumed a simple triangular model for the design hyetograph. Yen & Chow (1980) proposed a dimensionless triangular profile fitted by the method of moments and concluded that duration did not significantly affect the form of the design profile. Sutherland (1983) developed the triangular model further and took the antecedent wetness of the catchment into consider-ation in order to reduce the fitted profile into a representation of effective rainfall. A comparison of the performance of triangular and simple bimodal profiles when used as input to a rainfall-runoff model was carried out by Lambourne & Stephenson (1987). The results indicated that the adoption of a triangular profile gave the best estimate of peak discharge but the bimodal distribution gave a more reliable estimate of the volume of runoff.

The third subset of methods is empirical in nature. The average variability method was developed by Pilgrim *et al.* (1969) and is the method adopted in Australia to provide design profiles for 20 durations from ten minutes to 72 hours (Institution of Engin-eers, Australia, 1987). The approach is based on characterizing the mean variability of rainfall intensity during observed periods of heavy rainfall.

From a large number of events of a given duration, the sequence of periods of various ranks is arranged in the most likely order. The percentage of rain in a period of a given rank is calculated as the average of the percentages in the periods of that rank. Thus the resultant temporal distribution reflects the average sequence of depths within individual observed periods of heavy rainfall. The main advantages of the average variability technique are its simplicity and flexibility; design profiles can be defined for any duration provided that enough data are available.

A number of other empirical methods are reported in the literature. A broadly similar approach to that of average variability was adopted by the SOGREAH group in France to produce a median pattern centred on the period of most intense rainfall (Hall & Kneen, 1973). More recently, Srikanthan & McMahon (1985) developed a method which attempted to take account of the persistence inherent in the rainfall process. The resulting technique, however, does not display the same flexibility because design profiles are always centred on the peak, and unusual data are effectively discarded by the method.

In the current study, the average variability method was selected as the most appropriate to very long durations, since the technique allows design profiles to have more than one peak.

North-west Scotland

The study area was defined to consist of the catchments of the Conon, the Beauly and the Ness in north-west Scotland (Figure 1). These catchments are all greater than 1000 km² in area and are characterized by complex systems of reservoirs developed for hydroelectric power generation.

Climatic characteristics

As a result of the dominance of westerly winds across the region, north-west Scotland experiences heavy rainfall throughout the year. Although there is a decrease in both the number and the severity of depressions during the summer, frontal systems continue to provide most of the rainfall. The Highlands provide an effective topographic barrier to the westerly flow, and orographic enhancement increases the rainfall totals in north and west Scotland. A very sharp gradient in rainfall totals is evident across Scotland, with the east in a marked rain shadow. Average annual rainfall totals in the west can be as much as 2800 mm, compared to about 600 mm in the east.

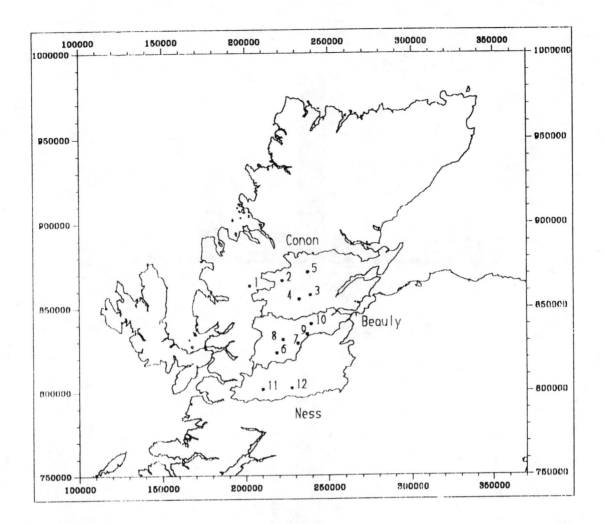

Figure 1   Map of the study region showing gauge locations

Flood-producing storms almost invariably occur in the winter months of October to March. They tend to take the form of an intense depression accompanied by heavy rainfall and the associated rise in temperature often causes significant snowmelt. The typical duration of the heaviest rainfall is two to three days, although such an event usually forms part of a sequence of weather systems lasting from seven to ten days. For this reason, realistic design profiles for durations of up to ten days are required in the region.

Some major storms

In an initial analysis, the characteristics of a number of severe storms experienced in the study region were investigated using daily raingauge data from the archive held at the Institute of Hydrology and synoptic information taken from Daily Weather Reports published by the Meteorological Office. Profiles of daily rainfall totals were constructed for the 15-day period centred on the highest depth. The profiles of three heavy rainfall episodes as measured at individual raingauges are given in Fig. 2. Each was produced by essentially the same sequence of events.

A rainfall peak in the early part of the profile represents an initial depression, the passage of which establishes a westerly airflow over Scotland. This flow in turn brings in a second, more potent system which is generally responsible for the highest daily rainfall totals in the sequence. The cold front associated with this system is left trailing over Scotland in the strong westerly airstream. The situation favours the formation of wave depressions on the cold front of the initial system and these account for the rainfall peaks towards the end of the profile.

Data

For the main analysis, 12 gauges situated within or close to the three catchments were selected, the major selection criteria being record length and continuity. The locations of the three catchments and the 12 selected raingauges are shown in Figure 1 and details of the gauges are given in Table 1. Average annual rainfall totals at the gauges range from 1115 mm to 2225 mm and altitudes from 25 m to 268 m. A 27-year data period from 1961 to 1987 was adopted.

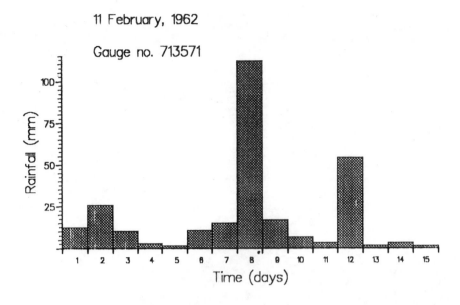

11 February, 1962

Gauge no. 713571

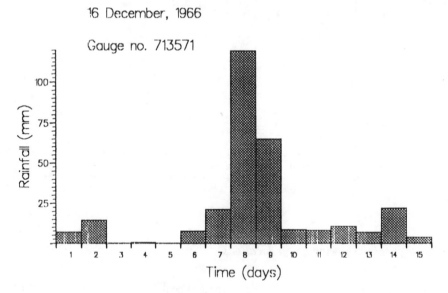

16 December, 1966

Gauge no. 713571

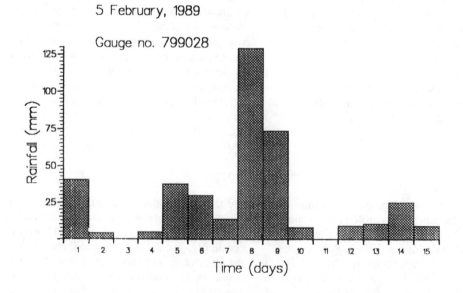

5 February, 1989

Gauge no. 799028

Figure 2 *Profiles of some heavy rainfall episodes in north-west Scotland (15-day profiles centred on the highest daily total)*

Table 1 Details of raingauges used in the study

Gauge number	Name	Average annual rainfall, SAAR (mm)	Altitude (m)
713571	Kinlochewe	2008	25
789210	Fannich Lodge	1872	268
789696	Loch Luichart	1115	50
790309	Bridgend	1300	107
791188	Blackbridge	1267	210
794463	Affric Lodge	1796	233
795076	Fasnakyle	1115	80
795625	Mullardoch Dam	1807	245
795917	Glassburn	1118	52
797209	Struy	1126	53
799028	Kingie Camp	2225	146
799626	Invergarry Dam	1431	90

Methodology

The data analysis was divided into two stages. First, an analysis of the characteristics of observed profiles of extreme rainfall was undertaken. For durations of three to 12 days inclusive, profiles of annual maximum rainfall totals were extracted from the daily record of each of the 12 raingauges. It is important to note that the profiles extracted were of fixed durations regardless of whether or not they represented complete storm events or sequences of events. Values of the mean, coefficient of variation (CV), skewness and kurtosis were then calculated for each observed profile in order to search for differences between the form of profiles of different seasons and durations.

In the second stage of the analysis, the average variability method was used to derive design profiles for the study region for a range of durations. The resultant profiles were then compared with those currently in use in the Highlands of Scotland.

Results

Characteristics of annual maximum profiles

Over 270 fixed-duration profiles were extracted from the daily records of the 12 gauges for each duration from three to 12 days, with the number of profiles decreasing slightly with increasing duration owing to the effect of missing data. The form of the profiles was very variable at all durations and no preferred patterns were discernible. Many profiles had multiple peaks, particularly at the longer durations.

Mean values of some basic statistics of the observed profiles of each duration are given in Table 2. The mean of each profile is expressed as a proportion of the duration in days and generally shows a downward trend with duration. Where the value of the mean is greater than 0.5, this indicates that the bulk of the total rainfall occurs in the latter half of the duration. This is the case for all durations up to seven days and corresponds with the negative values of mean skewness. Values of CV tend to increase with duration, indicating that the profiles of the longer durations are more variable. Kurtosis values decrease with duration as a result of the multiple peaks evident at long durations.

The possibility of seasonal differences in profile form was investigated, summer being defined as the period from April to September and winter from October to March. Many more annual maximum events were found to occur in winter than in summer, in the ratio 6:1. It was evident that, in addition to the tendency towards winter maxima, those that occurred in summer were more likely to be of shorter duration. This supports the idea of convective events being short-lived and more prevalent in summer.

The form of dimensionless mass curves (giving percentage rainfall against percentage duration) was inspected to detect possible seasonal differences. Figure 3 shows the summer and winter mass curves for the 5-day duration. In contrast to the results for other regions of the UK (Stewart & Reynard, 1991), very little difference was found between summer and winter mass curves for all durations. Significance tests on the mean statistics already discussed also

4.31

Table 2 Mean values of some statistics of the observed profiles

Duration (days)	No. of observed profiles	Mean/ duration	Coeff. of variation (CV)	Skewness	Kurtosis
3	273	0.508	0.500	-0.054	-0.77
4	273	0.507	0.519	-0.048	-0.75
5	272	0.507	0.554	-0.037	-0.83
6	272	0.508	0.543	-0.024	-0.79
7	272	0.511	0.551	-0.034	-0.83
8	272	0.497	0.570	0.038	-0.93
9	272	0.492	0.574	0.055	-0.93
10	272	0.497	0.571	0.031	-0.93
11	272	0.499	0.576	0.018	-0.94
12	271	0.498	0.579	0.035	-0.98

failed to detect substantial differences in the form of profiles of different seasons.

Design profiles

The average variability technique was used to produce design profiles for the study region for durations from three to 12 days inclusive. In view of the similarity observed in annual maximum summer and winter profiles, a single set of design profiles was produced for all seasons. For each duration, data from the 12 raingauges were pooled together to maximize the number of observed profiles on which each design distribution was based. Although some widespread events were responsible for the annual maxima at a number of gauges, it was felt that the

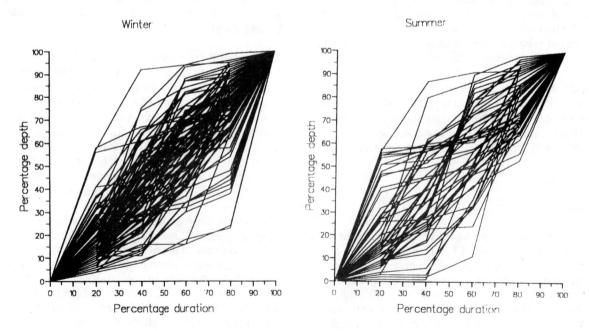

Figure 3 Seasonal mass curves for the 5-day duration

Table 3 *Statistics of average variability profiles for north-west Scotland*

Duration (days)	Mean/ duration	Coeff. of variation	Skewness	Kurtosis
3	0.54	0.42	-0.16	-0.83
5	0.56	0.57	-0.17	-1.61
7	0.60	0.47	-0.28	-1.04
9	0.44	0.65	0.37	-0.96
11	0.45	0.74	0.26	-1.38

average intergauge distance (33 km) was great enough for the pooling to be worthwhile. The resultant profiles for the odd-numbered durations are given in Figure 4 and corresponding shape descriptors are given in Table 3.

A clear progression in the form of the design profiles from one duration to the next is evident in Figure 4. The 3-day profile is slightly negatively skewed and becomes bimodal when the duration is extended to five days. In the case of the 5- and 7-day durations, the highest rainfall depth occurs at the end of the sequence. At the 9-day duration the peak is central and the profile shows a clear sequence of three events; four peaks are evident in the 11-day profile.

Discussion

The fact that long duration rainfall extremes often comprise a sequence of severe storms is clear from the average variability profiles for all durations, and comparisons can be drawn between the design profiles and those of real events (see, for example, Figure 2). The design profiles for the 5- and 7-day durations are particularly interesting since in both cases the rainfall peak occurs at the end of the sequence, which is the most severe case for a reservoir to withstand.

The practice of using nine profiles chosen subjectively from local raingauge records, which is used in the Highlands of Scotland, has already been discussed. Five of these profiles are based on 8-day rainfall durations and these are shown in Figure 5. Three of the profiles are negatively skewed and two have high rainfall totals at the end of the design duration. A particular advantage of the average variability profiles is that they are derived from annual maximum events of the design duration, rather than always being based on 8-day storms; they also display the mean variability typical of annual maximum events.

The decision to produce a single set of design profiles for the whole year was based on the results

of significance tests and reflects the recognition that frontal rainfall mechanisms are dominant in north-west Scotland in both winter and summer. However, this situation does not pertain to other upland regions of the UK. In similar analyses of temporal rainfall distribution in north-west England and north Wales, significant differences were found in the form of annual maximum profiles for different seasons (Stewart & Reynard, 1991). In these regions, although frontal rainfall is still dominant, convective storms are often responsible for exceptional rainfall totals over shorter durations.

The effect of return period on the form of the design profiles was tested by ranking the annual maximum profiles and deriving three average variability profiles for each duration based on the highest ten, 50 and 100 maxima. It was found that differences between the three profiles were minimal.

Further refinement of the design profiles remains to be carried out. For example, some adjustments may be necessary to make the progression with duration smoother, and confidence limits could be attached to the percentage of the total rainfall depth assigned to each period. The impact on reservoir flood estimates of using the new design profiles remains to be investigated.

Conclusions

Daily raingauge data from an area of north-west Scotland have been used to produce a set of design rainfall profiles for long durations relevant to spillway flood design on large, reservoired catchments. The profiles were derived using the average variability technique which is notable for the flexibility and simplicity of its approach.

The resultant design profiles are realistic when compared to the temporal distributions of some sequences of severe rainfall events experienced in the study region, and offer an objective alternative to the unimodal, symmetrical profiles recommended in the UK for design durations of up to three days.

4.33

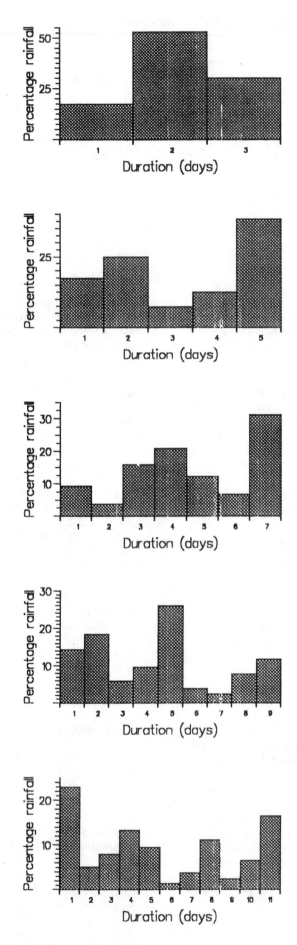

Figure 4 *Average variability profiles for the study region*

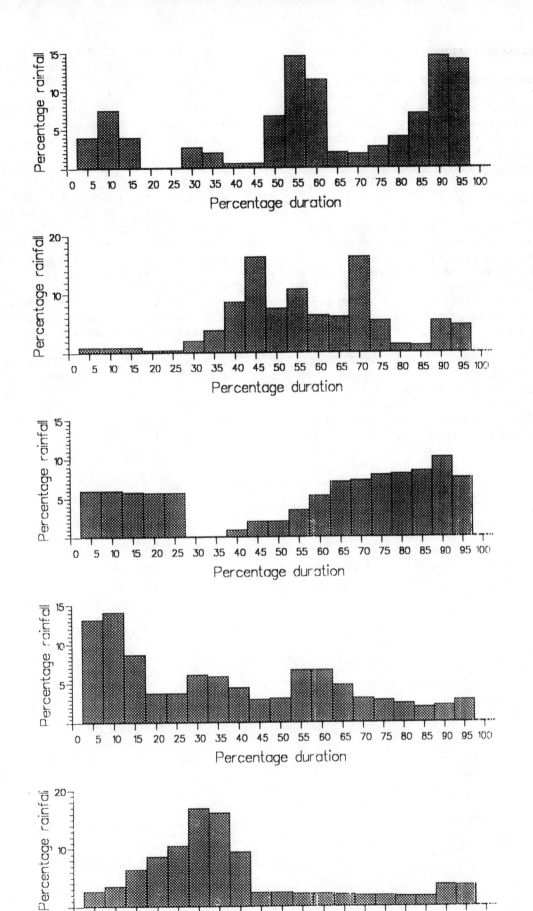

Figure 5 *Profiles of 8-day rainfalls in north-west Scotland currently used for design by Scottish Hydro-Electric plc*

4.35

Acknowledgements

The analysis presented in this paper forms part of a wider study of the spatial and temporal variability of extreme rainfall events in upland areas commissioned by the Department of the Environment (contract no. PECD7/7/190). The assistance of Mr R M Jarvis of Scottish Hydro-Electric plc in providing details of current design practice is gratefully acknowledged.

References

Hall, A. G. & Kneen, T. H. 1973. Design temporal patterns of storm rainfall in Australia. *Proc. Hydrology Symp., I.E. Aust.,* Perth 1973, 77-84.

Huff, F. A. 1967. Time distribution of rainfall in heavy storms. *Wat. Resour. Res.* 3, 1007-1019.

Institution of Civil Engineers. 1978. *Floods and Reservoir Safety: an Engineering Guide.* ICE, London.

Institution of Engineers, Australia. 1987. *Australian Rainfall and Runoff* (third edition). Sydney, Australia.

Johnson, F. G., Jarvis, R. M. & Reynolds, G. 1981. Use made of the Flood Studies Report for reservoir operation in hydroelectric schemes. In: *Flood Studies Report - Five Years On,* 85-90.

Thomas Telford Ltd, London.

Keifer, C. J. & Chu, H. H. 1957. Synthetic storm pattern for drainage design. *J. Hydraul. Div. ASCE,* 83 (HY4), 1332-1 - 1332-25.

Lambourne, J. J. & Stephenson, D. 1987. Model study of the effect of temporal storm distributions on peak discharges and volumes. *Hydrol. Sci. J.* 32, 215-226.

Natural Environment Research Council. 1975. *Flood Studies Report* (five volumes). NERC, London.

Pilgrim, D. H., Cordery, I. & French, R. 1969. Temporal patterns of design rainfall for Sydney. *Civ. Eng. Trans. I.E. Aust.,* CE11(1), 9-14.

Srikanthan, R. & McMahon, T. A. 1985. Temporal storm patterns re-examined. *Civ. Eng. Trans. I.E. Aust.,* CE27, 230-237.

Stewart, E. J. & Reynard, N. S. 1991. Temporal variations of extreme rainfall events in upland areas. Institute of Hydrology Report to the Department of the Environment.

Sutherland, F. R. 1983. An improved rainfall intensity distribution for hydrograph synthesis. Report No. 1/1983, Water Systems Research Programme, University of the Witwatersrand.

Yen, B. C. & Chow, V. T. 1980. Design hyetographs for small drainage structures. *J. Hydraul. Div. ASCE,* 106 (HY6), 1055-1076.

Soil moisture patterns beneath broadleaf forests in southern England during 1989 and 1990

P.T.W.Rosier

Abstract

Soil water content changes in a chalk soil have been measured beneath ash (*Fraxinus excelsior*) and beech (*Fagus sylvatica*) plantations at Black Wood near Winchester, Hampshire and also in a clay soil for an ash plantation at Old Pond Close near Olney, Buckinghamshire during 1989 and 1990 using a neutron probe. During 1989 and 1990 soil moisture deficits in excess of 200 mm occurred beneath all three plantations. At Black Wood all the changes in soil water content beneath the beech plantation were in the top 240 cm, while under the ash some small changes were found as deep as 340 cm. At Old Pond Close some changes were found below 180 cm. Comparisons are made between these measured soil moisture deficits and estimates of soil moisture deficits produced by the Meteorological Office MORECS system.

Introduction

The effect increased forestry activities in the wet upland areas of the UK can have on local hydrology and hydrochemistry has been well documented. At Plynlimon in mid-Wales the paired catchment experiment operated by the Institute of Hydrology showed that the evaporation from the forested part of the catchment would be twice that of the adjacent grassland catchment (Calder and Newson, 1979). The difference was due to the larger interception losses from the well-ventilated forest canopy during and immediately following rainfall. This would inevitably be reflected in a reduced water yield from the forested catchment. The enhanced ability of trees to scavenge acid pollutants from the atmosphere and to acidify upland streams has in turn been shown to affect wildlife which is dependent on the rivers for food supplies (UKAWRG, 1988).

In recent years improved agricultural practices have meant that large surpluses of cereal crops have been produced. The policy of the government now is to encourage farmers to take some land out of cereal production and to use it in other ways. One way is to encourage the planting of broadleaf trees and hence increase timber production. At present the UK produces about 10% of its timber requirements and by increasing the amount of broadleaf plantations this will also impact on amenity value and conservation of habitats (Blyth *et al.*, 1987). It is proposed that the new broadleaf plantations will be in the drier, lowland areas of the UK, which is in contrast to previous forestry plantation programmes which have been concentrated in the wet upland areas. The plantations will consist of small (about 5 hectares in size) irregular blocks. The tree species being considered for the plantations are ash (*Fraxinus excelsior*), sweet chestnut (*Castanea sativa*), sycamore (*Acer pseudoplatanus*), poplar (*Populus* sp.), beech (*Fagus sylvatica*) and cherry (*Prunus avium*).

Any change in land use has the potential to seriously impact water resources. Groundwater recharge and river flow are very sensitive to changes in water use because the difference between rainfall and evaporation can be quite small. The implications of this potentially major land use change have caused concern for the already limited water resources in southern England and led to the setting up of a project "the hydrological impacts of broadleaf plantations in lowland Britain". This project, started in 1988, has as its main aims to assess the effects of small-scale plantations on: (1) the water use and (2) the hydrochemical budgets.

The work reported here is one aspect of this multi-disciplinary project and (as the project is still ongoing) presents only an interpretation of data from 1989 and 1990.

The sites and measurements

Black Wood

The comparative study of ash and beech is being made at Black Wood, a 2.7 km² Forestry Commission woodland, completely surrounded by agricultural land, situated near Winchester (Grid Reference SU534428), Figure 1. It is primarily beech but with a small plantation of ash within it, and a small clearing near its centre. The beech trees were planted in 1933 and are about 21 m tall and have no undergrowth, but there is a leaf litter layer of 1 - 2 cm thickness. The ash trees were planted in 1952 and are about 16 m tall. The ash site has a vigorous undergrowth consisting mainly of hazel (*Corylus avellana*) and bramble (*Rubus* sp), along with Dog's mercury (*Mercurialis perennis*) and a number of other species appearing at different times of the year. The soil at both sites is of the Andover series (Jarvis, 1973) and consists of 25 cm of a dark brown silty loam with small flints, overlying a lightly stained chalk grading into *in situ* chalk at about 1.5 m.

Old Pond Close

The plantation is a small 25 ha Forestry Commission woodland, surrounded by agricultural land near Olney (Grid Reference SP877551), Figure 2. The plantation containing a small number of oak and poplar trees was planted in 1934 and the trees are about 16 m tall. There is a dense undergrowth of

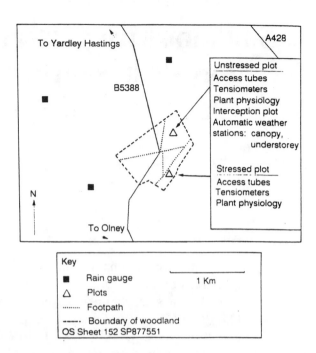

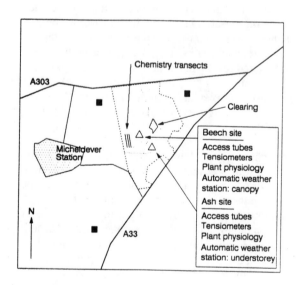

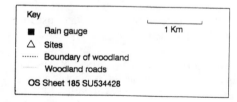

Figure 1 The Black Wood experimental site

Figure 2 The Old Pond Close experimental site

bramble and a mixture of grasses. The soil is of the Hanslope series (Hodge *et al.*, 1984) and consists of a dark greyish-brown clay loam which is slightly calcareous and overlies Oxford clay.

At each of the three sites, five randomly located access tubes for measuring soil water content using the Institute of Hydrology Neutron Probe system (Bell, 1976) were installed. Details of the access tubes and frequency of observations at each site are given in Table 1.

The neutron probe observations (count rate in the soil) are made every 20 cm to 210 cm and then every 30 cm to the bottom of the access tube. The soil moisture is expressed volumetrically in terms of moisture volume fraction (θ). The relationship between count rate in the soil and the moisture volume fraction is given by the equation:

$$\theta = a.R/R_w + b$$

where:
a = slope of the line
b = intercept of the line
R = count rate in the soil
R_w = count rate in the water standard.

The constants a and b vary with soil type but are well known for UK soils (Bell, 1976). The total water content of each access tube is the sum of all the individual water contents and is expressed in mm of water.

Because of the chalky soils at Black Wood it is difficult to determine precisely when the soils would be at field capacity, and therefore from which point soil moisture deficits start to occur. Chalk has the ability to conduct water even at low soil water

Table 1. Access tube details at Black Wood and Old Pond Close

BLACK WOOD - ASH
Frequency: weekly till 8 Mar 1990, then fortnightly

Tube Number	Max. reading depth (cm)	Start date 1989
01	250	4 May
02	250	14 Apr
03	320	20 Apr
06	340	20 Apr
09	340	14 Apr

BLACK WOOD - BEECH
Frequency: weekly till 8 Mar 1990, then fortnightly

Tube Number	Max. reading depth (cm)	Start date 1989
02	360	3 Mar
04	360	--"--
05	350	--"--
07	350	--"--
09	360	--"--

OLD POND CLOSE - ASH
Frequency: weekly till 19 Sept 1990, then fortnightly

Tube Number	Max. reading depth (cm)	Start date 1989
01	250	23 May
02	210	--"---
03	260	--"---
04	210	--"---
05	240	--"---

potentials (Wellings 1984) and thus the idea of field capacity is not well defined. From tensiometer measurements made at both sites it is probable that the soil profiles were saturated during March 1990, and this value (at which deficits started to occur) is used for the comparison with estimates made from MORECS (Meteorological Office Rainfall & Evaporation Calculation System, Thompson *et al.*, 1981).

At Old Pond Close no winter soil moisture measurements were available and hence a value for field capacity has not been determined. For ease of analysis a value of 950 mm for the field capacity was assumed and the MORECS values start from this point. Although this value is not strictly correct, varying the starting point will not alter the results of the comparison.

Black Wood and Old Pond Close are in MORECS squares 170 and 138 respectively, and estimates for both squares with a surface cover of deciduous trees were obtained using available water capacities of 131.3 mm (for the chalky soils at Black Wood) and 218.8 mm (for the clay soil at Old Pond Close). MORECS assumes that the trees are fully foliated and no account is taken of tree rooting depths.

Results and discussion

The large soil moisture deficits at Black Wood and Old Pond Close are a reflection of the particularly dry summers experienced in 1989 and 1990. Table 2 shows the monthly MORECS values of rainfall for squares 170 and 138. For square 170 the summer rainfall (May to September inclusive) for 1989 and 1990 was 20.2% and 22.5% respectively of the annual rainfall. For square 138 the summer rainfall for 1990 was 26% of the annual rainfall.

Table 2 Monthly rainfall values (mm) for MORECS squares 170 and 138 for 1989 and 1990

Month	Square 170		Square 138
	1989	1990	1990
January	33.7	126.9	61.6
February	86.6	175.5	86.3
March	89.8	8.1	15.5
April	65.2	29.9	36.7
May	26.4	16.1	5.8
June	37.8	43.5	40.3
July	18.8	18.1	21.9
August	36.0	33.5	21.9
September	27.0	41.1	26.9
October	87.5	72.7	49.0
November	46.9	40.9	35.1
December	165.7	70.2	50.2
Total	721.4	676.5	451.2

The time series of the total water contents (average of all five tubes) from the ash and the beech sites at Black Wood are shown in Figure 3. In May 1989 (when observations started) the mean total water content of the profile at the ash site was 1085 mm, and probably does not represent the profile at its wettest. However the change in mean total water content during the summer (to the beginning of September) was approximately 280 mm. The profile began to wet up during October 1989 and reached a maximum of 1150 mm in mid-February 1990. The

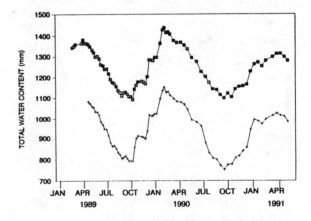

Figure 3   Time series of total soil water content beneath the ash (+) and beech (■) sites at Black Wood

soil then dried steadily from the end of March through to October 1990 and shows a deficit of 340 mm of which about 80 mm can be attributed to drainage as the trees did not come into leaf until mid-May. The beech site (average of all five tubes) shows a similar pattern to the ash. In 1989 the decrease in soil water content beneath the beech was about 250 mm, (from May until September). The profile was still wetting up during March 1989 (when observations commenced) and reached a maximum of 1380 mm during April. The profile then started to dry out until the beginning of September. The pattern for 1990 is very similar. The profile reached a maximum of 1440 mm total water content and steadily dried out from the end of March until the beginning of September when there was a deficit of about 380 mm (although again about 80 mm can be attributed to drainage during early spring as the trees were not in leaf).

Figure 4 shows soil moisture deficit estimates from MORECS plotted alongside the measurements from the neutron probe for the ash and the beech sites for 1990. Good agreement is found up to the beginning of June when the neutron probe measurements show a rapidly increasing deficit as compared to the MORECS estimates whose rate of change has started to slow down. The measurements show a maximum deficit of about 300 mm (for both the ash and the beech sites) in mid-September, whereas MORECS shows a maximum deficit of 131 mm at the beginning of September and remains constant for the rest of the month.

Figure 5 shows the comparison between the time series of the total water contents (average of all five tubes) from the ash site at Old Pond Close and the associated MORECS estimates. In May 1990 (when the measurements were started) the mean total water content of the profile was about 940 mm, and is unlikely to be the wettest profile for the year. The profile dries steadily until mid-September when the mean total water content was about 735 mm, a deficit for the summer of 205 mm. In comparison the MORECS estimates show a marked increase in the

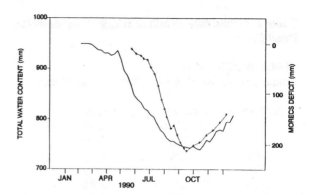

Figure 5 Comparison between measured soil water content beneath the ash (+) and MORECS estimates (—) of soil moisture deficit at Old Pond Close

rate of change in the deficit from the end of April. At that time MORECS has the tree buds bursting (day 108: 18 April) although very few trees are in leaf until the end of May. The maximum MORECS deficit for the year of 210 mm compares favourably with the measurements. However the timing of the maximum deficit was different, with MORECS estimating the maximum deficit in mid-October whereas the measurements show the maximum deficit occurring a month earlier in mid-September. The measurements show the profile starting to wet up from mid-September while the MORECS estimates do so from mid-October, and from this point the measurements and estimates agree reasonably well.

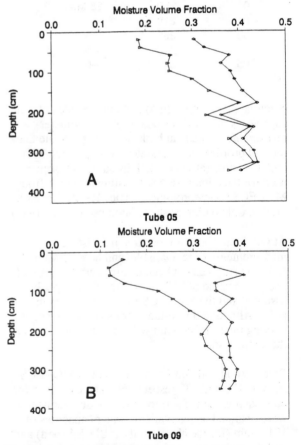

Figure 6 The driest and the wettest soil moisture profiles from one ash and one beech tube at Black Wood for 1989

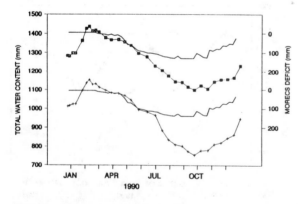

Figure 4 Comparison between measured soil water content beneath the ash (+) and beech (■) sites and MORECS estimates (—) of soil moisture deficit at Black Wood

Figure 6a shows the driest (31 August) and the wettest (4 May) soil moisture profiles from one of the ash tubes, (the other four ash tubes show a similar pattern) for 1989 from Black Wood. The pattern was repeated in 1990, though the data are not presented here. For both years there was still some change in soil water content at the lowest measurement depth of 340 cm. This may have been due to the roots of the trees extending beyond this depth or drainage from the profile. By implication it does mean that the soil moisture deficits beneath the ash could have been larger than were actually measured. In Figure 6b the driest (31 August 1989) and the wettest (30 March 1989) soil moisture profiles from one of the beech tubes are shown, again a similar pattern for the other four beech tubes is found. For both years the profile shows soil water depletion in the top 240 cm with very little change below this, implying that the rooting depth of the trees is well within the measurement range of the access tubes.

Figure 7 shows the driest (19 September) and the wettest (23 May) profiles for 1990 for two groups of access tubes from Old Pond Close - Figure 7a those that show changes beneath 180 cm, albeit rather small and Figure 7b those that do not. As in the case of the ash trees at Black Wood, if the trees are deep rooted it is possible that the roots are extending beyond the lowest measurement depth. This implies that the soil moisture deficits could have been larger than were actually measured.

Concluding remarks

The soil moisture patterns beneath the ash and the beech plantations at Black Wood are very similar for both 1989 and 1990, and show soil moisture deficits in excess of 250 mm observed at both sites. It is probable that the ash trees are deeper rooted than the beech and this may explain why changes in the soil moisture occur at lower depths. At Old Pond Close a soil moisture deficit in excess of 200 mm was observed beneath the ash for 1990. Small changes in soil moisture were observed at lower depths in some access tubes, which may be the result of tree roots extending beyond the measurement range of some of the access tubes.

Generally there is poor agreement between the soil moisture measurements and the MORECS estimates of soil moisture deficit at both Black Wood and Old Pond Close. At Black Wood this may be due to the choice of value used in MORECS for the available water capacity for chalky soils. Even so, by using the value for soils of 'high water capacity' (a value of 219 mm) the MORECS estimates would still not have reached the maximum deficits as measured by the neutron probe. At Old Pond Close the comparison of MORECS estimates with the neutron probe measurements again shows poor agreement with the measured soil moisture deficits. MORECS does estimate rapidly increasing deficits from mid-April although few trees are even in leaf. However, the maximum measured deficit and the maximum MORECS deficit do agree reasonably well, though the timing of when the maximum deficit is reached differs.

Acknowledgements

This work is funded by the National Rivers Authority, the Directorate of Rural Affairs (DOE) and the Natural Environment Research Council. I would like to thank Marc Tarrant and Catriona Pullen who have assisted in the collection and the analysis of the soil moisture data from Black Wood and Old Pond Close.

References

Bell, J.P. 1976. Neutron probe practice. *I.H.Report No 19*, Institute of Hydrology, Wallingford.

Blyth, J., Evans, J., Mutch, W.E.S. & Sidwell, C. 1987. *Farm Woodland Management*, Farming Press, Ipswich.

Calder, I.R. & Newson, M.D. 1979. Land use and upland water resources in Britain - a strategic look. *Wat. Resour. Bull.* 16, 1628-1639.

Hodge, C.A.H., Burton, R.G.O., Corbett, W.M., Evans, R. & Seale, R.S. 1984. Soils and their use in Eastern England. Soil Survey of England

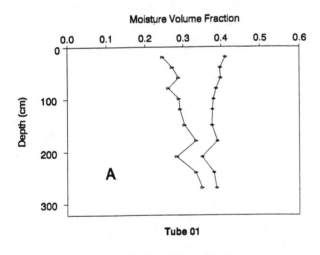

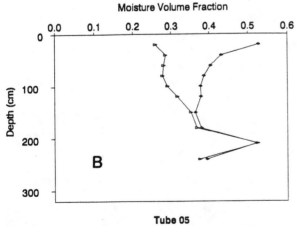

Figure 7 The driest and the wettest soil moisture profiles from two ash tubes at Old Pond Close for 1990

and Wales, Bulletin No. 13, Harpenden, UK.

Jarvis, M.G. 1973. Soils of the Wantage and Abingdon District (Sheet 253). *Memoirs of the Soil Survey of England and Wales*, Harpenden, UK.

Thompson, N., Barrie, I.A. & Ayles, M. 1981. The Meteorological Office Rainfall and Evaporation Calculation System: MORECS (July 1981).

Met. Office Hydrological Memorandum No.45.

UKAWRG, 1988. United Kingdom Acid Waters Review Group, second report. Acidity in United Kingdom Fresh Waters. HMSO. 1-61.

Wellings, S.R. 1984. Recharge of the upper chalk aquifer at a site in Hampshire, England. 1. Water balance and unsaturated flow. *J. Hydrol.* 69, 259-273.

Session 5

Snow and Ice

Hydrological inferences from meltwater quality data: the unfulfilled potential

M. Sharp

Abstract

Studies of the quality characteristics of meltwaters draining from glaciers and ice sheets have the potential to provide important information about the character of subglacial drainage systems and their evolution over time. To date, however, this potential is largely unfulfilled because field monitoring programs have been designed without due regard to insights provided by theoretical analyses of subglacial water flow and solute acquisition by glacial meltwaters. This has resulted in measurement of inappropriate parameters, neglect of important issues and the choice of weak and inappropriate interpretative procedures. This paper reviews the implications for solute acquisition of what is known about the hydraulic behaviour of arterial conduit and linked-cavity drainage systems, and suggests ways in which unresolved questions about subglacial hydrology might be answered using water quality data. Those water quality parameters which are likely to be sensitive indicators of subglacial hydraulic conditions are identified, and recommendations are made for the design of future monitoring programs. Particular emphasis is placed on the need for complimentary work which will allow interpretations of water quality data to be rigorously tested.

Introduction

In the field of glacier dynamics, the decade of the 1980s was marked by an increasing appreciation of the coupling between the internal hydrology and flow of glaciers and ice sheets which are temperate at their beds (e.g. Iken, 1981; Bindschadler, 1983; Iken & Bindschadler, 1986; Kamb & Engelhardt, 1987). Relations were derived to describe the motion of such ice masses over beds composed respectively of rigid bedrock (Kamb, 1987; Fowler, 1987a, 1987b) and unlithified, permeable and potentially deformable sediments (Clarke, 1987; Boulton & Hindmarsh, 1987), and these incorporate the subglacial water pressure as one of the principal controlling variables. This pressure depends upon the meltwater flux, the ice mass geometry (which controls the hydraulic gradient and the tendency for ice flow to close down drainage passageways), the structure of the drainage system and the hydraulic geometry, sinuosity and boundary roughness of the major drainage routeways. Drainage system characteristics control both the magnitude of the water pressure associated with a given water flux, and the form of the water pressure/flux relationship (Rothlisberger, 1972; Walder, 1986; Kamb, 1987).

Thus, temporal and spatial variations in the character of subglacial drainage systems may play an important role in explaining such aspects of glacier flow as seasonal velocity variations and the occurrence of ice streams and glacier surges. Furthermore, since different types of drainage system display different characteristic flow velocities, residence times and water storage behaviours, they exert a profound influence on the relationship between surface melting and meltwater runoff.

Unfortunately, the application and testing of theoretical models of subglacial water flow is severely restricted by lack of knowledge of critical drainage system remnants exposed on recently deglaciated bedrock surfaces (Walder & Hallet, 1979; Hallet & Anderson, 1980; Sharp et al., 1989) and of the properties of eskers (Shreve, 1985). Conditions at the glacier bed are highly dynamic, however, and it is hard to relate such static observations to variable flow conditions. Direct observation of the relevant parameters in active subglacial environments is constrained by their physical inaccessibility. There is therefore a need to find indirect methods of determining drainage system characteristics and their variation in time and space.

It has been argued that the analysis of data relating to the quantity and quality of meltwaters exiting from the termini of glaciers has the potential to fulfil this role (e.g. Collins, 1977; 1979). This makes intuitive sense because meltwaters demonstrably pick up solute and suspended sediment during their passage from glacier surface to glacier terminus, and their ability to do so presumably varies depending upon such factors as their rate of flow, residence time, flow routing and access to supplies of atmospheric oxygen and carbon dioxide. All of these factors will be dependent upon drainage system characteristics. The challenge is to identify those water quality parameters which are sensitive indicators of these characteristics, to work out how to interpret their patterns of variation, and to design and implement programs of measurement which collect the necessary information at appropriate temporal and spatial scales.

Existing studies of meltwater quality characteristics have had limited success in this regard, and have yet to provide significant insights into the character and behaviour of subglacial drainage systems. Indeed, a recent review of englacial and subglacial hydrology makes no mention of such studies (Hooke, 1989). It is possible to identify a number of reasons for this but the fundamental problem is that field measurement programs have been designed without regard to the insights provided by theoretical analyses of subglacial water flow (e.g. Rothlisberger, 1972; Walder, 1986; Kamb, 1987) and processes of solute acquisition (Raiswell, 1984; Souchez & Lemmens, 1987). Many programs have been technology-led; for instance, electrical conductivity has often been measured because it is cheap and easy to do (Fenn, 1987). Furthermore, they have failed to monitor the most appropriate parameters (anions have rarely been monitored although they provide important information about processes of solute acquisition), failed to address issues of fundamental importance to the interpretation of water quality data (e.g. the source of protons consumed in weathering reactions), employed weak and inappropriate interpretative procedures (e.g. simplistic mixing models, and descriptive rating and time series methods), and failed to make independent measurements (e.g. dye tracer, water balance and borehole water pressure studies) which allow proper testing of the interpretations proposed. This is not to deny that significant progress has been made in other areas (e.g. in water quality forecasting and the estimation of sediment and solute yields), but simply to argue that the contribution to our understanding of subglacial hydrology has been minimal.

In this paper I try to identify those questions relating to the behaviour of subglacial drainage systems which might be answered by the analysis of water quality data, and suggest the sorts of measurements which are required. To do this, it is necessary to couple understanding of the behaviour of different types of subglacial drainage system with that of processes of solute acquisition in glacial environments (Raiswell, 1984). Limitations of space preclude a comprehensive treatment, so I deal with two types of drainage system for which theory is particularly well-developed: the ice-walled conduit system (Rothlisberger, 1972) and the linked-cavity system (Walder, 1986), and with solutes rather than suspended sediments. This should, nonetheless, suffice to exemplify the approach which I wish to promote.

Hydrological questions to be tackled

Given the present level of understanding, it remains necessary to concentrate attention on some of the most basic questions concerning subglacial hydrology. These questions are important, nevertheless, and only when we learn how to answer them will we be able to proceed to ask more sophisticated ones. The questions are: (a) what type of drainage system(s) underlie(s) a particular glacier?; (b) do(es) the system(s) evolve(s) over time?; (c) if so, what factors are responsible for this evolution?, and (d) what flow conditions exist within the system(s) - are drainage pathways completely or partially water-filled, and is this situation time and space-dependent? Only when we can answer these questions will we begin to understand the runoff response of glaciers, their water storage behaviour, and the coupling between their hydrology and their flow.

Solute acquisition by glacial meltwaters

Four principal processes are involved in the acquisition of solutes (ions and neutral species) by meltwaters (Raiswell, 1984; Souchez & Lemmens, 1987; Tranter et al., in prep.). Ion exchange is the rapid, reversible exchange of ions between a solution and a solid surface (Stumm & Morgan, 1981). Surface exchange of base cations from freshly comminuted mineral surfaces for protons in solution is a rapid and largely irreversible process which occurs in the initial stages of water-sediment reaction (Lerman, 1979). It alters the mineral surface in such a way that it becomes difficult to exchange the adsorbed protons for dissolved base cations. It thus results in an increase in pH and a reduction in the partial pressure of carbon dioxide ($p(CO_2)$) of the liquid. This initiates gaseous diffusion reactions (carbonation) which tend to restore the $p(CO_2)$ in the liquid to equilibrium with that in the atmosphere and renew the supply of protons (by dissociation of H_2CO_3 into bicarbonate and hydrogen ions). These protons are then consumed in reactions which involve the slow (incongruent) dissolution of the mineral lattice, and are replaced largely by base cations. Continued weathering by this means demands renewal of the proton source.

The primary factors governing the extent of solute acquisition by glacial meltwaters are (i) the chemistry of the source waters. This may vary through a melt season as a consequence of the initial leaching of solute from the seasonal snowpack (Johannessen et al., 1977), and spatially across a glacier surface as a consequence of variations in the balance between snow and ice sources and in the degree of contact with supraglacial sediment; (ii) the availability of protons, which may be derived from snowpack leaching, carbonation, or oxidation reactions, particularly those involving sulphide minerals (e.g. pyrite; Raiswell, 1984); (iii) the duration of contact between meltwaters and weatherable rock material; (iv) the grain size, shape and mineralogical properties of particulate rock material in the subglacial environment; and (v) the ratio between meltwater volume and the surface area of rock material available for weathering.

Different types of drainage system may be characterised by different proton sources, rock availability and weatherability, and rock-water contact times, and hence by differing magnitudes and pathways of solute acquisition. Temporal changes in these properties of any one type of system may result from varying source water composition and water flux. Where different parts of a single glacier are underlain by different types of drainage system (e.g. Humphrey *et al.*, 1986; Willis *et al.*, 1990), bulk water chemistry reflects mixing of waters from the different systems, which will often be non-conservative (Raiswell, 1984).

The above discussion points to an important linkage between those reactions which renew the proton supply (carbonation, pyrite oxidation), and those which consume protons (ion exchange, surface exchange, lattice dissolution). This provides a natural basis for the classification of subglacial weathering environments. Where the reactions which supply protons keep pace with those which consume them, the $p(CO_2)$ of the liquid remains in equilibrium with that of the atmosphere, and the system is said to be open (Thomas & Raiswell, 1984). Where the two sets of reactions proceed at different rates, however, the system is said to be closed (Raiswell & Thomas, 1984), with high $p(CO_2)$ if protons are supplied more rapidly than they are consumed (so that pH is lowered and CO_2 must diffuse out of solution to restore equilibrium with the atmosphere), or low $p(CO_2)$ if the reverse occurs. It is important to realise that the causes of closed system conditions can be physical (i.e. lack of access to atmospheric CO_2 in full subglacial conduits) or kinetic (i.e. CO_2 is available, but diffuses into solution too slowly to replace protons consumed in weathering reactions) (Raiswell, 1984).

Although all three types of weathering environment are known to occur, insufficient data on meltwater chemistry have been published to ascertain spatial and temporal changes in their relative importance within individual glaciers, or to permit evaluation of their hydrological significance. Raiswell (1984) suggested that 'supraglacial' and 'englacial' waters, which he argued had short water-rock contact times, limited access to weatherable sediment and/or free access to atmospheric CO_2 sources, were likely to have open system characteristics. By contrast, he argued that 'subglacial' waters, with long residence times, access to large amounts of sediment, and restricted access to atmospheric CO_2 would have closed system characteristics.

This argument, however, concentrates on carbonation as the principal proton source, and assumes that supraglacial waters are in equilibrium with the atmosphere and that weathering of suspended sediment

transported by waters flowing through major subglacial conduits is minimal (although the latter is discussed in the context of post-mixing reaction). It is also confused by the usage of the term 'englacial' in the sense proposed by Collins (1979, p.349), which includes 'arterial conduits located at the bed', and by imprecise definition of the hydrological environment from which 'subglacial' waters are believed to be derived. It is therefore useful to re-evaluate the implications for solute acquisition of what we know about two of the principal types of subglacial drainage system - the arterial conduit, and the linked-cavity system.

Arterial drainage conduits

Rothlisberger (1972) argued that much of the meltwater draining from glaciers would be routed via a relatively small number of ice-walled conduits. Dye tracer studies have confirmed the existence of such a system beneath the ablation areas of a number of glaciers during the later parts of summer melt seasons (Collins, 1982; Burkimsher, 1983). Such conduits are characterised by high flow velocities, short and discharge-dependent residence times and limited storage capacity. Water flow is confined to a relatively small proportion of the glacier bed. Under steady state conditions there is an inverse relationship between water pressure and discharge, but the reverse is true under transient conditions of rapidly varying water flux (Spring & Hutter, 1982). Whilst Rothlisberger assumed that conduits would always flow full of water, others have argued that steady state open channel flow may occur, particularly when discharges are high, bed slopes steep and overlying ice thin (Lliboutry, 1983; Hooke, 1984). Transient open channel flow is likely when discharges are low and/or declining. The occurrence of open/closed channel flow is of fundamental importance as a control on the location of drainage conduits, and on the manner in which the drainage system adjusts to varying water flux.

From a hydrochemical point of view, probably the most significant characteristic of arterial conduits is the short residence times (of the order of a few hours) associated with them. These will mean that solute acquisition is either limited or dominated by rapid reactions. When solute acquisition is limited, water characteristics will be inherited largely from the supraglacial source. Although Raiswell (1984) suggests that supraglacial meltwaters are likely to have open system characteristics, this is not necessarily the case. Thus, high $p(CO_2)$ waters may occur during the early stages of snowmelt when they are enriched in protons leached from the snowpack. Such waters are likely to be characterised by relatively high concentrations of atmospherically-derived NO_3^-, Cl^- and SO_4^-, also leached from the snowpack. Retention of high $p(CO_2)$ characteristics by bulk meltwaters may, however, demand a physical drainage environment which restricts degassing (i.e. full conduits), or residence times which are too short to allow re-equilibrium with the atmosphere. Low

$p(CO_2)$ supraglacial waters may also be possible, for instance on heavily crevassed glaciers with short supraglacial residence times which do not permit ice-derived meltwaters to equilibrate with the atmosphere (temperate glacier ice is often significantly depleted in CO_2 compared with air-equilibrated meltwater; Weiss et al., 1972). Insufficient measurements have been made to properly characterise the chemistry of supraglacial meltwaters, and special techniques may be required to determine accurately the pH and bicarbonate contents of these very dilute solutions.

Modification of the hydrochemical properties of source waters will depend upon the extent to which these waters have access to supplies of weatherable sediment. Rapid, turbulent flows may be capable of mobilising suspended sediment but sediment supplies are likely to be limited by the restricted spatial extent of the conduit system. It is nevertheless clear that meltwater streams can carry very high concentrations of suspended sediment (Gurnell, 1987). This may be delivered to major conduits by a more-distributed drainage system, perhaps at times when the drainage system as a whole undergoes major reorganisation (Collins, 1989; see below). The extent to which sediment acts as a source of solute will depend upon precisely where it is introduced to the major conduits. If this occurs close to the glacier terminus, limited weathering is likely, but if it occurs close to the conduit head, more extensive weathering is possible. In the latter case, protons will be consumed rapidly in ion exchange and surface exchange reactions, but residence times may be too short to permit re-supply of protons by carbonation or pyrite oxidation.

This will be particularly true if conduits are full and access to CO_2 sources is restricted. Waters draining via major conduits are therefore likely to derive their protons primarily from carbonation which occurs before they enter the glacier (Raiswell, 1984) or, in the early season, from snowpack leaching. In the former case, bicarbonate will be the dominant anion found in the waters. In the latter case, NO_3^-, Cl^- and SO_4^- will have greater relative importance. Bulk waters may be either open system or closed system, low $p(CO_2)$ in character, depending upon the extent to which suspended sediment has been weathered. Temporal variations in suspended sediment concentration may thus be reflected in the $p(CO_2)$ of bulk meltwaters.

Linked-cavity Systems

Where glaciers slide over irregular bedrock topography, cavities often open up in the lee of bedrock bumps. The pressure in such cavities is less than the average ice overburden pressure, so they become the focus of local meltwater drainage. Since the overall pressure gradient within an ice mass continues to drive water flow towards the ice margin, however, hydrological linkages develop between adjacent cavities, creating a linked-cavity drainage system (Walder, 1986; Kamb, 1987). Such a system is

distributed (in that water flow occurs widely over the glacier bed) and has considerable storage capacity (Hallet & Anderson, 1980). Drainage is, however, constricted at inter-cavity linkages so flow rates are slow and only weakly-dependent upon discharge (Walder, 1986). Residence times are therefore an order of magnitude longer than in arterial conduit systems (Walder, 1986). Cavities are opened by the sliding process, and therefore exist throughout the year. They are, however, enlarged by enhanced sliding if water at a pressure in excess of the local ice pressure drains into them (Iken, 1981). They may therefore be water-filled or partially air-filled. They are most likely to be water-filled under conditions of rising water flux at the start of the melt season (Iken et al., 1983).

The potential for solute acquisition in a linked-cavity system is considerable. Although water flow velocities may be insufficient to mobilise large volumes of suspended sediment, the widespread nature of flow will ensure that waters come into contact with weatherable material. Limited mobilisation of fine-grained material may even enhance solute acquisition by ensuring that solute sources do not become exhausted over time. Long residence times favour solute acquisition, and permit slower reactions such as lattice dissolution and pyrite oxidation to become important. The considerable storage capacity of linked-cavity systems buffers the waters within them against dilution by surface-derived meltwaters. It thus seems probable that the hydrochemical characteristics of waters draining from linked-cavity systems will differ considerably from those of source waters. These characteristic may, however, be highly variable, depending upon whether the cavities are completely or partially water-filled, because access to supplies of oxygen and carbon dioxide will exert a strong influence on the nature of the weathering reactions which can take place.

Where cavities are water-filled, proton supply by carbonation will be restricted. Pyrite oxidation may continue, however, releasing protons which are consumed in weathering reactions. If, as is often the case, the dominant weathering reaction involving long residence time waters is carbonate dissolution (Raiswell, 1984), neutralisation of the acidity released by pyrite oxidation results in a significant increase in the bicarbonate content of the waters with no associated change in their pH:

$$4FeS_2 + 15O_2 + 8H_2O \rightarrow 2Fe_2O_3 + 16H^+ + 8SO_4^- \quad (1)$$

$$16CaCO_3 + 16H^+ \rightarrow 16Ca^{2+} + 16HCO_3^- \quad (2)$$

According to equation (3) below, this results in an increase in the $p(CO_2)$ of the waters:

$$p(CO_2) = (H^+ HCO_3^-)/(K_H K_1) \quad (3)$$

where K_H is the Henry's Law constant ($10^{-1.5}$ atm) and $K_1 = 10^{-6.4}$ moles l^{-1}. Thus, the combination of pyrite oxidation and carbonate dissolution in water-filled cavities produces high $p(CO_2)$ waters which are enriched in calcium, bicarbonate and sulphate (Tranter *et al.*, in prep.). This tendency will be enhanced in the early melt season when acid snow-melt may drain via the linked-cavity system.

In reality, the situation may be more complicated because pyrite oxidation in water-filled cavities may be restricted by the lack of an oxygen source. Thus, water-filled cavities may become reducing environments in which species such as nitrate are reduced to replace oxygen consumed in pyrite oxidation. This process may be relatively slow, so that solute acquisition in full cavities is limited by the physical constraint on gaseous diffusion reactions. In this case, waters draining from water-filled cavities may be characterised by low dissolved oxygen levels and nitrate concentrations. The physical constraint on degassing which exists in water-filled cavities may allow high $p(CO_2)$ waters to survive if the linked cavity system provides the primary drainage route-way from the glacier. The long residence times in linked cavity systems will, however, allow degassing to occur in partially water-filled cavities, so that high $p(CO_2)$ waters are unlikely to drain from such a system. Furthermore, the $p(CO_2)$ of meltwaters may be lowered rapidly if cavity-derived waters drain into arterial conduits and come into contact with large quantities of weatherable suspended sediment.

Drainage reorganisation

Collins (1989) has noted that suspended sediment is commonly flushed from glaciers in pulses which are independent of discharge variations, and argued that such pulses are indicative of reorganisation of the subglacial drainage system. Since availability of suspended sediment may be a major influence on the hydrochemical characteristics of meltwaters draining via arterial conduits, it is useful to consider what such reorganisation may involve. Arterial conduits which develop during the summer melt season are likely to be closed down by ice deformation during the winter (Rothlisberger & Lang, 1987), and must therefore re-form each year. Cavities, however, are formed by the process of sliding and will persist through the winter and act as the major subglacial drainage pathway in the early melt season. The process of conduit formation involves a concentration of water flow into restricted areas of the glacier bed, and causes a sharp reduction in subglacial water pressure (Fowler, 1987a; Kamb, 1987). It is thus likely to result in a steep local water pressure gradient between the residual distributed drainage system and the incipient conduit, and in strong water flow from distributed system to conduit. This flow may be responsible for injecting suspended sediment into conduits during episodes of channel growth. Dye tracer studies at the Haut Glacier d'Arolla, Switzerland, indicate that headward growth of conduits occurs discontinuously throughout the melt season (Nienow *et al.*, in prep.), thus creating conditions which favour the lowering of $p(CO_2)$ in waters draining via major conduits. The process of

conduit growth may initiate drainage of cavities which had filled with water earlier in the season, thus triggering a switch from reducing to oxidising conditions within residual cavities. This may be marked by the reappearance in bulk meltwaters of species which were reduced under full cavity conditions (e.g. nitrate).

The way forward

The above discussion leads to four major conclusions which must be taken into account in the design of water quality monitoring programs intended to shed light on subglacial hydrological conditions.

(1) Temporal variations in the character of source waters are largely unknown but changes in acidity, $p(CO_2)$ and anion/cation concentrations should be anticipated. These changes may be reflected in the hydrochemistry of bulk meltwaters either directly (through inherited characteristics which as NO_3^- and Cl^- loading) or indirectly (through variations in the weathering potential of the waters). There is thus a need to monitor the chemistry of supraglacial waters, and to include measurements of pH and the concentrations of anions and dissolved gases in the program.

(2) The two types of drainage system considered differ markedly from each other in terms of the residence times of waters passing through them. This may be reflected in the extent of solute acquisition during subglacial drainage, the source of protons consumed in weathering reactions, and the nature of the weathering reactions themselves. Whilst measurements of a parameter such as electrical conductivity may be useful for quantifying the extent of solute acquisitions, they shed no light on the processes by which this has occurred. Monitoring of sulphate and bicarbonate concentrations should help to do this.

(3) Processes of solute acquisition within a given type of drainage system are likely to vary depending upon whether or not the system is water-filled. It is not, therefore, safe to assume that major changes in meltwater chemistry necessarily reflect changes in the type of subglacial drainage system. Water-filled conditions inhibit gaseous diffusion reactions which supply CO_2 and O_2 to meltwaters, and thus limit both pyrite oxidation and proton supply by carbonation. Whilst this may result in low $p(CO_2)$ waters, it should also be remembered that degassing is restricted in water-filled systems and that, where high $p(CO_2)$ waters can develop (as when pyrite oxidation and carbonate dissolution occur together in water-filled cavities), this may permit their survival. In linked-cavity systems, where residence times are long, water-filled conditions may create a reducing environment. Such changes are only likely to be detected by a relatively comprehensive monitoring program, which includes measurements of pH, anion and base cation concentrations and dissolved oxygen.

(4) When the character of subglacial drainage systems evolves over time, the process of drainage

reorganisation may create conditions which differ from those which occur in stable drainage systems of either type. In particular, conduit growth may initiate the transition from wholly to partially water-filled cavities, and may be important in controlling the supply of weatherable suspended sediment to downstream sections of conduit. Interactions between suspended sediment supply and weathering processes may be particularly important as an influence on the hydrochemistry of waters draining via arterial conduits. It will therefore be necessary to include measurements of suspended sediment concentration in any monitoring programme.

In summary, it can be concluded that for meltwater quality monitoring programs to have any prospect of elucidating subglacial hydrological conditions, they should include parallel measurements of the pH, dissolved oxygen content, major anion and base cation concentrations and suspended sediment content of both supraglacial and bulk meltwaters.

Although measurements of the electrical conductivity of meltwaters are cheap and easy to make, they provide no direct information about the character of subglacial weathering processes and, when collected in isolation, are unlikely to clarify the subtleties of subglacial hydrological conditions. This will demand a much broader hydrochemical database. Although there may be strong relationships between electrical conductivity and the concentrations of individual cations and anions (Gurnell & others, submitted), these relationships are empirical and likely to vary between glaciers. They can only be established, therefore, if concentrations of cations and anions are measured directly. Measurements of anion and cation concentration are thus a fundamental part of any water quality monitoring program designed to elucidate subglacial hydrological conditions. In view of the scatter which inevitably characterises statistically-defined relationships, it seems preferable to utilise such direct measurements for hydrological inference rather than synthetic records of anion and cation concentration constructed from electrical conductivity data.

The major benefit of electrical conductivity measurements is that they can be readily obtained using continuous recording devices. Whilst this may be important if one's objective is estimation of solute yield or water quality forecasting, it seems unlikely that major changes in subglacial hydrological conditions occur sufficiently rapidly for this to be essential if the objective is hydrological inference. For the purpose of monitoring seasonal evolution of the subglacial drainage system, daily or even weekly measurements of the range of parameters described above will provide far more information than continuous monitoring of electrical conductivity alone (Gurnell & others, submitted). Repeat sampling over 24-hour periods may also be useful to determine the interactions which occur between different components of the drainage system over diurnal discharge cycles.

In addition to clarifying the type of measurement programme required to provide the information necessary to evaluate subglacial hydrological conditions, it is important to consider how this information should be interpreted. It should be stressed that hydrochemical data provide only indirect information about hydrological conditions. Although they do permit reconstruction of the dominant processes by which meltwaters have acquired their solute load, we are still dependent upon the insights provided by theoretical models to evaluate the hydrological conditions under which these processes are most likely to have operated. To a large extent, therefore, interpretations are constrained by the nature of available models, and we must be aware of the risk of reinforcing rather than rigorously testing these models.

Two courses of action seem advisable if we are to minimise this risk. First, we should endeavour to make independent measurements which allow us to evaluate the consistency of our interpretations. For instance, dye tracer experiments provide direct information about the residence time of meltwaters within glaciers, and this can be used to infer the structural characteristics of subglacial drainage systems and their patterns of change over time (Willis et al., 1990). By combining such experiments with water quality monitoring, it should be possible to determine the quality characteristics of meltwaters draining from different types of drainage system, and the water quality response to drainage evolution. Replication of such studies will lead to a firmer basis for the interpretation of water quality data collected in isolation. Second, we should be extremely cautious about employing procedures such as simplistic two-component mixing models (Collins 1977, 1979; Gurnell & Fenn, 1984) to interpret water quality data before we have made the detailed hydrological and hydrochemical measurements required to rigorously evaluate the assumptions which they make (e.g. two drainage components, unique and unchanging component chemistries, conservative mixing of drainage components). The above discussion suggests that the assumption of constant component chemistries is extremely unlikely to be correct, and it will result in calculation of component discharge fluctuations which are really a reflection of varying component water chemistries. Premature application of mixing models may therefore lead to erroneous conclusions about the behaviour of subglacial drainage systems. Such conclusions will only serve to confuse rather than further our understanding of subglacial hydrology.

Acknowledgements

The ideas embodied in this paper were developed in relation to work carried out under NERC grant GR3.7004A, and sharpened by stimulating discussions with Martyn Tranter, Giles Brown, Ian Willis, Peter Nienow and Chris Smart. I am grateful to Martyn Tranter, Byrn Hubbard and Tracy Brennand for their comments on an earlier draft of the manuscript. The paper was written while I was on sabbatical leave at the University of Alberta. I acknowledge receipt of a Royal Society/NSERC scientific exchange award, and thank Professors John England and John Shaw for their hospitality.

References

Bindschalder, R. 1983. The importance of pressurised subglacial water in sliding and separation at the glacier bed. *J. Glaciol.*, 29, 3-19.

Boulton, G.S. & Hindmarsh, R.C.A. 1987. Sediment deformation beneath glaciers: rheology and geological consequences. *J. Geophys. Res.*, 92(B9), 9059-9082.

Brukimsher, M. 1983. Investigations of glacier hydrological systems using dye tracer techniques: observations at Pasterzengletscher, Austria. *J. Glaciol.*, 29, 403-416.

Clarke, G.K.C. 1987. Subglacial till: a physical framework for its properties and processes. *J. Geophys. Res.*, 92(B9), 9023-9036.

Collins, D.N. 1977. Hydrology of an alpine glacier as indicated by the chemical composition of meltwater. *Zeitschrift für Gletscherkunde und Glazialgeologie,* 13, 219-238.

Collins, D.N. 1979. Quantitative determination of the hydrology of two alpine glaciers. *J. Glaciol.*, 23, 347-361.

Collins, D.N. 1982. Flow routing of meltwater in an alpine glacier as indicated by dye tracer tests. *Beitrage zur Geologie der Schweiz - Hydrologie*, 28, 523-534.

Collins, D.N. 1989. Seasonal development of subglacial drainage and suspended delivery to melt waters beneath an alpine glacier. *Ann. Glaciol.*, 13, 45-60.

Fenn, C.R. 1987. Electrical conductivity. In Gurnell, A. M. & Clark, M. J. (eds.) *Glacio-fluvial sediment transfer: an alpine perspective.* John Wiley and Sons, 377-414.

Fowler, A.C. 1987a. Sliding with cavity formation. *J. Glaciol.*, 33, 255-267.

Fowler, A. C. 1987b. A theory of glacier surges. *J. Geophys. Res.*, 92(B9), 9111-9120.

Gurnell, A. M. 1987. Suspended Sediment, In Gurnell, A. M. and Clark, M. J. (eds.) *Glacio-fluvial sediment transfer: an alpine perspective.* John Wiley and Sons, 305-354.

Gurnell, A. M. & Fenn, C. R. 1984. Flow separation, sediment source areas and suspended sediment in a proglacial stream. *Catena Suppl.*, 5, 110-119.

Gurnell, A. M., Brown, G. H. & Tranter,M. (In press). A sampling strategy to describe the temporal hydrochemical characteristics of an alpine proglacial stream. *Hydrological Processes.*

Hallet, B. & Anderson, R.S. 1980. Detailed glacial geomorphology of a proglacial bedrock area at Castleguard Glacier, Alberta, Canada. *Zeitschrift für Gletscherkunde und Glazialgeologie,* 16, 171-184.

Hooke, R. le B. 1984. On the role of mechanical energy in maintaining subglacial water conduits at atmospheric pressure. *J. Glaciol.*, 30, 180-187.

Hooke, R. le B. 1989. Englacial and subglacial hydrology: a qualitative review. *Arctic & Alpine Res.*, 21, 221-233.

Humphrey, N., Raymond, C. F. & Harrison, W. D. 1986. Discharges of turbid water during mini-surges of Variegated Glacier, Alaska, USA. *J. Glaciol.*, 32, 195-207.

Iken, A. 1981. The effect of the subglacial water pressure on the sliding velocity of a glacier in an idealised numerical model. *J. Glaciol.*, 27, 407-421.

Iken, A., Rothlisberger, H., Flottron, A. & Haeberli, W. 1983. The uplift of the Unteraargletscher at the beginning of the melt season - a consequence of water storage at the bed? *J. Glaciol.*, 29, 28-47.

Iken, A. & Bindschadler, R.A. 1986. Combined measurements of subglacial water pressure and surface velocity of the Findelengletscher, Switzerland: conclusions about the drainage system and sliding mechanism. *J. Glaciol.*, 32, 101-119.

Johannessen, M., Dale, T., Gjessing, E.T., Henriksen, A. & Wright, R.F. 1977. Acid precipitation in Norway: the regional distribution of contaminants in snow and the chemical concentration processes during snowmelt. *IAHS Publication No. 118*, 116-120.

Kamb, B. 1987. Glacier surge mechanism based on linked cavity configuration of the basal water conduit system. *J. Geophys. Res.*, 92(B9), 9083-9100.

Kamb, B. & Engelhardt, H.H. 1987. Waves of accelerated motion in a glacier approaching surge: the min-surges of Variegated Glacier, Alaska. *J. Glaciol.*, 33, 27-46.

Lerman, A. 1979. *Geochemical processes: water and sediment environments.* Wiley-Interscience, 481 pp.

Lliboutry, L. 1983. Modifications to the theory of intraglacial passageways for the case of sub-glacial ones. *J. Glaciol.*, 29, 216-226.

Raiswell, R. 1984. Chemical models of solute acquisition in glacial meltwaters. *J. Glaciol,* 30, 49-57.

Raiswell, R. & Thomas, A.G. 1984. Solute acquisition in glacial meltwaters. I. Fjallsjokull (south-east Iceland): bulk meltwaters with closed-system characteristics. *J. Glaciol.*, 30, 35-43.

Rothlisberger, H. 1792. Water pressure in intra- and sub-glacial channels. *J. Glaciol.*, 11, 177-204.

Rothlisberger, H. & Lang, H. 1987. Glacial hydrology. In Gurnell, A.M. and Clark, M.J. (eds.) *Glacio-fluvial sediment transfer: an alpine perspective.* Chichester, John Wiley and Sons, 207-284.

Sharp, M., Gemmell, J.C. & Tison, J-L 1989. Structure and stability of the former subglacial drainage system of the Glacier de Tsanfleuron, Switzerland. *Earth Surf. Proc. & Land.*, 14, 119-134.

Shreve, R.L. 1985. Esker characteristics in terms of glacier physics. Katahdin esker system, Maine. *Bull. Geol. Soc., America,* 96, 639-646.

Souchez, R.A. & Lemmens, M.M. 1987. Solutes. In Gurnell, A.M. and Clark, M.J. (eds.) *Glacio-fluvial sediment transfer: an alpine perspective.* Chichester, John Wiley and Sons, 285-303.

Spring, U. & Hutter, K. 1982. Conduit flow of a fluid through its solid phase and its application to intraglacial channel flow. *Int. J. Engng Sci.,* 20, 327-363.

Stumm, W. & Morgan, J.J. 1981. *Aquatic chemistry: an introduction emphasising chemical equilibria in natural waters.* New York, Wiley-Interscience.

Thomas, A.G. & Raiswell, R. 1984. Solute acquisition in glacial meltwaters. II. Argentiere (French Alps): bulk meltwaters with open system characteristics. *J. Glaciol.,* 30, 44-48.

Tranter, M., Brown, G.H., Raiswell, R. & Sharp, M. (In prep.) On solute acquisition by alpine glacial meltwaters. To be submitted to *J. Glaciol.*

Walder, J.S. 1986. Hydraulics of subglacial cavities. *J. Glaciol.,* 32, 439-445.

Walder, J.S. & Hallet, B. 1979. Geometry of former subglacial water channels and cavities. *J. Glaciol.,* 23, 335-346.

Weiss, R.F., Bucher, P., Oeschger, H. & Craig, H. 1972. Compositional variations of gases in temperate glaciers. *Earth & Planet. Sci. Lett.,* 16, 178-184.

Willis, I.C., Sharp, M. & Richards, K.S. 1990. Configuration of the drainage system of Midtdalsbreen, Norway, as indicated by dye-tracing experiments. *J. Glaciol.,* 36, 89-101.

Alpine glacier hydrology inferred from a proglacial river monitoring programme

A.M. Gurnell, M.J. Clark, M. Tranter, G.H. Brown & C.T. Hill

Abstract

This paper describes and interprets time series of discharge, suspended sediment concentration, electrical conductivity and selected solutes from a monitoring programme on the proglacial river of the Haut Glacier d'Arolla during June-August 1989, inclusive. These data were collected as part of an integrated glacio-hydrological study of the Haut Arolla basin, but this paper concentrates upon the glacio-hydrological inferences that can be made from twice-daily sampling of the river close to the times of maximum and minimum flow. Analysis of these time series data indicates five hydrologically distinct periods in the ablation season which may correspond to changes in the source areas and the routing of meltwater within the basin.

Introduction

As part of an integrated study of the glacio-hydrology of the Haut Arolla glacier basin, Valais, Switzerland, time series of the climatic inputs to the basin (incident radiation, air temperature, wind speed and direction, relative humidity and precipitation) and the proglacial river outputs (discharge, suspended sediment concentration, electrical conductivity, pH and the concentration of a range of solutes, including Ca^{2+}, Mg^{2+}, K^+, Na^+, SO_4^{2-}, NO_3^-, HCO_3^-) were collected from June to August inclusive, 1989. Many of these time series were monitored with a resolution of one hour, but in the case of the solute data full ablation season monitoring was based on two meltwater samples a day, collected at 10.00h and 17.00h to approximately match the timing of maximum and minimum flow. This paper concentrates on the magnitude of processes in the proglacial river at these times and uses these data to interpret the effects of the changes in the source areas and routing of meltwater in the basin.

A high level alpine glacier, such as the Haut Glacier d'Arolla, has a short ablation (melt) season. The data presented here for June-August inclusive, span this season in 1989 from initially complete snow cover across the basin to the first snow of the following winter season. Thus, the data represent periods of snow melt progressing from the proglacial zone and gradually extending up-glacier to reveal the maximum amount of glacier ice by the end of August. Meltwater is initially generated almost entirely by snowmelt but by the end of the observation period the majority of the meltwater is derived from icemelt. In addition, the active sources of the snow and ice meltwater cover an increasing area as the melt season progresses, so that the centre of gravity of the area contributing meltwater moves gradually up-glacier and away from the proglacial monitoring site throughout the monitoring period. There are some small hanging glaciers within the basin, which would be affected by the spatial shift in processes described above. There is no attempt to separate the role of these glaciers in the present paper. Thus, reference to the Haut Glacier d'Arolla should be taken to include all areas of permanent snow and ice located upstream of the proglacial river monitoring site.

Field and laboratory methods

The full justification for the twice daily sampling programme for solutes is presented elsewhere (Gurnell et al, 1991), but in the context of the present paper it is important to establish the degree to which such sampling times reflect the extremes of hydrochemical processes in a system which is largely driven by the diurnal pattern of radiation input. Many researchers have illustrated how the diurnal rhythm of radiation input is reflected in a delayed but positive response in discharge (e.g. Rothlisberger & Lang, 1987) and suspended sediment concentration (e.g. Gurnell, 1987), and a delayed but inverse pattern in electrical conductivity and the concentration of many solutes (e.g. Collins, 1979; Fenn, 1987a and b; Tranter & Raiswell, in press) resulting from the dilution of longer residence time waters by the diurnal inputs of fresh meltwater. Although there may be lags or leads between maximum and minimum diurnal discharge and the sediment and solute concentrations transported, such lags or leads rarely exceed two hours in small glacier basins such as the Haut Arolla Basin (e.g. Gurnell *et al*, 1988). The basin of the Haut Glacier d'Arolla has a compound accumulation area consisting of two main basins which feed the glacier tongue. The basin has an area of 12 km², of which 6 km² is covered by permanent snow and ice, and an altitudinal range of 2560 m at the glacier snout and main river gauging site rising to 3838 m at the highest point on the watershed. The sampling times of 10h and 17h (local time) were selected on the basis of discharge records from previous summer melt seasons. The hourly discharge and electrical conductivity observations for the 1989 ablation season reported here suggest that such sample times were sufficiently near to the maximum and minimum levels of both of these variables to give a reasonable reflection of the changing behaviour of diurnal extremes in the time series monitored.

Early in the season diurnal discharge cycles were absent, but by mid June the cycles were established with the minimum and maximum flow (11h and 20h) and maximum and minimum conductivity (11h and 19h), slightly later than the sampling time. During July and August, minimum discharge and maximum conductivity occurred between 8 and 10h, maximum discharge occurred between 16 and 20h (most commonly at 17 or 18h), and minimum conductivity occurred between 15 and 18h (most commonly at 15 or 16h). This suggests that the time series collected at 10h and 17h provide a good representation of the range of diurnal discharge and conductivity, and are, therefore, likely to provide a reasonable represent-ation in the range of the other variables monitored.

The observations of discharge and solute and suspended sediment concentrations presented in this paper were obtained as follows:

Continuous discharge records (in m³s⁻¹) were supplied by Grande Dixence S.A., who monitor flows at a rectangular weir located in their meltwater intake structure, 1 km from the glacier snout. All other variables were monitored close to the glacier snout.

Solute concentrations were determined from hand samples of meltwater. *Bulk meltwater samples* were immediately vacuum filtered through a 0.45 μm cellulose nitrate filter membrane, using a Nalgene filter unit and handpump. Apparatus and filter paper were rinsed three times with filtrate, wetting all inside surfaces. An aliquot of 150 ml was then rapidly filtered, and decanted into two Azlon poly-propylene bottles, which were also rinsed three times with filtrate. This first, rapidly filtered solution was used for pH and alkalinity determinations. A second 150 ml aliquot of sample was then filtered and decanted into two rinsed bottles. One solution was acidified with 1 ml of 50% Analar HNO_3^- and used for cation analysis, while the other unacidified solution was used for determination of anions. An

Orion SA250 portable meter, with a Ross combina-tion electrode (81555C) and automatic temperature compensator (917001) was used for the determination of pH. During June and July standard BDH buffer powder solutions of pH 7.00 and 9.20 were used to calibrate the electrode. Orion low-ionic strength buffer solutions were used during August 1989. Buffers and sample solutions were placed in a water-bath at room temperature to further reduce ambient temperature effects. Precision of replicate measure-ments was typically ±0.2 pH units (range 0.01-0.44). *Total alkalinity* was determined by titration of 25 ml of filtered solution with 1 mmol HCl to an endpoint of 4.5 using a mixed BDH indicator. Titre volumes ranged from 1.10 - 11.20 ml. Precision was ±2%.

Continuous recording of *electrical conductivity* was obtained (in μScm^{-1}) from a pHOX 57 (Mk. 2) conductivity and water temperature recorder, with a resin carbon electrode probe (cell constant 1.00), connected to a Delta-T logger. Accuracy for EC is ±5%. *Major cation and anion concentrations* in the bulk meltwater samples were determined on return to the laboratory. Concentrations were estimated in $\mu equiv\ l^{-1}$ and are presented in this way throughout the present paper. Storage time ranged from 100 - 200 days. Ca, Mg, Na, K were determined by atomic absorption spectrophotometry on a Pye-Unicam SP9 spectrophotometer, using an air-acetylene flame. Ca and Mg were determined in absorption mode, whereas Na and K were determined in emission mode. A releasing agent $(La(NO_3)_3)$ and an ionisation suppressant (CsCl) were added to the samples prior to analysis (Brown and Tranter, in prep.). Accuracy of the major cation analysis is ±5%, as determined from standard additions. Precision of replicate measure-ments is also ±5%. SO_4^{2-} and NO_3^- were determined by ion chromatography on a Dionex 4000i Ion Chromatograph using an IonPac AS4A analytical column. Precision is ±3%.

Suspended sediment concentration was estimated (in mgl^{-1}) from continuous turbidity measurements using a Partech 7000-series model 3RP suspended solids monitor fitted with a single head probe. Calibration values of suspended sediment concentration were estimated at a two-hourly resolution by filtration of meltwater samples, collected using an Isco pump sampler, and filtered through pre-weighed Whatman 40 filter papers.

Temporal patterns within and between time series

Figures 1 to 3 present the time series of some of the variables monitored at 10h and 17h at the proglacial monitoring station over the 92-day field season. The time series have been smoothed using a five-day, unweighted, running mean, so that the underlying patterns in the series are apparent and are not disguised by day-to-day detailed variability in the data. The discharge data (Figure 1) can be used to subdivide the time series into periods of differing hydrological characteristics. There is an initial period

5.10

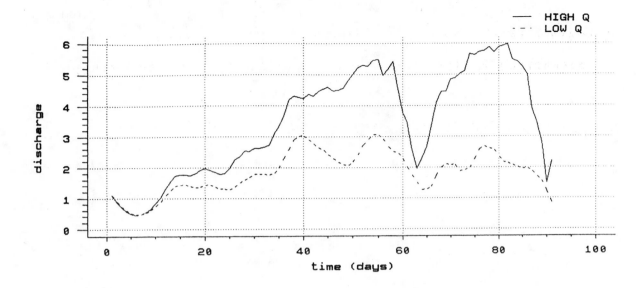

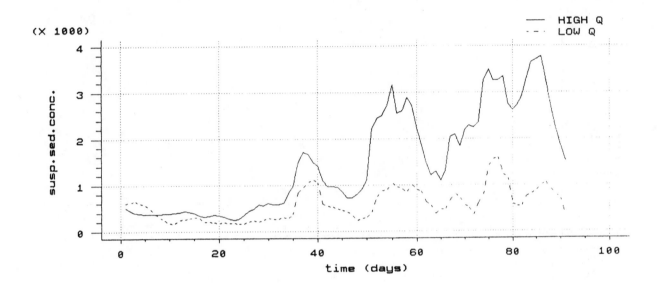

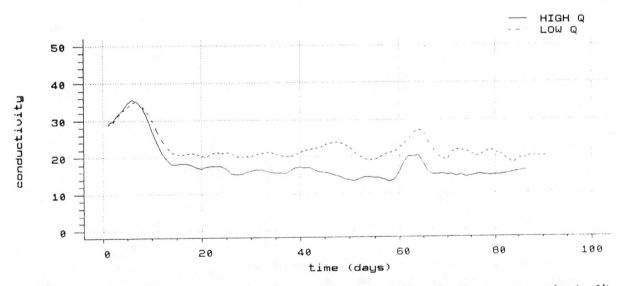

Figure 1   Discharge (m³s⁻¹), electrical conductivity (μScm⁻¹) and suspended sediment concentration (mgl⁻¹) at 10.00h (LOW Q) and 17.00h (HIGH Q), June-August inclusive, 1989

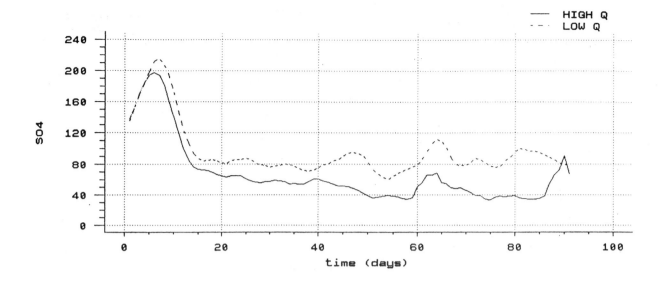

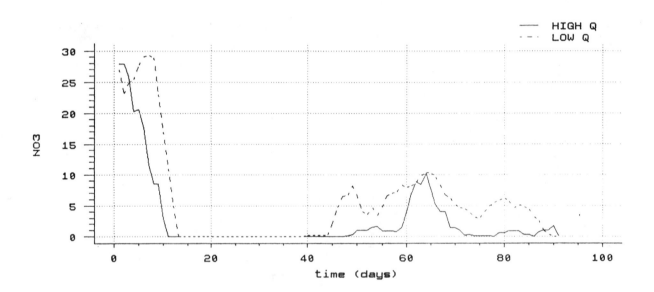

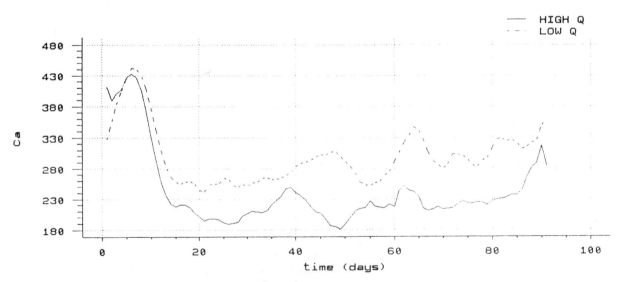

Figure 2 *SO$_4$, NO$_3$ and Ca (μequiv l^{-1}) at 10.00h (LOW Q) and 17.00h (HIGH Q), June-August inclusive, 1989*

5.12

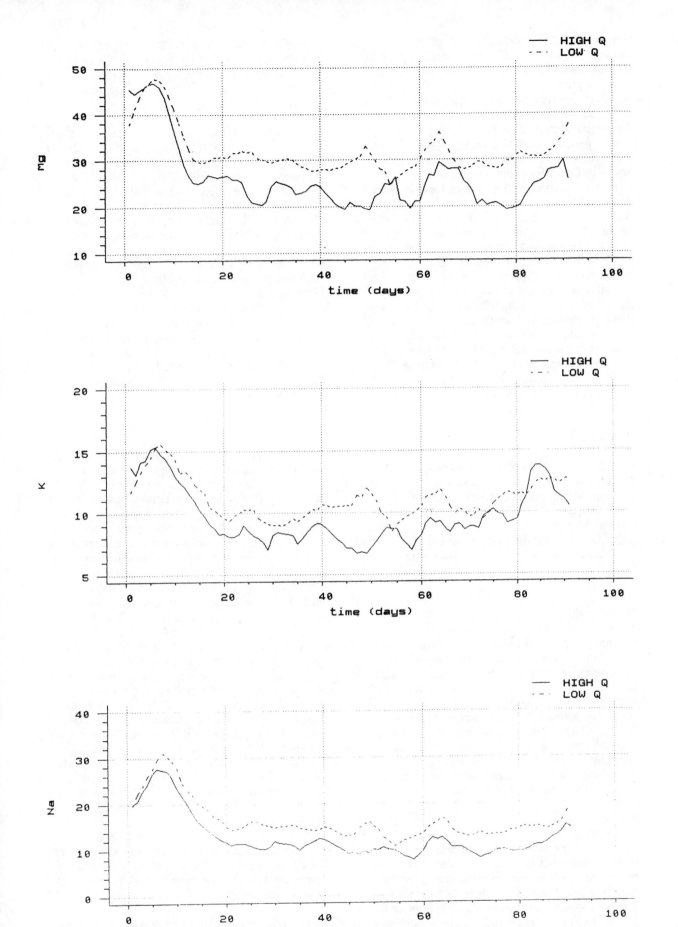

Figure 3   Mg, K and Na (μequiv l⁻¹) at 10.00h (LOW Q) and 17.00h (HIGH Q), June-August inclusive, 1989

of decreasing flow, followed by a slight flow increase, but with no identifiable diurnal rhythm in the melt (Period 1, days 1-8). This is followed by a period of gradually increasing flow, with subdued diurnal cycles (Period 2, days 9-16). Period 3 (days 16-38) shows a progressive increase in flow and in the diurnal range of flow. Period 4 (days 39-67) is another period of high discharges. It shows fluctuating low flows (two higher periods with an intervening lower flow period) but progressively increasing high flows, indicating an overall increase in diurnal flow amplitude, but not in 'baseflow' over the period. A snow fall event and several days of cold weather at the end of the period reduced high and low flows and diurnal flow amplitude dramatically. Period 5 (days 68-92) shows even greater diurnal flow amplitude than period 4 superimposed on slightly lower background flows. Again a snowfall event at the end of the period results in a dramatic fall in high and low flows and diurnal flow amplitude. These periods, which are identified from the discharge record, will form the framework for describing the time series presented in Figures 1 to 3 and then, in the following section, for interpreting the observed patterns in the context of the hydrological evolution of the glacier system through the melt season.

Period 1

During this period the low and relatively invariant flows are accompanied by relatively low and invariant suspended sediment concentrations and high solute concentrations. The solutes present high concentrations during low flows and also the concentrations fall away rapidly towards the end of the period as the discharge stabilises and starts to increase.

Period 2

During period 2 the gradual increase in discharge magnitude and the appearance of clear diurnal cycles in discharge are accompanied by a decrease in solute levels but an increase in the diurnal amplitude of fluctuations in concentrations of most solutes and in conductivity. NO_3 forms an exception to this pattern, since both its level and its diurnal range decrease. By the end of period 2, NO_3 is no longer detectable in the meltwater and does not become detectable again until the commencement of period 4. Suspended sediment concentration remains relatively stable during this period, although at the diurnal timescale, cycles in concentration become discernible.

Period 3

The gradual rise in both the magnitude and the amplitude of diurnal cycles in discharge are accompanied by similar trends in suspended sediment concentration. However, suspended sediment concentration shows a change in the rate of increase, from an initial gradual rise up to day 28, followed by a much more abrupt rise to a peak at the end of the period. Conductivity and solute concentrations remain low through the period but it is significant that all solutes,

to varying degrees, show an increase to a peak during high flows at the end of the period. This is particularly marked in the Ca high flow time series.

Period 4

Although high flows continue to increase until the snowfall at the end of this period, low flows fall and then peak again prior to the final low at the end of the period. The peaks in high flow and low flow suspended sediment concentration and in high flow conductivity and solute levels at the boundary between periods 3 and 4 mirror the peak in low flow discharges and the associated commencement of a period of increasing diurnal flow range. Conductivity and solute levels show peaks in low flow samples mirroring the lows in the low flow discharge levels. Similarly a peak in conductivity and solute levels during diurnal high flows mirrors the dip in high flow discharges caused by the snowfall event at the end of the period. NO_3 shows the same timing of peaks in concentration at high and low flows as the other solutes, but its fluctuations are far more marked and develop from a period where NO_3 was undetectable in the meltwater.

Period 5

This period is characterised by high discharge levels and high diurnal discharge ranges sandwiched between depressed discharges resulting from the effects of the two snowfall events at the ends of periods 4 and 5. Although there is only a single and prolonged peak in discharge during this period, there are two clear peaks in suspended sediment concentration in both the high and low flow time series. The first peak at high flows is slightly lower that the second and is associated with a smaller diurnal range such that the first peak in suspended sediment concentration in low flows is actually higher than the second peak. Conductivity remains low and relatively invariant during this period, but some solutes (e.g. Na, Mg, SO_4, and Ca) show a marked increase in concentration, particularly during the diurnal high flow, at the end of the period when discharge is depressed by a snow fall event. NO_3 concentrations appear to be negatively correlated with suspended sediment concentration rather than discharge variations at both high and low flows, whereas SO_4 and Ca tend to show an inverse relationship with suspended sediment concentration at low flows only, and K shows a positive relationship at high flows only.

Discussion

The patterns discerned in the time series provide a fascinating insight into the evolution of meltwater source areas and glacial drainage pathways through the ablation season.

The proglacial records during periods 1 and 2 are predominantly driven by snow melt. The transient snowline had not receded past the glacier snout by the end of period 2. In period 1 the air temperature at the glacier snout remained below freezing point and the discharge appears to be predominantly a recession flow from the snowpack from a warmer period at the commencement of monitoring, super-imposed upon a small background flow of long-residence time meltwater. The low suspended sediment concentrations are compatible with recession flow conditions (the source areas will be predominantly proglacial and will be located on the banks, bed and immediate flood plain of the pro-glacial stream) and the high conductivity and solute concentrations reflect the early phase of snowmelt when solutes are preferentially released from the snow pack, coupled with significant concentrations from the background flow. Thus the rapid decrease in conductivity and solute concentrations during period 2 results from the increase in meltwater being generated and the increase in the proportion of that meltwater coming from snow pack which has already experienced some melt and thus the major prefer-ential elution phase. Diurnal variations in solute concentration during phase 2 result from the effects of mixing of meltwaters of different residence times within the snow pack and the influence of longer residence time meltwater from the glacier itself, particularly towards the end of this period. The total disappearance of NO_3 at the end of period 2 is difficult to explain. It may result from the overdeep-ening of much of the glacier bed (revealed by radio-echo sounding through the ice) which may create a water storage zone at depth within the glacier up-stream of the lip of the overdeepened section. Altern-atively, there may be chemical reasons for the disap-pearance of nitrate associated with sulphide weather-ing, which are discussed in Sharp et al, (in prep.).

Period 3 shows a gradual increase in discharge reflecting increased meltwater generation both from snowmelt as the snowline moves up glacier (exposing approximately half of the main glacier tongue - about one third of the total glacier length - by the end of the period), and ice melt from the lower albedo glacier ice revealed by the retreating snow. The fact that the amplitude of diurnal discharge variations is small but slowly increases through the period, suggests that drainage of the glacier ice commences inefficiently (water goes into storage and is released in a damped way through the diurnal discharge cycle) but that the drainage system within and below the glacier gradu-ally improves during the period. Decreasing albedo also accelerates daytime melt and rapidly increases the high flows. Even at the end of period 3, the diurnal flow amplitude is not very great and it is possible to imagine the glacial drainage system gradually developing and rationalising down-valley of the snowline as it progresses up-glacier. Rothlisberger and Lang (1987) give an excellent description of how meltwater on alpine glaciers enters crevasses and goes into local storage early in the season. The crevasses then gradually propagate to the bed, where water may be stored in a rather dis-jointed series of cavities and other smaller stores. These eventually join up and a properly structured drainage system develops which can drain meltwaters

efficiently. The relatively thin ice in the lower section of the Haut Glacier d'Arolla tongue would probably permit the survival of the largest conduits from one ablation season to another, but this restrict-ed system would be progressively extended by the above processes within each ablation season. This type of drainage evolution and its propagation up-glacier, down-valley of the transient snow line would be expected to produce a pattern of increasing dis-charge, with increasing diurnal range. The peak in suspended sediment concentration, conductivity and solutes at the end of this period are probably a result of the expansion of the evolving drainage network across a substantial area of the lower glacier bed. Such a process would tap water that has been in resi-dence long enough to acquire an increased solute load and it would also expose the increasing flow levels to sediments stored within that area of the bed.

The progressive increase in peak discharge accompanied by a reduction in low flows at the beginning of period 4 is consistent with the mode of development of the drainage system described above. A high diurnal discharge amplitude is associated with a well developed system of conduits beneath the glacier that can efficiently drain meltwater from the glacier surface to the proglacial monitoring site. This change is also reinforced by the fact that the maxi-mum cross correlation between incident radiation and proglacial discharge changes from 8h in periods 1 and 2 and 6h in period 3 to 4h in period 4; equivalent figures for the response of discharge to air tempera-ture are 6h in periods 1 and 2, 5h in period 3 and 2h in period 4 (Gurnell et al, in prep.). Thus, it appears that the junction between periods 3 and 4 is marked by a sudden change in the glacial drainage from a relatively diffuse system to a more rational arrange-ment of conduits. This is associated with the release of solutes and sediments from the affected area of the glacier bed. This area must occur in the lower third of the glacier because inputs of meltwater on the glacier surface to such a system are heavily affected by the position of the transient snowline. The absence of NO_3, through the storage hypothesis, is also indic-ative of this location, because the glacier surface is steep here and so NO_3 generated by preferential elution from the snow pack would have drained efficiently from the basin during the earlier snowmelt phase (periods 1 and 2). However, the change in diurnal discharge range during this period is support-ive of the sulphide weathering explanation for the NO_3 pattern, since the increased range suggests more efficient and free glacier drainage which would be associated with a better oxygen supply to the glacier bed.

After the initial change in the drainage early in period 4, peak discharge and diurnal flow amplitude continue to increase but sediments and solutes initial-ly show signs of exhaustion and also, in the case of solutes, decreased residence time of meltwater in the developing conduit system. However, after day 50, high flow and low flow suspended sediment concentration increases to a peak around day 55. This

5.15

is accompanied by an increase in low flow discharge and in high flow concentrations in Mg and Na. This period is also indicative of adjustments in the subglacial drainage system so that new solute and sediment sources are tapped. The transient snowline continues to recede during period 4, reaching the upper end of the main glacier tongue (about two thirds of the total glacier length) by the end of the period.

The junction between periods 4 and 5 is marked by a period of snowfall and cold weather. Such weather is associated with a dramatic fall in discharge. Meltwater draining from the glacier during this period shows high concentrations in solutes, indicative of the gradual release of longer residence time water with negligible dilution from short residence time meltwater. However, the discharge level and diurnal amplitude soon recovers and the remainder of period 5 up to the final snowfall event is characterised by the highest flows and diurnal flow amplitudes of the season. This implies high ablation coupled with a well developed drainage system over much of the glacier basin. However, it is apparent from the sediment and solute record, that this drainage system continues to evolve in a stepped fashion. The two clear suspended sediment peaks are associated with a variety of adjustments in the solutes, indicating the tapping of subglacial source areas as the main drainage system expands up glacier and laterally across the glacier bed.

Conclusion

The description and discussion of high flow and low flow proglacial time series has allowed us to make a number of inferences about the evolution of drainage in the Haut Glacier d'Arolla basin during the 1989 ablation season. In particular, we have been able to identify the influence of four groups of factors:

(i) The impact of changing from a predominantly snowmelt-driven to a predominantly icemelt-driven flow regime.

(ii) The impact of the changing nature of glacier drainage in time and in space as the transient snowline retreats and the meltwater drains through an increasingly integrated glacial drainage network.

(iii) The fact that the evolution in the drainage network does not take place in a smooth fashion, but that there are clearly identifiable steps in this evolution, where suspended sediments and solutes respond in a pulsed fashion as sections of the glacier bed are connected in to the main drainage conduit system.

(iv) The possibility that some temporal patterns (specifically in NO_3 behaviour) may be interpreted in the light of information on the subglacial topography or the subglacial weathering environment.

Of particular significance is the degree to which the glacio-hydrological inference demonstrated in this paper is dependent upon synthesis of the various physical and chemical time series rather than interpretation of any particular subset of the data.

Acknowledgements

The authors thank Martin Sharp for his very helpful comments on an early version of the manuscript. The Natural Environment Research Council are very gratefully acknowledged for the provision of a research grant (GR3/7004) and a research studentship (GT4/88/AAPS/56) to support integrated studies within the Upper Arolla basin. Grande Dixence S.A. provided discharge data and logistical support for which the authors thank them very sincerely.

References

Brown, G.H. & Tranter, M. (in prep.). Accurate determination of cation concentrations in glacial meltwaters.

Collins, D.N. 1979. Hydrochemistry of meltwaters draining from an alpine glacier. *Arctic and Alpine Research* 11, 307-324.

Fenn, C.R. 1987a. Electrical conductivity. In A.M. Gurnell & M.J. Clark (eds) *Glacio-fluvial Sediment Transfer: An Alpine Perspective.* Wiley, Chichester, 377-414.

Fenn, C.R. 1987. Sediment transfer processes in alpine glacier basins. In A.M. Gurnell & M.J. Clark (eds) *Glacio-fluvial Sediment Transfer: An Alpine Perspective.* Wiley, Chichester, 59-85.

Gurnell, A.M. 1987. Suspended sediment. In A.M. Gurnell & M.J. Clark (eds) *Glacio-fluvial Sediment Transfer: An Alpine Perspective* Wiley, Chichester, 305-354.

Gurnell, A.M., Warburton, J. & Clark, M.J. 1988. A comparison of the sediment transport and yield characteristics of two adjacent glacier basins, Val d'Herens, Switzerland. In M.P. Bordas & D.E. Walling (eds) *Sediment Budgets* I.A.H.S. Publication 174, 431-441.

Gurnell, A.M., Brown, G.H. & Tranter, M. 1991. A sampling strategy to describe the temporal hydrochemical characteristics of an alpine proglacial stream. Submitted to *Hydrological Processes.*

Gurnell, A.M., Clark, M.J. & Hill, C.T. (in prep.). Analysis and interpretation of patterns within and between hydroclimatological time series in an alpine glacier basin.

H. Rothlisberger & Lang, H. 1987. Glacial hydrology. In A.M. Gurnell & M.J. Clark (eds) *Glacio-fluvial Sediment Transfer: An Alpine Perspective.* Wiley, Chichester, 207-284.

Sharp, M., Tranter, M., Brown, G.H., Nienow, P. & Willis, I.C. (in prep.). Hydrological behaviour of the Haut Glacier d'Arolla, Valais, Switzerland, as inferred from the hydrochemistry of glacial meltwaters.

Tranter, M. & Raiswell, R. (in press). The composition of the englacial and subglacial components in bulk meltwaters draining the Gornergletscher. *J. Glaciol.*

Extreme snow melt in the UK

J.A. Mawdsley, A.K. Dixon & A.C.Adamson

Abstract

Snow melt can on occasions significantly contribute to winter flooding in the UK, which is reflected in the Flood Studies Report's recommendation that a snow melt rate should be added to the probable maximum precipitation to obtain the probable maximum flood for the winter season. The melt rate proposed by the FSR is 42 mm d^{-1}, but this figure has been questioned by Archer (1981) who has produced data to suggest that it is too low. In this paper, extreme snow melt rates are considered from an energy budget point of view. Extreme snow melt rates occur in the UK when warm fronts move in from the Atlantic and produce large temperature and humidity gradients between the air and the cold snow pack. As a result, the most significant terms in the energy budget are the sensible heat and condensation terms.

Using data for historic events in the north east of England for a period similar to that used by Archer, snow melt rates in excess of 70 mm d^{-1} were obtained from sensible heat energy source alone. These results support the earlier observations of Archer. There appears to be no obvious meteorological reason why the combination of extreme snow melt rates and a deep snow pack could not occur at sometime in the future. Therefore, the FSR recommendation of 42 mm d^{-1} should be reviewed and a higher figure used in the interim.

An attempt was made to estimate the probable maximum snow melt rate (PMSM) by using the estimated maximum values of temperature, wind speed, and humidity to calculate the sensible and condensation energy terms. Results for three locations in the UK were found and results close to or exceeding 200 mmd^{-1} were obtained at all locations.

Introduction

Rapid snow melt often occurs in the UK during rainfall events and contributes significantly to the resulting flood peak. Some of the worst flood events which have occurred in the winter have had a significant snow melt contribution (Johnson and Archer,1972; Rodier and Roche,1985). This is reflected in the Flood Studies Report's (FSR) recommendation (NERC, 1975) that a snow melt rate should be added to the probable maximum precipitation to obtain the probable maximum flood for the winter season. The point melt rate proposed by the FSR is 42mm d^{-1}, but this value has been questioned by Archer (1981), who has produced data to suggest that, for the north east of England at least, it is too low. This conclusion has not been universally accepted. At a British Hydrological Society meeting in 1984, G.Reynolds suggested that for the highlands of Scotland the value was too high and he thought Archer's data were suspect. Subsequently, D. W. Reed at the Institute of Hydrology, conducted a review of these and other data but the report has not yet been published.

In this paper, extreme snow melt rates are considered from an energy budget point of view: an approach that has not been used by the previous researchers. Large amounts of energy are required to melt snow, and it is the available energy which controls the rate of snow melt. The full energy budget is complex and requires data for meteorological variables, which are not generally available, before the melt rate at a point can be calculated. However, most of the extreme snow melt rates observed in the UK occur as a result of warm fronts moving in from the west. In this situation it is the sensible and latent heat terms which dominate the energy budget, and data does exist for estimates of these terms to be made. In this paper, these data have been used to estimate the snow melt rates for a number of events at a location in NE England close to the locations used by Archer. Some of these data are compared with the values of Archer. In addition, this and other locations within the UK are considered to try to estimate the likely probable maximum snow melt rates (PMSM) which perhaps should be used in PMF studies instead of the 42 mm d^{-1} presently recommended.

Energy budget

To melt snow requires approximately 335×10^3 J kg^{-1}. This energy enters the snow pack as short or long wave radiation, as sensible heat, Q_h, (i.e. heat conducted to the snow from the warm air above), as energy from condensation, Q_c, as energy transferred from warm rain falling on the snow, Q_r, or as heat conducted from the warmer ground beneath the snow, Q_g. If the snow is already at 0°C then any surplus energy entering the snow pack will cause snow melt. If the snow pack has been lying for some time, it may have a temperature less than 0°C, in which case the surplus energy must first warm the pack up to zero before melt will occur. A pack in this condition is said to have a cold content. For the rest of this paper it is assumed that the cold content of the pack is zero and hence the pack is ready to melt. This is generally the situation in much of England and Wales.

The full energy budget can be expressed as

$$Q_m = Q_{sn} + Q_{ln} + Q_h + Q_c + Q_r + Q_g \text{ (Wm}^{-2}) \quad (1)$$

where Q_m is the energy consumed in snow melt, Q_{sn} is the net energy entering the snow pack from solar radiation (short wave), Q_{ln} is the net energy absorbed from long wave radiation, and the other terms are as previously defined.

In situations where high melt rates are of interest, the last two terms are small in comparison to the others. Therefore, they are not considered in detail in this paper. The radiation terms are large when there are clear skies. However, most of the rapid melt rates observed in the UK occur as a result of warm fronts travelling across the UK from the west. In these situations the skies are covered in cloud, often with rain, and as a result the sensible and condensation terms are the major terms in the energy budget. These are the types of situation observed by Archer. Both the dominant terms, Q_h and Q_c, are described by equations based on turbulent transfer theory because of the importance turbulent eddies play in the transport of the heat and water vapour from the air to the snow surface.

The equations can be written:

$$Q_h = p_a c_p C_h u (T_a - T_s) \quad (2)$$

$$Q_c = p_a L C_v u (q_a - q_s) \quad (3)$$

where c_p is the specific heat of air, u the wind speed, T the temperature, q the specific humidity, p_a the air density, L the latent heat of vapourisation and C_h and C_v are the turbulent transfer coefficients for sensible heat and water vapour, respectively. The subscripts a and s refer to the air above the snow and the snow surface, respectively.

If the temperature and humidity are measured at the same height above the snow surface, Z_a, and the wind speed at height, Z_u, then the two turbulent transfer coefficients are equal and expressed as

$$C_h = C_v = k^2 / [\ln(Z_a/Z_o) + 5.2(Z_a/L)][\ln(Z_u/Z_o) + 5.2(Z_u/L)] \quad (4)$$

where k is von Karman's constant (taken as 0.4), Z_o is the roughness length of the snow (the height at which the wind speed would become zero if the logarithmic profile were extrapolated close to the ground), and L is the Monin-Obukhov stability length (Brutsaert, 1982).

Two terms provide difficulties when applying these equations - the roughness length and the stability length. The roughness length depends on the shape of the snow surface and how smooth it is, but in a way which is not well understood. Consequently there is some uncertainty about the appropriate value for this term. To estimate the stability length, measurements of temperature, wind speed, and humidity at several levels are required. However, if the snow surface is taken as one of the levels and the air at the snow surface is assumed to be at 0°C and saturated, then an estimate of L can be made using an iterative procedure. Thus the equations can be applied but with some uncertainty attached to the values estimated. This will be discussed more fully later.

The radiation terms can be estimated using empirical equations, if the sunshine hours or cloud cover are known (e.g. Shaw, 1988; Bras, 1990). Uncertainties with these terms are not so important for our studies, because of the dominance of the sensible and condensation terms in the type of conditions considered here.

The atmospheric stability is an important factor when considering turbulent transfer processes, because it strongly influences the size and intensity of the turbulent eddies. Generally when snow is lying on the ground the stability will be stable because the snow is cooler than the air above it; as a result the turbulent eddies will tend to be damped out. The transfer coefficients decrease as the atmosphere becomes more stable.

The Monin-Obukhov length is defined by the equation

$$L = -u_*^3 p_a c_p T_b / gk Q_h \quad (5)$$

where T_b is the air temperature in degrees Kelvin, g is the acceleration due to gravity, and u_* is the friction velocity, which can be calculated from the equation

$$u_* = ku/[\ln(Z_u/Z_o) + 5.2\ Z_u/L] \quad\quad (6)$$

Historic melt rates in NE England

Data are not available in the north east of England to apply the full energy budget. As the sensible heat and condensation terms are normally the dominant ones, the other terms have been ignored. Unfortunately, data were not available for us to calculate the condensation term, hence the energy calculated is almost certainly an underestimate of the energy available for snow melt as only the sensible heat term has been calculated for the historic events.

To calculate the sensible heat, measurements of temperature and wind speed above the snow surface are required. A data set at Widdybank Fell close to Cow Green reservoir was available for the period from November 1969 to March 1985 with the exception of the period from December 1974 to April 1978. Cow Green is located on the upper Tees at an altitude of 513 m and close to two of the sites analysed by Archer - Langdon Beck and Harwood Beck. The temperatures and wind speeds were measured at 9.00 a.m. approximately 2 m above the snow surface. In addition snow depths were also measured close to this location.

Events were selected from the data record when snow was on the ground and was melting, and the contribution to this melt from sensible heat was calculated. From these results the days when the sensible heat was in excess of 150 Wm^{-2} were selected and the results for some of these days are shown in Table 1. If all of the sensible heat was consumed in melting the snow and this rate of 150 Wm^{-2} persisted all day, then 38.7 mm of melt would occur. Given that the radiation terms have not been calculated, this is approximately the 42mm d^{-1} quoted by the FSR, assuming no contribution from condensation.

The sensible heat was calculated using equations (2), (4)-(6). The stability length had to be calculated by an iterative procedure as the heat flux is required in equation (5). The values of the stability are shown in Table 1 as the Z_a/L values.

The roughness length depends on the shape and the smoothness of the snow surface but not in a well defined way. There are no data to help decide on the appropriate value for Widdybank Fell. A value of 1×10^{-4}m was chosen, which is towards the high end of the range of values quoted by Morris (1982), but there is considerable relief in this area so that the value is likely to be higher than for many sites.

There were 324 events analysed and 9% of these had a sensible heat rate of 150 Wm^{-2} or more. Some of these are shown in Table 1, including the largest of them - the remaining results can be found in Dixon (1985). The largest sensible heat rate calculated is

the 278 Wm^{-2}, or 72 mmd^{-1}, on the 29/4/81. The snow depth measurements show a decline of 70mm on this day, but the density of the snow is unknown.

Table 1 Snowmelt rates at Widdybank Fell

Date	Air Temp °C	Wind Speed ms^{-1}	Stability Z_a/L	Qh Wm^{-2}	Qh mmd^{-1}
31/1/85	4.80	15.89	0.0133	167	43.1
12/1/84	7.70	16.21	0.0203	271	69.9
14/1/83	5.90	14.67	0.0191	188	48.5
15/1/83	6.00	15.33	0.0136	200	51.6
29/4/81	10.00	13.08	0.0401	278	71.7
23/12/80	7.40	17.13	0.0175	276	71.2
7/3/74	8.10	14.87	0.0253	260	67.1
10/1/74	6.40	11.28	0.0350	154	39.7
11/1/74	8.30	11.79	0.0412	208	53.7
18/11/69	6.70	14.36	0.0226	208	53.7
19/11/69	6.67	15.38	0.0196	223	57.5

It is clearly quite common for this location for there to be sufficient energy to melt snow well in excess of a rate of 42mmd^{-1} from sensible heat alone, but this rate may not persist for 24 hours. Unfortunately the data were not available to establish this point with certainty, but there are a number of occasions when these rates were recorded on consecutive days, which strongly implies these conditions would persist for at least 24 hours. This will be discussed more in the next section. Unfortunately a good comparison can not be made with Archer's results primarily because of the different times during the day when the measurements were made. However, it seems self evident from our results, that from an energy budget point of view, the rates of melt quoted by Archer are not unreasonable, and therefore it is likely that his results are correct. To assess whether these results are likely to occur at other locations in the UK, and to see how high the melt rates could reach in extreme conditions, an attempt has been made in the next section to estimate the probable maximum snow melt rate.

Probable maximum snow melt rates

To try and assess the probable maximum snow melt rate that could occur within parts of the UK, the important terms in the energy budget — namely the sensible heat and condensation terms — were considered to see how large they could become under extreme conditions. To widen the discussion beyond the north east of England, sites are also reported in other parts of the UK - specifically the northeast of Scotland, the southern Pennines, from Belper to Ilkley.

Extremely high melt rates may occur at a point, but doubt is sometimes expressed as to whether these rates can be sustained over a large catchment. To try to counter this argument, data were obtained for a number of locations within these three regions (see Table 2) and averaged prior to the calculations of the sensible and latent heat terms. The stations are naturally at different elevations, but no account was taken of this when averaging. This averaging will help reduce some very high observations at specific locations and produce values more likely to be observed over a large area. It is the best that can be done with the sparse data available at present.

Temperatures vary significantly with altitude. To be able to compare melt rates between these three regions, it was thought helpful if the air temperatures used were all corrected to the same altitude - in this case 300m AOD was chosen. The lapse rate used to make this correction is debatable, but a value from the middle of the range of values often quoted was taken, namely 7°K per km (Barry, 1981). The average elevation of the stations where data were used was considerably below 300m in most cases (Table 2). The relative humidities were also adjusted to the same reference level of 300m using corrections from Lacy (1977).

The data required to estimate the probable maximum daily mean values of Q_h and Q_c are ideally the highest expected daily mean values of wind speed, air temperature, and relative humidity. Resources were not available to undertake an analysis of historic data sets, so that published data had to be used. Unfortunately, to our knowledge, an attempt to maximise these data has not been undertaken or published, and therefore we used the maximum observed values where possible (Met Office 1968 a). For 24 hour mean wind speeds, even this was not published so that values which are exceeded on about 10% of occasions were used (Met. Office 1968 b). Thus all data are likely to be below the maximum values. When maximising terms in equations, the question of whether they can occur simultaneously has to be considered. Generally the fronts which produce very warm temperatures with high humidity can be accompanied by high winds, but it is not clear whether there are physical mechanisms which would preclude them all being maximised simultaneously. Therefore, the maximum melt rates estimated using these data are not necessarily an underestimate. Following Dixon's (1985) work, which showed that when wind speeds and sensible heat rates are high the atmospheric stability is close to neutral, we assumed this to be the case when calculating Q_c and Q_h using equations (2) and (3). The roughness length was again taken to be 1×10^{-4} m. The snow surface was assumed to have a temperature of 0°C and the air at the surface was assumed saturated. The data and resulting fluxes are shown in Table 2 for the three regions.

Calculations were performed for each month from December to April (Adamson, 1989) but only the results for March are reported here.

These values will only occur with overcast skies. The net radiation was estimated under these conditions

and was typically 10% of the sensible heat value. The energy advected by the warm rain was typically of a similar order, whereas the ground heat flux was an order of magnitude smaller (Adamson, 1989).

Table 2 Daily mean data, sensible heat and condensation fluxes for March

Region	No. Stns	Mean Elev'n m	Air Temp. °C	Rel. Humid. %	V_{10} ms^{-1}	Q_h Wm^{-2}	Q_c Wm^{-2}
NE Scotland	13	88	12.3	91.5	8.1	169	140
NE England	9	73	13.2	90.5	9.0	202	192
S Pennines	8	141	14.1	86.0	8.5	204	167

(V_{10} = wind speed at 10 m)

If the other energy values are assumed to be 20% of Q_h, then the total energy potentially available for snow melt at 300m elevation over a catchment in these regions of the UK is shown in Table 3.

Table 3 Probable maximum snow melt rates

Region	Q_m Wm^{-2}	Snow Melt mmd^{-1}	Snow Melt (Higher Wind Speed)
NE Scotland	371	96	155
NE England	473	122	210
S Pennines	445	115	223

The wind speed data are not maximum values. A few data were obtained from the Meteorological Office of maximum recorded daily mean wind speeds at 10m above the ground. There are only a few locations within these regions, but the data do suggest that values closer to 30-40 knots should be used, which is 15-20 ms^{-1} [the data for 10 locations have wind speeds ranging from 19-45 knots]. With a wind speed of 15.5 ms^{-1} for the three regions, the snow melt rates shown in the last column of Table 3 were obtained.

For all the energy to be used to melt snow, the pack must be ripe at the start of the event, and, of course, there must be at least that amount of snow water equivalent lying on the catchment. Archer (1981) shows that in NE England this amount of snow has been observed, and presumably in Scotland it is more common.

Discussion

The historic melt rates reported for Widdybank Fell in northeast England were obtained assuming sensible heat to be the only energy source. If the melt rates are compared with the probable maximum sensible heat for the northeast of England shown in Table 2 (the Q_h values), it can be seen that the historic values are larger than the supposed maximum values. This is primarily because the observed wind speeds are significantly larger than the speeds used for the PMSM calculations. There are several possible explanations for this: first, the wind speeds used for the PMSM estimates are not maximum values; second, the wind speeds measured at Widdybank Fell, which are essentially instantaneous readings observed at 10 a.m., may not persist for 24 hours; third, the PMSM calculations are performed for catchments at 300 m elevation whereas Widdybank Fell is over 500 m AOD. It seems likely that all contribute to the difference, but it is probable that the true maximum wind speeds are greater than the data used, and the melt rates obtained using the higher wind speeds are likely to be closer to the true PMSM.

From the PMSM calculations it is clear that the energy from condensation can be very large and almost as large as the sensible heat terms. Contributions from condensation would increase the historic melt rates even more, but data were not available for us to perform these calculation. However, there is some doubt, at least in our own minds, as to whether both the sensible and condensation energy terms and rainfall can achieve their maximum values simultaneously. More research is required to establish this. However, the weather conditions which produce heavy winter rain are the same conditions which will cause sensible and condensation terms to be large. Therefore, until this research has been conducted, it would be safer to assume that they can occur simultaneously.

There are a number of semi-empirical equations which have been developed to estimate snow melt rates. These equations contain terms which clearly relate to sensible heat, condensation, and advected energy from warm rain. One such equation was published in the Flood Studies Report volume II (NERC, 1975) attributed to the Met Office but based on a Canadian equation of Bruce and Sporn. The equation is:

$$M=T_a(1.32+0.394ku)-0.3ku(T_s-T_d)+0.0125PT_a \quad (7)$$

where M is the melt rate in mm d^{-1}, k is a factor between 0.3 and 1.0, T_d is the dew point temperature, and P the rainfall; all other terms are as before, except that the wind speed is in knots. If the rainfall is assumed to be 200 mm, k = 1.0, and the other data taken from Table 2 for the northeast of England, the melt rate is 226 mm d^{-1} which is very similar to the results shown in Table 3. There are other equations from around the world which also give very large melt rates with the same data inputs (e.g. WMO, 1969). Using these data may be extrapolating the equations beyond the range of their development but the similarity between the equations and the more detailed energy budget suggest that the errors

introduced by extrapolation may not be great. We should note here that it is assumed the equation published in FSR is in error, and the form shown here is correct, i.e. in the second term, it is the difference between T_s and T_d rather than T_a and T_d which is intended. If used as published, the condensation term would be negative at all times which, with a humidity gradient towards the snow pack, cannot be correct.

The roughness length chosen was towards the higher end of the range but is by no means the largest value that has been proposed.

The PMSM rates are estimates of rates that could occur across the whole catchment. The runoff processes could cause the peak runoff rates at the outlet from the catchment to exceed these.

Conclusions

The energy budget estimates of snow melt rates at Widdybank Fell, which is close to two of Archer's sites - Harwood Beck and Langdon Beck, offer supporting evidence for the melt rates observed by Archer, although, due to limitations in the data, firm confirmation cannot be claimed.

The estimates of PMSM are uncertain and they can only be considered preliminary estimates. It is likely that the values shown in the last column of Table 3 will be closest to the true values of probable maximum snow melt rates for catchments at 300 m AOD. The values range from 150-220 mm d^{-1} for the three locations. These values are of the same order as the probable maximum precipitation values used in estimating the probable maximum flood in the winter. They are far in excess of the 42 mm d^{-1} which the FSR recommends should be used.

Comparable values have been obtained for other countries in the world using a similar procedure. Therefore, it seems prudent for hydrologists to use much larger values for snow melt rates when calculating PMF, certainly in excess of 75 mm d^{-1}. Further a research project should be commissioned to study probable maximum snow melt rates in greater detail.

Acknowledgements

This work was carried out when all the authors were at the University of Newcastle upon Tyne. The views expressed are our own and not necessarily those of our current employers. We would like to thank the Nature Conservancy Council for the data from Widdybank Fell, Dave Archer for so clearly identifying the problem and for his useful advice, and NERC for supporting two of the authors whilst they carried out this work.

References

Adamson, A.C. 1989. The prediction of extreme rates of snowmelt using model component maximisation. Unpublished MSc Thesis.

University of Newcastle upon Tyne.

Archer, D.R. 1981. Severe snowmelt runoff in north-east England and its implications. *Proc. Instn Civ. Engrs*, Part 2, 71, 1047-1060.

Barry, R.G. 1981. *Mountains, Weather and Climate.* Methuen, London.

Bras, R.L. 1990. *Hydrology: An Introduction to Hydrologic Science.* Addison Wesley, Massachusetts.

Brutsaert, W. 1982. *Evaporation into the Atmosphere: Theory, History and Applications.* Reidel, Holland.

Dixon, A.K. 1985. A study to determine extreme snowmelt rates in north east England. Unpublished MSc thesis, Univ. of Newcastle upon Tyne.

Johnson, P.J. & Archer, D.R. 1972. The significance of snow in Britain, Proc. WMO Symp, Banff, 1098-1110.

Lacy, R.E. 1977. Climate and building in Britain: a review of meteorological information suitable for use in the planning, design, construction and operation of buildings. HMSO, London.

Meteorological Office 1968 a. Averages of temperature for the UK, 1941-70. Bracknell.

Meteorological Office 1968 b. Tables of surface wind speed and direction over the UK. Bracknell.

Morris, E.M. 1982. Sensitivity of the European hydrological system models. Proc Exeter symposium, IAHS, Publication No. 138, 221-231,Wallingford.

NERC 1975. *Flood Studies Report* Vol.I-V, London.

Rodier, J.A. & Roche, M. 1984. World catalogue of maximum observed floods. IAHS, 143, Wallingford.

Shaw, E.M. 1988. *Hydrology in Practice.* Van Nostrant Reinhold, London.

World Meteorological Organisation, 1969. Estimation of maximum floods. WMO, Tech note 98, Geneva.

The significance of snow on immediate flood risk estimates

M. R. Futter

Abstract

Flood risk in the winter months responds to both catchment wetness and the amount of snow lying on the catchment. A model exists that can estimate the risk of exceeding some critical flow, taking into account seasonal and prevailing catchment conditions (Ettrick *et al.*, 1987). This model is based on the use of conditional probability distributions, where the parameters of the distributions are related to the prevailing hydrological variables of a catchment. The model is fitted to three catchments to give flood risk estimates conditional upon baseflow, as a measure of catchment wetness, and the presence or absence of snow on the catchment at the time of prediction. The model estimates are higher for the snow compared to the no snow conditions.

Looking in more detail at the model fitting, these results are shown to be solely due to an increase in the rate of events rather than to the magnitudes of event peakflows. The conditional peakflow probability distributions suggest that the presence of snow on the catchment has a dampening influence on the precipitation-runoff processes. It is hypothesised that this may be due to the storage potential of the snow, and that routing of any melt or rainfall through the snow results in attenuation of that input.

Introduction

Most rivers show a strong seasonal variability in flood risk. However, there is also a large variation in the risk of flooding in a specified season from one year to the next due to changes in hydrological conditions: in the snow melt season the amount of snow lying on the catchment affects the flood risk, and in the summer months, in temperate regions, the soil moisture content is likely to influence the flood risk by controlling the proportion of rainfall that infiltrates into the soil.

Models of seasonal flood risk have been developed, e.g. Todorovic (1978) and North (1980). However, it is only recently that a model has been published (Ettrich *et al.*, 1987) which estimates the immediate risk of a flood exceeding some critical flow, taking into account the season and prevailing catchment conditions.

The model is based on a probability distribution of peakflows conditional on catchment wetness and precipitation covariates, and on the precipitation exceeding some threshold. A precipitation threshold, rather than a flow threshold, is used to define events, so that peak flows from a wide range of values of the covariates are included in the fitting data set. As precipitation cannot be forecast accurately, the assumption is made that the value of this covariate would not be known at the time of making the prediction and, therefore, a seasonally varying probability distribution is used. This is then integrated out to obtain a distribution of peakflows conditional only on the catchment wetness and the precipitation exceeding a threshold value. The model was originally developed to consider summer flood risk estimates, with the conditioning variables of catchment average (time of concentration) rainfall total and, as an index of catchment wetness, baseflow.

In this paper, extension of the model to give all year round immediate flood risk estimates is outlined. Consideration is given to the peakflow distribution conditioning variables, with the result that modifications are made to these variables. The model is then fitted to several catchments with the resulting flood risk estimates reflecting catchment wetness, exceedence of the precipitation threshold and the presence or absence of snow on the catchment at the time of prediction.

Flood risk in the winter months

In the summer months one would expect the flood risk to be dependent upon catchment wetness and the forecast rainfall amount. In the winter months the amount of snow on the catchment available for melt must also be important, since it represents a further source of runoff. The importance of snowmelt in the UK to the occurrence of peakflows is well know and has been documented by Johnson (1975) and Rodier and Roche (1985). Thus, in applying the model to give immediate flood risk estimates, consideration must be given to any snow stored on the catchments. This snow has the potential to contribute to any future peakflow event, as does precipitation falling as rain. Thus, the contributing precipitation does not just include the rainfall within the catchment time of concentration, but also melt from precipitation that has fallen and has been held in storage from a greater number of days in the past. In considering the influence of snow on the flood risk, two different fits of the model are required, one that describes the situation with no snow on the catchment, and the second that gives an estimate when snow is present.

Consideration was initially given to the influence of frozen ground and its impact on the runoff potential of the catchment. Frozen ground has been assumed by many to be a relatively common occurrence that reduces the losses via infiltration and percolation from a snowmelt event, therefore giving enhanced runoff with a quicker time to peak and larger peak magnitude compared with non-frozen ground conditions. The example often quoted is the March 1947 flood of rain and snowmelt (NERC, 1975). This is believed to have been aggravated by the long spell of cold weather that preceded it, and which might have frozen the top layers of the soil. However, others (for example, Archer, 1981) have argued that the very high flows were not the result of frozen ground, but were due to the presence of a very large water equivalence in the snow pack. They have suggested this was the result of the snow being on the ground for a very long period of time, and they have argued that the densities of the snowpack could have reached 0.4 g cm^{-3} after repeated snowfalls and freezing. Once the snowpack was ripe, they have suggested that high runoff values were reached because of very high yields.

Literature does exist investigating both the effect of soil freezing on infiltration, for example Gurnell and Midgely (1987) and Prevost et al. (1987), and the occurrence of frozen ground under snowpacks, for example English et al. (1987). However, the vast majority of this research is confined to North America. The conclusions to be drawn from this research are varied. For instance, under forested areas, the infiltration properties of frozen soils can be maintained or even enhanced. In contrast, with non-forest cover, freezing may have a much more influential effect on reducing the infiltration potential of the soil, but that it is uncommon for infiltration to be completely impeded. In terms of the occurrence of frozen ground under snowpacks, the literature suggests that the presence of snow on the soil surface acts as an insulating layer, confining the ground heat flux to the surface and lower layer of the snow pack. However, Archer (pers. comm.) has commented that he does know of upland catchments, for example sections of the Upper Tees, which have frozen under little or no snow cover. Given these results, the influence of frozen ground does not seem to be generally significant on the level of winter flood risk. Therefore, in applying the model to estimate the immediate flood risk, continued use of baseflow as a measure of catchment wetness seems reasonable.

The model

The model postulates a distribution of peakflows, q, conditional on catchment wetness, w, and depth of available precipitation (AP), y, given that AP exceeds some threshold, y_0. This distribution is represented by:

$$g(q|y,w,y>y_0) \qquad (1)$$

As the AP will not be known over the immediate period, this distribution can be combined with a distribution of AP, that is:

$$h(y|y>y_0) \qquad (2)$$

to give a distribution of peak flows conditional on catchment wetness at the time of prediction and the occurrence of an AP event which exceeds the threshold. Thus:

$$F(q|w,y,y>y_o) = {}_o\!\int^q \int_{y_o}^\infty g(q|y,w,y>y_o).h(y|y>y_o)dydx \qquad (3)$$

where it is assumed that AP is independent of catchment wetness.

If the AP events are assumed to occur according to a Poisson Process, and if ψ is the average number of AP events exceeding y_o in time interval δt, then the probability of at least one exceedence of the critical flow level of interest, c, in time δt is given by:

$$\Pr\{q>c\} = 1-\exp[\psi(F(c)-1)] \qquad (4)$$

Both the conditional peakflow and AP distributions in equation (3) and the rate parameter, ψ, in equation (4) have the potential to change seasonally and when there is snow on the ground. However, it was initially assumed that the conditional peakflow parameter-covariate relationships would remain unaltered. This distribution represents the rainfall-runoff processes in the model, and given the evidence from the literature reviewed earlier, it seems reasonable to assume that these would not significantly change either seasonally or between the snow and no snow situations.

When precipitation is falling as snow, it may be held in storage on the catchment and melt some days later, possibly at the same time as a rainfall event. This melt would be added to the rainfall to either increase the AP if the rainfall alone is greater than the melt, or take an event AP total over the threshold for inclusion in the fitting data set. However, if the precipitation fell as rain, no storage would take place over such a long time period. Thus, the expected value of a snow events AP distribution should be higher than that for a no snow events one. The rate parameter, ψ, in Equation (4), would also be expected to be higher for periods when snow is on the ground. Again, this is because snow represents stored precipitation awaiting release. The catchment is not starting at a zero base level before exceeding the event defining AP threshold, as is the case with rainfall alone, but at a level somewhat higher than zero and therefore closer to that threshold.

Fitting the model

The model was fitted to three catchments, those of the Rivers Browney, Dearne and Ure. The River Browney catchment covers an area of 178.5 km^2 in County Durham, England; it varies in height between 100 and 300 metres O.D. and has a geology dominated by Carboniferous coal measures. The River Dearne catchment above Barnsley in South Yorkshire covers an area of 119 km^2 and varies in height from 150 m to over 860 m O.D., with its geology also dominated by Carboniferous coal measures. The River Ure catchment above Kilgram Bridge in the Yorkshire Dales, covers an area of 510 km^2 and varies in height from 98 m O.D. at Kilgram Bridge to over 660 m O.D. The geology consists of Carboniferous limestones and sandstones.

Fitting of the model took place on a snow, no snow and all events basis. A 10 mm 2-day AP threshold was used to define events for the River Browney data, a 14 mm 2-day AP threshold for the River Dearne and 32.5 mm 3-day AP threshold for the River Ure. For each catchment, exponential distributions were used to describe the AP distributions in Equation (3) for the snow, no snow and all events situations. For the conditional peakflow distributions, use was made of the Weibull distribution, with the scale parameter of the distribution, α, made a function of the baseflow and AP, for example:

$$\alpha = [C_o + (y - y_o)*C_1 + W*C_2]^{-1} \qquad (5)$$

Maximum likelihood techniques were used to estimate the distribution parameters.

In the previous section of this paper, the expected behaviour of the distributions and rate parameter under the snow and no snow conditions was described. In the fitting of the model to each of the catchments, these assumptions were tested and Table 1 presents a summary of the findings of these tests.

The model immediate flood risk estimates

Based on the model fitting to the catchment data, immediate flood risk estimates were made for each of the catchments, conditional on baseflow, exceedence of the AP threshold and the presence or absence of snow. For the Rivers Browney and Dearne the critical flow of interest was set at 20 m^{3}s^{-1}, while for the River Ure this was increased to 100 m^{3}s^{-1}. The estimates are presented in Figures 1, 2 and 3 respectively. For the River Browney, both baseflow and snow are important factors in determining the

Table 1: Summary of Model Fitting Details

Model Attribute	Expected Behaviour	Observed Catchment Behaviour		
		Browney	Dearne	Ure
AP Distribution	Conditional on presence or absence of snow	as proposed	as proposed	based on all events
Rate Parameter	Conditional on presence or absence of snow	as proposed	as proposed	as proposed
Peakflow Distribution Parameters	Based on all events	Conditional on presence or absence of snow	Conditional on presence or absence of snow	Conditional on presence or absence of snow

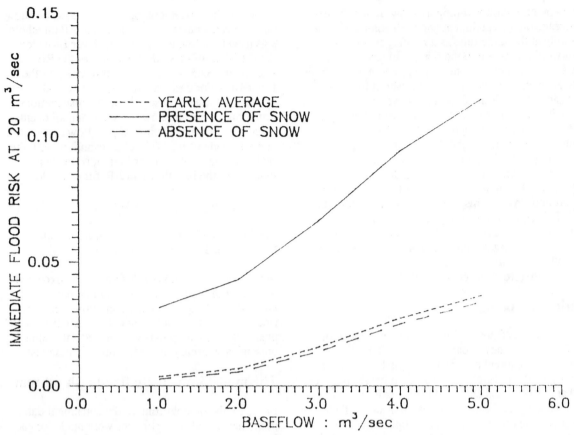

Figure 1   River Browney immediate flood risk estimates at 20 cumecs, conditional on baseflow and the presence or absence of snow

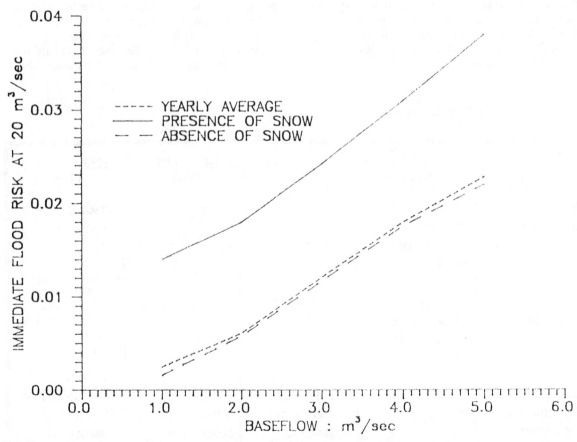

Figure 2   River Dearne immediate flood risk estimates at 20 cumecs, conditional on baseflow and the presence or absence of snow

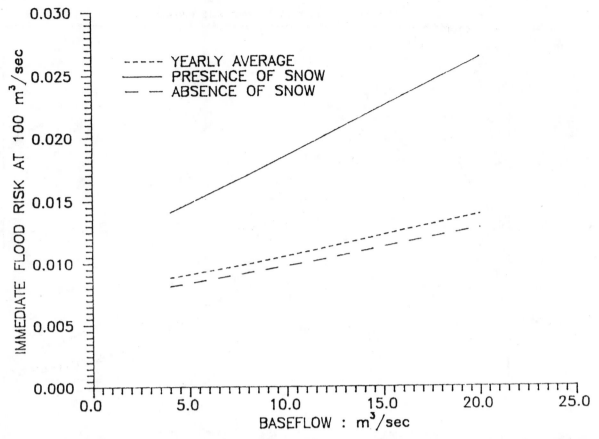

Figure 3 River Ure immediate flood risk estimates at 100 cumecs, conditional on baseflow and the presence or absence of snow

level of flood risk. At a baseflow of 1.0 m³s⁻¹, the estimated flood risk is over 11 times greater with snow on the catchment compared with the no snow situation. This falls to just over 3 times with a baseflow of 5.0 m³s⁻¹. In the case of the RiverDearne, baseflow and snow are also important in estimating the level of flood risk. At a baseflow of 1.0 m³s⁻¹, the estimated flood risk is over eight times greater for the snow than the no snow situation, while at a baseflow of 5.0 m³s⁻¹, the ratio of risk estimates is greater than 1.7.

The River Ure results present a slightly different situation. Here, the relative importance of snow on the catchment has increased slightly as the baseflow has increased. Also, for the no snow conditions, the flood risk estimates are less responsive to baseflow for this catchment compared with the Rivers Browney and Dearne.

Discussion of results

In fitting the model to the catchment data sets, the observed behaviour of the peakflow distribution parameter-covariate relationship did not agree with the hypothesized behaviour for any of the data sets. Figures 4, 5 and 6 present the snow and no snow conditional peakflow distributions for the Rivers Browney, Dearne and Ure respectively. All three figures show clear differences between the distributions, and suggest that the presence of snow

on the catchment has a restraining and dampening influence on the precipitation-runoff processes.

A possible explanation for this may be related to the storage potential of the snowpack for any rainfall and melt. Figure 7 illustrates the influence routing through a snowpack has on a pulse of melt at the snowpack surface. The routing has resulted in a lag time and attenuation of the pulse. For larger rainfall and melt releases, this same potential storage will become relatively less influential, so that the lag time and attenuation of the melt and rainfall will both decline. Figure 8 (Anderson, 1978) shows the time lag of any melt as a function of the ratio of the water equivalent of the solid portion of the snowcover (mm), to the excess liquid water (mm per 6 hours). This illustrates that for a given snowcover, increasing the excess liquid water reduces the lag, and presumably the attenuation. At higher peakflows, the distributions for each catchment are generally similar, suggesting that the influence of the snowpack has reduced as the melt and rainfall amounts have increased, and that there seems to be little difference between the distributions for higher peakflow snow and no snow events. Figures 9a, b, c and d compare the fitted conditional snow and no-snow River Browney peakflow distributions, standardised to AP values 10mm and 20mm above the AP threshold, and for baseflow values of 0.5 and 2.5 m³s⁻¹. These distributions are responding in the manner hypothesized above, that is, the higher the AP value, the smaller

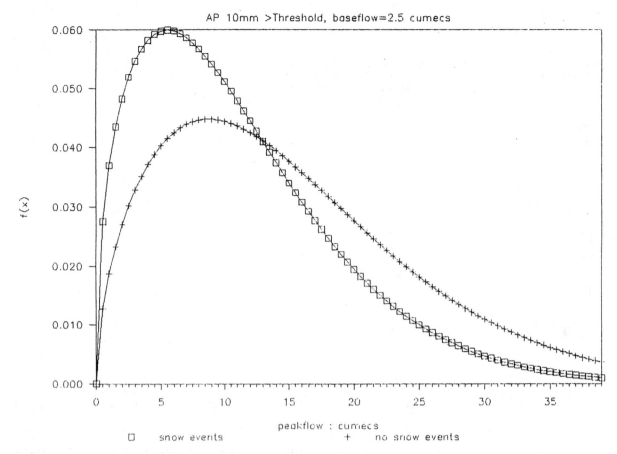

Figure 4 River Browney peak flow distributions

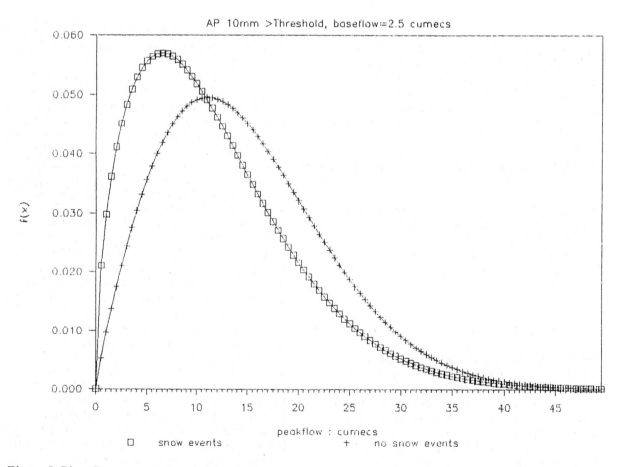

Figure 5 River Dearne peak flow distributions

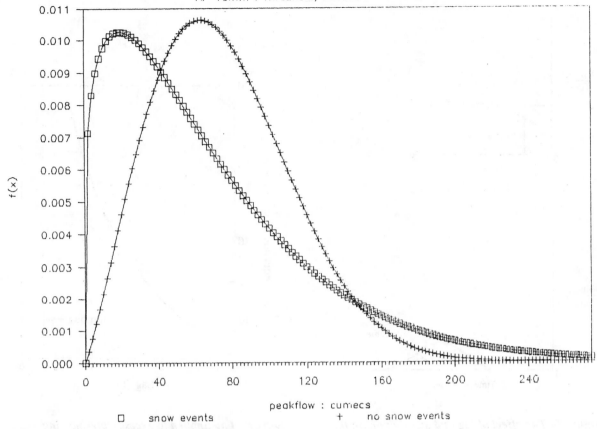
AP 10mm >Threshold, baseflow=10 cumecs

Figure 6 River Ure peak flow distributions

the difference between the snow and no snow distributions for a given baseflow value. The maximum difference between the cumulative distribution functions (cdfs), based on Figures 9a and 9b, falls from 0.276 to 0.110, while for the cdfs in Figures 9c and 9d, the differences fall from 0.174 to 0.114. Similar results were found for the River Dearne, but for the River Ure, there was little difference between the cdfs when increasing the AP value for a fixed baseflow. Thus, the River Ure conditional peakflow distributions are not as responsive to change in the covariate values compared with the distributions for the Rivers Browney and Ure.

When making the flood risk estimates, the conditional peakflow distributions are tending to create negative differences between the snow and no snow situations, while the AP distributions and rate parameters are counteracting this to produce the expected flood risk estimates that are higher for the snow than the no snow situation.

The importance of prior catchment wetness to flood risk is also highlighted by these results. However, the sensitivity of the flood risk to this catchment wetness seems to be less on the River Ure catchment than on the other study catchments. An indication as to the expected hydrologic response of the three catchments can be based on their soils. Boorman and Hollis (1990) have proposed hydrologically based classification of the soils of England and Wales. Based on their classification, the soils of the River Ure are dominated by peat. The presence of this layer limits infiltration and provides a lateral pathway for rapid response in the uppermost parts of the soil. The classification also suggests that the hydrological response of the Rivers Browney and Dearne is controlled by soils which are slowly permeable and where the baseflow makes an important contribution to the long-term average of the total flow. The River Ure results therefore indicate that application of the model is not recommended for all catchments.

Conclusions

The model estimates have illustrated the importance of snow on the catchment, at the time of prediction, to the levels of flood risk. The model has also shown that catchment wetness is an important factor influencing flood risk.

Acknowledgements

The research for this paper was carried out by the Author as part of his PhD at the Department of Civil Engineering, University of Newcastle upon Tyne. Therefore, thanks are due to the supervisors of the research, Drs John Mawdsley and Andrew Metcalfe. Funding for the research was provided by the Natural Environment Research Council.

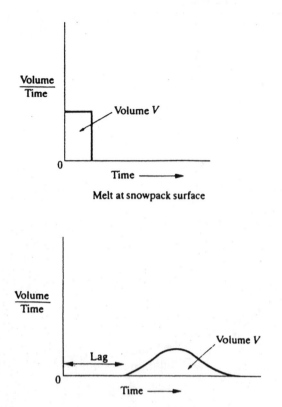

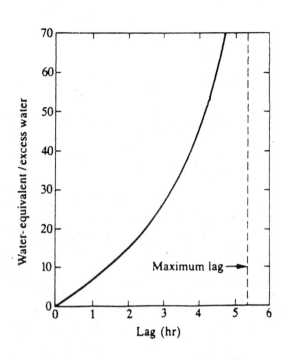

Figure 7   The effect of lag and attenuation on the routing of snowmelt (from Bras, 1990)

Figure 8   Lag applied to excess water moving through a snow cover (from Anderson, 1978)

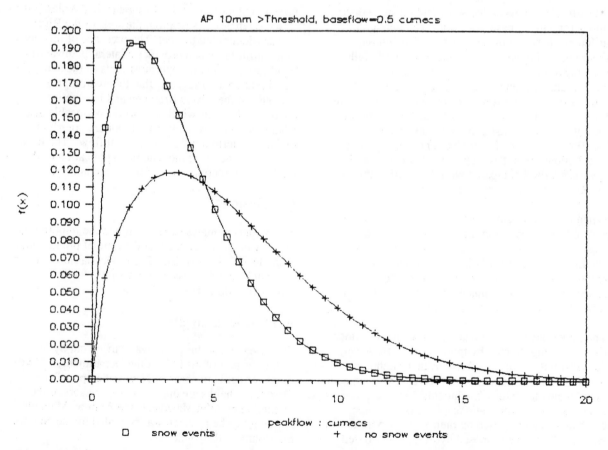

Figure 9(a)   River Browney peak flow distributions, AP 10mm > threshold, baseflow=0.5 cumecs

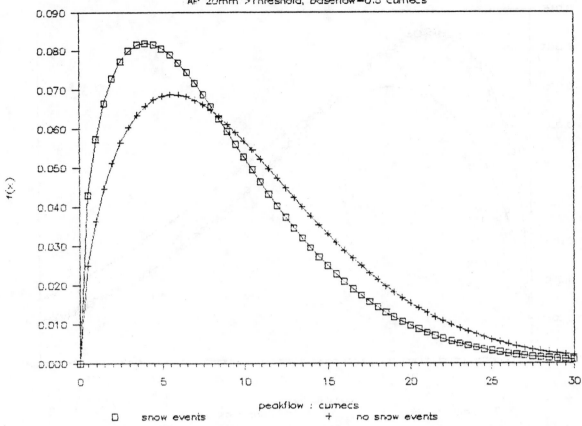

Figure 9(b)   River Browney peak flow distributions, AP 20mm > threshold, baseflow=0.5 cumecs

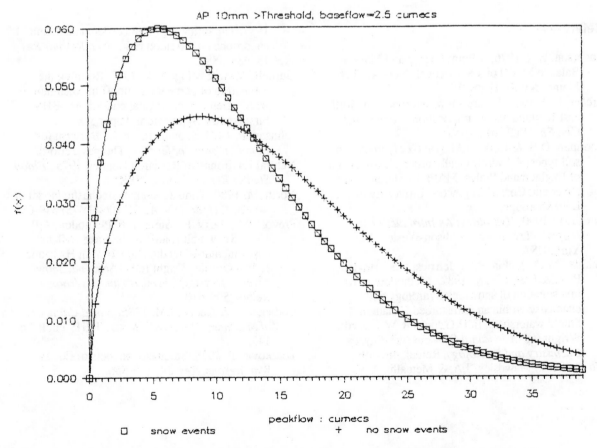

Figure 9(c)   River Browney peak flow distributions, AP 10mm > threshold, baseflow=2.5 cumecs

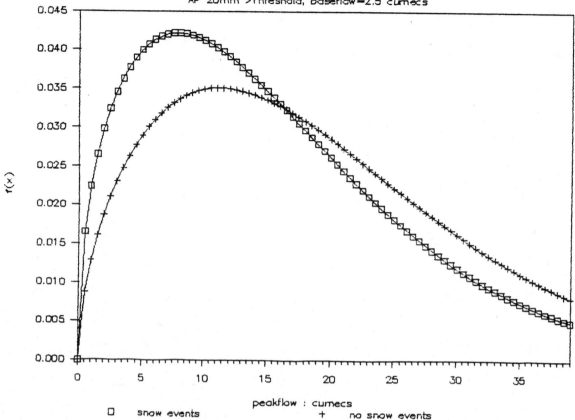

Figure 9(d) *River Browney peak flow distributions, AP 20mm > threshold, baseflow=2.5 cumecs*

References

Anderson, E.A. 1976. A Point Energy and Mass Balance Model of a Snowcover. NOAA, Tech. Memo. NWS - Hydro 19.

Archer, D.R. 1981. Severe snowmelt runoff in North-east England and its implications. *Proc. Inst. Civ. Eng.* Pt.2, 1047-1060.

Boorman, D.B. & Hollis, J.M. (1990). Hydrology of soil types: A hydrologically based classification of England and Wales. MAFF Conference of River and Coastal Engineers, University of Loughborough.

Bras, R.L. 1990. *Hydrology: An Introduction to Hydrologic Science*. Addison-Wesley, New York, USA.

English, M.C., Jenkin, R.G., Jeffries, D.S., Hazlett, P.W. & Foster, N.W. 1987. Methodology for investigation of snowmelt hydrology and chemistry within an undisturbed Canadian Shield watershed. In H.G.Jones & W.J.Orville-Wright (eds.) *Seasonal Snowcovers: Physics, Chemistry and Hydrology*, Reidel, 467-499.

Ettrick, T.M., Mawdsley, J.A. & Metcalfe, A.V.

1987. The influence of antecedent catchment conditions on the flood risk. *Wat. Resour. Res.* 13, 481-488.

Gurnell, A.M. & Midgely, P. 1987. Refining the estimation of percentage runoff in catchments with extreme hydrological conditions. BHS First Annual Symposium, Paper 3.

Johnson, P. 1975. Snowmelt. In T.J.Darwent (ed.) *Flood Studies Conference*, Thomas Telford.

Natural Environment Research Council 1975. *Flood Studies Report*, Vol. 1, NERC.

North, M. 1980. Time dependent stochastic model of floods. *J. Hydr. Div. ASCE* 106(HY75) 649-655.

Prevost, M., Barry, R., Stein, J. & Plamodon, A.P. 1987. Snowmelt runoff in the Lake Laflame experimental watershed, Quebec. In H.G.Jones & W.J.Orville-Wright (eds.) *Seasonal Snowcovers: Physics, Chemistry and Hydrology*, Reidel, 599-610.

Rodier, J.A. & Roche, I.M. 1985. *World Catalogue of Maximum Observed Floods*. IAHS Publ. No. 143.

Todorovic, P. 1978. Stochastic models of floods. *Wat. Resour. Res.* 14, 345-356.

Session 6

Large Data Bases for Hydrology

Integrating hydrological databases - GIS and other solutions

M.J.Clark & A.M.Gurnell

Abstract

Large databases have come to play an essential role in both research and operational contexts, yet they continue to offer problems as well as potential. The challenge of building and managing a single large database is very considerable, but these difficulties are multiplied when several databases are to be integrated within a single descriptive or analytical process, particularly if such integration requires inter-departmental, inter-agency or international co-operation. Data definition standards are a primary prerequisite for database construction and integration, but in practice many deficiencies remain, even in such relatively well-ordered sciences as hydrology. Data structures are equally important to successful data management and database integration. Not only do they have massive influence on the response of database manipulations (possibly as significant as the fundamental contrasts between hierarchical, relational and object oriented database structures), but they can also act as major constraints in the ease of data transfer between systems. Data transfer within and between systems continues to yield problems, but technological advance is such that such hurdles should be substantially reduced over a timescale of one to two years. This suggests that in future the problem of system inter-compatibility (local or national) is likely to be seen largely in terms of data structures rather than identity of file format or operating system. However, such access to multiple data sets offers limited analytical potential without a technology capable of synthesising such data, and in this context few fields offer greater potential than GIS. Provided that data are geocoded (an attribute that is available or possible with most hydrological data) remarkable descriptive and conceptual power is available through the synthetic functions of GIS. With large databases, data capture has dominated much effort to date, but there are signs of a growing interest in GIS analysis. Some of the most useful advances centre on the integration of data from multiple sources, especially maps, images and numerical data.

The challenge of large hydrological databases

Large hydrological databases have come to play an essential role in both research and operational contexts, yet they continue to offer problems as well as potential. Examples of successful implementations (e.g. IAHS, 1989) offer an invaluable guide to the nature of the problems to be faced, and provide indications of the available solutions, but it is also helpful to provide a more general context by assessing the principles of database design, construction and use. A generic approach of this type highlights the components from which an effective database can be built, and also defines criteria and standards through which existing databases can be evaluated and, if necessary, refined. Such refinement can never be a trivial operation with a large database, but it does nevertheless represent a fundamental professional responsibility, as well as being practically unavoidable in a context of rapid technological and analytical change. It is also important at a generic level to acknowledge the contractual, copyright and legal issues that a large database might embody, especially if it is the product of a multi-participant effort (Montgomery, 1990). Clear conceptualisation of the nature, structure and management of the database is thus as important as its incorporation of robust scientific standards (Mounsey and Tomlinson, 1988).

The challenge of building and managing a single large database is very considerable, particularly when disparate data sets and data sources are involved. These difficulties are multiplied when several separate databases are to be integrated within a single operational or analytical process, particularly if such integration requires inter-departmental, inter-agency or even international co-operation. Nevertheless, as the modelling and management operations based on complex databases increase in scope, the need for integration of discrete data sets and databases becomes ever more pressing.

The technical requirements for such integrative procedures involve data standards, data structure standards, data transfer standards and integrating technologies (within which Geographic Information Systems (GIS) represent a recent advance). It is characteristic of most specialist disciplines that effort initially tends to concentrate on ensuring scientific rigour and data quality while permitting some neglect of robust information handling standards. In order to contribute towards the establishment of sound working practice, this paper presents a generic overview of large database technical requirements rather than examining the specific detail of any one database.

Data standards

It has long been recognised that instrument and sampling (spatial and temporal) design exercise a significant influence on the precision and accuracy of data (Gurnell, 1987: Clark *et al*, 1988), and parameter definition may also mask substantial variations particularly where surrogate variables are involved. It may appear self-evident that data definition standards are a prerequisite for database construction and integration, but in practice many deficiencies remain, even in such relatively well-ordered sciences as hydrology.

Responding to the increasing need for organised data interchange and archiving, most branches of physical science have moved towards defined policies on data quality (CNIG, 1990), often spearheaded by internationally supported structures such as the World Data Centers. Nevertheless, even within these formal contexts, scope for improvement has been recognised (Barry, 1988, 1989). The functions of such a strategy have been summarised in the context of arctic hydrology by Clark (1991) in terms of three distinct aims, each with its own specific data requirements:

To permit aggregation of data sets. (This requires standardized units and measurement techniques, together with quasi-equivalent attributes of the sampled population).

To permit comparison, classification and assessment of variability in time or space. (This requires either standardization, or a sufficiently comprehensive documentation of data, sampling and population attributes to distinguish real from artificial differences between data sets).

To permit explanation of patterns within the combined data sets. (Hypothesis building and speculative reasoning are possible provided that data are thoroughly documented, but rigorous model building and hypothesis testing require standardized data.)

It follows that large database compilation and management require detailed attention to "data quality" as well as to the more obvious technical aspects of recording, storage, retrieval and distribution of data. Such attributes of data quality determine both the precision and accuracy (representativeness) of the information held within the database, while storage and presentation media/format influence the robustness of the information and its ability to respond to changed needs and resist deterioration. It is axiomatic that data quality should be optimised, and where optimum is something less than maximum the data documentation should incorporate both an error assessment and a suitable disclaimer. This is a matter of good operational practice and business efficiency, not an admission of failure.

An excellent example of the interaction between data standards and database attributes is presented by Boorman *et al*. (1991) in the context of the Hydrology of Soil Types (HOST) data set. This major database raised a number of issues concerning the extent to which data acquisition techniques influence the nature of the data held and (indirectly) the precision and accuracy of inferences from those data. The example is also particularly interesting since it represents a successful implementation of a large database in which the size forced some of the data attributes that had to be adopted.

Data structures

Data structures are equally important to successful data management and database integration (Roald and Beldring, 1991). Not only do they have massive influence on the response of database manipulations (possibly as significant as the fundamental contrasts between hierarchical, relational and object oriented database structures), but they can also act as major constraints in the ease of data transfer between systems. This is particularly important in the case of complex spatial topologies such as those involved in the apparently simple task of designating river reaches for operational data gathering and storage (Davenport, 1990). While some database designers opt for the robustness of established database shells such as ORACLE or SQL, others still prefer the tailored attributes of customised or in-house database software. Regardless of the database shell, the data structure that is to reside within it still imposes a major influence on the success of a project, yet there is little hydrologically-specific literature on which to base such a design.

As file transfer standards improve, with consequent enhancement of the ability to transfer data between systems or to migrate a complete database from one system to another, perhaps the major hurdle to effective data integration lies in the absence of agreed data structures. Where an agency or institution is seeking to implement a robust long-term information strategy, priority should be given to achieving agreed data definitions and structures, rather than concentrating on relatively trivial short-term incompatibilities between current hardware or software systems. The achievement of complete uniformity of, or compatibility between, systems is a hollow victory unless it is accompanied by such underlying data standards. Both logical organisation (entities and attributes) and relationships (topology) are involved in defining a data structure capable of transfer or integration.

Data transfer and system interconnection

Most conventional hydrological studies and data sets have been designed to accord with often unwritten scientific protocols which establish a degree of data standardisation (particularly in hydro-meteorology), but assume individual responsibility for, and ownership of, methodology and data. However, when data are to be integrated within and between major databases, a substantially different approach is required, based on co-operative research structures and joint data management responsibilities (Clark, 1991). More specifically, the increasing emphasis on integrated research and operational systems places ever greater emphasis on the connectivity between data systems, and on the data transfer that such connectivity permits. Similar requirements may be generated in the construction of multiparticipant commercial data sets.

System interconnectivity first appears as a large database constraint at the data import/export level (Parks & Sene, 1991), but also poses a major challenge when enquiry or analytical tasks are proposed. A major database is of restricted use unless its contents are accessible to the widest possible range of applications, including those operated by people with limited IT expertise. Access to small standalone interactive systems is already effective through such common devices as pull-down menus or touch screens, and is destined to get still simpler. Large systems are being demystified by embedding them in user-friendly shells. Software standards such as Open Systems, UNIX and X-windows offer the hope that the individual will be able to transfer between systems, or use multiple systems, without meeting problems of incompatibility. A GIS training development project currently under way at the GeoData Institute includes a core illustrative module concerning river corridor information handling. The project is part of an IT Training Initiative of the Information Services Committee, which has a broad computing responsibility for the UK University and Polytechnic sector. Although the focus is on Higher Education, it includes the vital interface with the professional user community, and in this context reflects the growing emphasis on highly portable information systems which minimise reliance on any

one system. With this broadly Open Systems aspiration, the project module will offer an effective basis of GIS training for the water industry.

Networks (local and wide) are the key to meeting the needs of scientific database users, so that individuals, departments and indeed the whole institute can liaise effectively in information management and use. To this end, hydrologists have become familiar with the design or use of standardised user interfaces, common or compatible data structures, and clearly mapped navigable routes via interface formats between data sets and software systems. Software and systems are already under development to handle networks of medium or small processors (including PCs) to share the total available queue of computing tasks (a kind of distributed multicomputing) and, with rather more hardware and software ingenuity, to split up the large tasks into multiple simultaneous strands (distributed parallel computing) (Gaffney & Zannetti, 1990; IBM, 1990). Any organisation with several computers, however small, may already have the basis for building its own supercomputer.

However, information system integration using large databases demands much more than a means of transferring data or computing tasks from one system to another on a one-off basis. Prototypes are already in place to permit the user to gain real-time access to databases on different computers (mixed vendors and variable platforms) in distant locations (different countries if appropriate), without needing to know where the data are or what format they are held in. Basic to such approaches is the concept of metadata - a standardised dictionary of information which defines data in such a way as to allow compatible transfer to be achieved (Tom, 1990: Gaffney and Zannetti, 1990). The system of the mid-1990s should gather in, manipulate and distribute data effortlessly, provided that the political, managerial and financial obstacles are overcome! As always, it will be the people, not the machines, that provide the greatest hurdles, and it is already clear that many scientists and scientific institutions are too protective of their data to permit the effective interchange which is becoming technically feasible.

Data transfer within and between systems continues to yield problems, but technological advance is such that such hurdles should be substantially reduced over a timescale of a few years. This suggests that in future the problem of system inter-compatibility (local or national) is likely to be seen largely in terms of data structures rather than identity of file format or operating system. Developments in multi-system linkage using a metadata approach offer bright medium term prospects for hydrologists engaged in multi-variate and multi-national projects.

Integrative technologies - the role of GIS

Access to multiple data sets offers only very limited analytical potential in the absence of a technology capable of synthesising such data, and in this context few techniques offer greater potential than GIS. Provided that data are geocoded (an attribute that is present or possible with most hydrological data), remarkable descriptive and conceptual power is available through the synthetic functions of GIS.

With large databases, data capture has dominated much effort to date, but there are now signs of a growing interest in GIS analysis. Some of the most useful advances centre on the integration of data from multiple sources, especially maps, images and numerical data. This task of integration is of such fundamental significance that it seems worthy of consideration in its own right.

Spatial integration involves one of two subtly different approaches - first, the *ad hoc* design and implementation of holistic studies at the large region scale; second, the *post hoc* synthesis between previously-completed spatially or thematically distinct small-area studies. GIS can assist in both contexts, though it is most easily implemented in conjunction with studies or data sets specifically designed for this purpose.

It is possible in some circumstances to regard GIS as little more than a sophisticated front end to a large database, but even when the focus is on asset management (e.g. Elkins, 1990) such a categorisation underplays the scope of the system. Although the GIS does impose an element of spatial data structure, and may provide communications potential through its use of interface format files, its fundamental role lies in the extent to which it adds to functions or attributes that would alternatively be available in a non-spatial database. This enhancement may lie simply in the power of visualization, but is more likely to be a product of spatial synthesis or spatial modelling. Similar advances are possible where GIS is used to provide a spatial structure for time-series data, as is the case with the WIS package developed with the participation of the Institute of Hydrology.

By thus manipulating the database content, operational GIS applications can be developed that carry the database far beyond a merely custodial role. In the context of channel management for flood defence, asset and hydrological databases can be combined to evaluate the land/property at risk from flooding; use this information to build performance targets for flood defence; monitor the actual flood regime and thus flood defence performance; and thereby assess the level of performance as adequate, inadequate or excessive.

The requirements for such a "value added" GIS database application for NRA- Thames Region use are discussed by Mills *et al.* (1989) and Clark *et al.* (1990), and an operational prototype is described by Clark *et al.* (1991). The significance of this application is that it provides a very specific manipulation of a largely general database: the same data are available for incorporation within a number of other procedures or models.

Conclusions and priorities

It is clear that both operational and scientific procedures gain much from access to large databases, and particularly from integration and comparison of data from studies which are distinct in date as well as in place. It follows that agreed data definitions and diagnostic indices, together with common standards or guidelines for inter-calibrated sampling and instrumentation guidelines, will be essential to the achievement of high-resolution temporal or spatial analysis or monitoring of hydrological systems. Clark (1991) suggests that there are many opportunities for such standardised data and database management, yet the potential benefits will remain elusive unless the low incentive to impose standardisation is compensated by the strong support of professional agencies and research sponsoring bodies. This is particularly important in ensuring that emerging data standards comply with general database or GIS requirements, not just a set of discipline-specific norms which would be inadequate as a basis for interdisciplinary data integration. It has been noted by Tom (1990) that "*the development of standards is a long and arduous journey*", but the benefits at its destination makes the journey worthwhile.

Hydrology is not alone in confronting major opportunities for the enhancement of large database policy. In seeking to define a policy for cold regions scientists, Clark (1991) has proposed a multi-stage approach. Priority would be accorded to increasing awareness of the nature and scale of operator and instrumental variance in data collection (including spatial and temporal sampling design); breaking down the widespread neglect of detailed methodological debate; and designating agreed indices of the relevant main hydrological variables. Guidelines should be established for data documentation for publication and archiving of data sets or data-derived statements, and a preferred format for data archiving and indexing should be agreed. Careful documentation of measurement conventions can also help greatly in reducing the problem of comparing or merging data from different databases. Professional associations such as the British Hydrological Society have an important role to play in promulgating guidelines for the application of these preferred formats and acquisition standards to new data sets. Within defined key subject areas, the documentation of significant existing data sets can also be improved by reference back to authors, originators, or their original records. Another priority is to create and publicise cross-referenced and interactive directories of major databases, and to provide location-independent access to directories and data sets, using central agencies as network gateways. Finally, it will be necessary to develop hardware- and software-independent archiving approaches, and establish any necessary upgrades to the data management infrastructure applied to these archives. Only then will it be possible to claim that the full potential of large hydrological databases is being realised.

References

Barry, R.G. 1988. Permafrost data and information: status and needs. In *Proc. V Int. Conf. on Permafrost*, Trondheim, Norway, 1988, 1, 119-122.

Barry, R.G. 1989. Workshop on permafrost data and information. Glaciological Data, Report GD-23, World Data Center A for Glaciology, 107 & 121-2.

Boorman, D.B., Hollis, J. & Lilly, A. 1991. The production of the Hydrology Of Soil Types (HOST) data set. In: *Proc. BHS 3rd National Hydrology Symposium, 1991*. (This volume)

Clark, M.J. 1991. The Svalbard contribution to global studies of arctic hydrology and sediment transfer. In *Proc. Norwegian Hydrological Society Conference on Arctic Hydrology*, Longyearbyen (Svalbard), September 1990. (In press)

Clark, M.J., Gurnell, A.M., Davenport, J. & Azizi, A. 1991. Integrated river channel management through Geographic Information Systems. *Proc. IWEM 91, Water and the Environment*, 30 April-2 May, Birmingham, 17.1-17.11

Clark, M.J., Gurnell, A.M., Candish, C. & Mills, D.N. 1990. Flood defence assessment through GIS. In *Proc. AGI Second National Conference and Exhibition*, GIS - The key to managing information, 5.1.1 - 5.1.3.

Clark, M.J., Gurnell, A.M. & Threlfall, J.L. 1988. The implications of investigative design for the study of fluvial sediment transfer in arctic and subarctic regions. *Zeitschrift für Geomorphologie*, 71, 147-156.

CNIG 1991. Geographic Information Exchange Standards: Summary Report on the Preliminary Investigation. Conseil National de l'Information Géographique.

Davenport, J. 1990. Linking GIS applications and research. *Mapping Awareness*, 4, 49-53.

Elkins, P. 1990. Water under the bridge - the background to Southern Water's experience with GIS, *Mapping Awareness*, 4, 38.

Gaffney, P.W. & Zanetti, P. 1990. Environmental Sciences at Bergen Scientific Centre: Key Strategies. Bergen Scientific Centre, IBM.

Gurnell, A.M. 1987. Suspended sediment. In Gurnell, A.M. & Clark, M.J. (eds) *Glacio-fluvial Sediment Transfer: an Alpine Perspective*. John Wiley & Sons, Chichester, 305-354.

IAHS 1989. *FRIENDS in Hydrology: Proc. Bolkesjø Symposium, April 1989*. International Association of Hydrological Sciences Publication 187.

IBM 1990. AIX and Parallel Computing: Tools/ Support. Bergen Scientific Centre, IBM.

Mills, D.N., Clark, M.J. & Gurnell, A.M. 1989. Criteria for selection of river basin G.I.S. applications. *Proc. Automated Mapping and Facilities Management AM/FM European Conference* V, AM/FM - A Competitive Edge; October 1989, Montreux, Switzerland, 207-212.

Montgomery, G.E. 1990. Multiparticipant GIS projects require contractual and legal obligations. *GIS World*, 3, 105-6.

Mounsey, H. & Tomlinson, R. 1988. *Building Databases for Global Science*. Taylor & Francis, London, New York, Philadelphia.

Parks, Y.P. & Sene, K. 1991. Hydrological data transfer systems. In *Proc. BHS 3rd National Hydrology Symposium, 1991*. (This volume)

Roald, L.A. & Beldring, S. 1991. Development of a new national database in hydrology in Norway. In *Proc. BHS 3rd National Hydrology Symposium*, 1991. (This volume)

Tom, H. 1990. Geographic Information Systems standards: a federal perspective. *The 1990 GIS Sourcebook*, GIS World Inc., Fort Collins, 281-284.

The production of the Hydrology Of Soil Types (HOST) data set

D.B. Boorman, J. Hollis & A. Lilly

Abstract

The Hydrology of Soil Types (HOST) data set represents a classification of soils that has been developed especially for hydrological applications. A description of how existing archives of time-series and geographical data that cover the whole of the UK have been combined to produce HOST is presented as an example of how large data sets may be used in hydrology. Various problems of managing and combining large data sets are considered.

Introduction

The Flood Studies Report (NERC, 1975) made use of a hydrological classification of soils to assist flood estimation at ungauged sites. This classification scheme was based on the Winter Rainfall Acceptance Potential (WRAP) and was a recognition of the major influence of soil type on both hydrological processes and catchment response. WRAP was developed from a theoretical consideration of runoff processes by soil scientists and hydrologists, and was not based on the widespread analysis of hydrological data (see Farquharson et al., 1978). Although the WRAP system has few classes (five) and is of limited resolution (it is derived from 1:1,000,000 base maps), it is at the core of the Flood Studies Report (FSR) rainfall-runoff method of design flood estimation, and has been used in many design studies over the last 15 years. It is also engrained in other design procedures (e.g. WASSP, Department of the Environment, 1981).

Problems encountered in the use of WRAP are easily appreciated by considering the estimation of standard percentage runoff (SPR), which is percentage runoff derived from event data, adjusted to standard rainfall and catchment conditions, and averaged for a catchment (see Figure 1). To estimate SPR at ungauged sites, the FSR gave the values 15, 30, 40, 45 and 50% to the five WRAP classes. Across a boundary between classes SPR can change by a factor of 2 or 3, and this factor will be carried forward in the flood estimate. Clearly mapping at a larger scale would remove some of this uncertainty, but users have also commented on the poor discrimination and limited range of the WRAP classification scheme. Downland chalk catchments have typical responses of just a few percent and some small, upland catchments have a standard response of over 60% (see, for example, Boorman 1985).

An opportunity to revise the scale of the WRAP map came in the mid-1980s when the Soil Survey and Land Research Centre (SSLRC) and Macaulay Land Use Research Institute (MLURI) completed the mapping of soils at 1:250,000. However, rather than merely produce a WRAP map at a more detailed scale, it was considered worthwhile to use the large hydrological databases held by the Institute of Hydrology (IH) to assist in the definition of classes. Thus the Hydrology Of Soil Types (HOST) project was born as a collaborative venture between these three organizations. Soil mapping at 1:250,000 has not been completed for Northern Ireland but the Department of Agriculture of Northern Ireland has been involved in the HOST project and in the preparation of a HOST map and data set for Northern Ireland.

The aim of this paper is not to describe the details of the HOST classification and how it was derived, but to use HOST as an example of a project that has used large data bases in a hydrological application. The next two sections describe the data sets that were already available or prepared specifically for HOST, and a brief account of how they were used in developing the classification. Problems encountered by the HOST project are described in a discussion section and will have relevance for other users, or potential users, of the many large data bases that are available to them.

Data sets

The time-series data come from the Surface Water Archive (SWA) and the Flood Event Archive, both held at IH. SPR values were available from the 1910 events on 210 catchments described by Boorman (1985), and from an additional 683 events collected subsequently from the same and other catchments. However, for many of these catchments insufficient

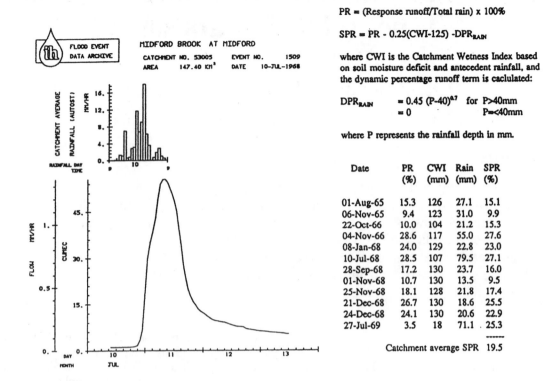

PR = (Response runoff/Total rain) x 100%

SPR = PR - 0.25(CWI-125) -DPR$_{RAIN}$

where CWI is the Catchment Wetness Index based on soil moisture deficit and antecedent rainfall, and the dynamic percentage runoff term is caclulated:

$$DPR_{RAIN} = 0.45 (P-40)^{0.7} \quad \text{for} \quad P>40mm$$
$$= 0 \quad\quad\quad P=<40mm$$

where P represents the rainfall depth in mm.

Date	PR (%)	CWI (mm)	Rain (mm)	SPR (%)
01-Aug-65	15.3	126	27.1	15.1
06-Nov-65	9.4	123	31.0	9.9
22-Oct-66	10.0	104	21.2	15.3
04-Nov-66	28.6	117	55.0	27.6
08-Jan-68	24.0	129	22.8	23.0
10-Jul-68	28.5	107	79.5	27.1
28-Sep-68	17.2	130	23.7	16.0
01-Nov-68	10.7	130	13.5	9.5
25-Nov-68	18.1	128	21.8	17.4
21-Dec-68	26.7	130	18.6	25.5
24-Dec-68	24.1	130	20.6	22.9
27-Jul-69	3.5	18	71.1	25.3

Catchment average SPR 19.5

Figure 1   The calculation of percentage runoff (PR) and standard percentage runoff (SPR) from event data

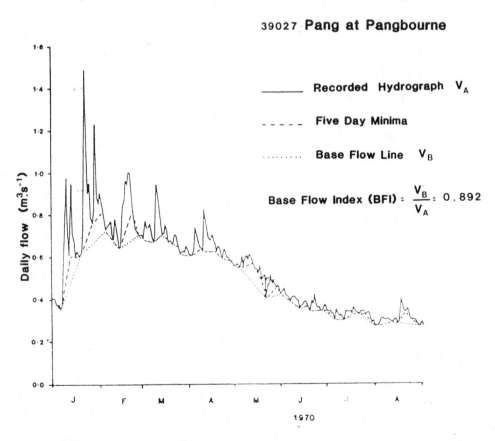

Figure 2   The calculation of base flow index (BFI) from daily mean flow data: River Pang at Pangbourne, 1970 [Reproduced from Gustard et al., 1989]

events are available to give an acceptable value of SPR and only 202 could be used for HOST. So that a much larger number of catchments could be used, the base flow index (Gustard *et al.*, 1991) was used as an alternative index of catchment hydrological response within HOST. Base flow index (BFI) is derived from daily flow data (see Figure 2) which were readily available on the SWA. Daily data from about 1100 catchments were available although only 826 were considered suitable for the HOST study as catchments with flow records dominated by artificial influences were rejected. As SPR and BFI are well correlated (correlation coefficient of 0.75), BFI was seen as an acceptable analogue for SPR, and in practice most of the work in developing HOST used BFI. Figure 3 shows the distribution of catchments for which these hydrological indices were available.

SSLRC and MLURI have produced maps showing the distribution of soil map units at a scale of 1:250,000 for England and Wales, and Scotland respectively. The soil maps have been digitised and are stored as both vector and raster data sets; the raster sets being held at 1km and 100m resolution. Soil map units comprise a limited number of soil series that occur together in the landscape. Soil series are distinguished by precise definitions of soil and substrate properties that can be assessed by soil survey. However SSLRC and MLURI have different classifications for soil series and hence different map units. For England and Wales, SSLRC show 299 map units containing 417 soil series, while for Scotland, MLURI depict 590 map units containing 552 series.

In addition to the map data, there exist databases containing information about the physical properties that characterise the soil series, and the proportions of series within the map units. For England and Wales alone there are physical property data for about 4000 soil layers describing over 1000 soil profiles. To make the best use of these data, the soil series was adopted as the key soil unit within the HOST project. The physical properties that were available at the start of the HOST project were: depth to a slowly permeable layer, depth to a gleyed layer, the integrated air capacity (IAC) and presence of a peaty top soil. However, at an early stage in the project it was seen to be necessary to include a geological component and a soil-hydrogeological classification was derived; where appropriate this also contained information about the depth to an aquifer or groundwater. These six properties, and their use in the HOST classification, are described in Table 1.

The link between soil type and hydrological response was made via the topographic catchment boundary, again available in digital form at IH. For each catchment the digitised boundary was overlain on the gridded soil map and the percentage cover of each soil series was calculated.

The HOST classification

A number of soil classification schemes were derived based on conceptual models of catchment response and feedback from applying the schemes to estimate the hydrological parameters. Examples of the

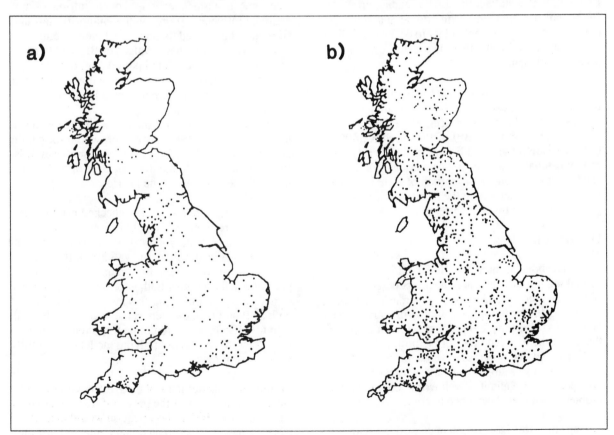

Figure 3 The distribution of catchments for which (a) SPR and (b) BFI data were available

Table 1 Descriptions and use of soil properties within HOST

Soil hydrogeology: Used to differentiate mechanisms of vertical water movement (e.g. intergranular or fissure flow) and to distinguish between permeable, slowly permeable and impermeable substrates

Depth to aquifer or groundwater: Indicates time taken for excess water to reach the water table.

Presence of a peaty topsoil: Indicates saturated surface conditions for most of the year; limits infiltration and provides lateral pathway for rapid response in the uppermost part of the soil.

Depth to a slowly permeable layer: Such a layer impedes downward percolation of excess soil water causing periodic saturation in the overlying layer. Storage is reduced and there is an increased response to heavy rainfall.

Depth to gleyed layer: Gleying is the presence of grey and ochreous mottles within the soil caused by intermittent waterlogging.

Integrated air capacity: The average percentage air volume over a depth of 1m. Used as a surrogate for permeability in permeable soils, and as a measure of storage capacity in slowly permeable and impermeable soils.

models, and the class definitions, can be found in Boorman and Hollis (1990).

The resulting scheme comprises 29 HOST classes and will be available as digital data sets in a raster form at both 1 km and 100 m resolution. Because the classification is series based many HOST classes may be present within each 1 km or 100 m cell. Thus although the HOST scheme can be represented as a map (e.g. showing only the dominant HOST class) this masks the true complexity of the data set. Figure 4 shows the distribution of HOST Class 23 which is the most extensive class covering almost 14% of England, Wales and Scotland. The shading on the figure indicates that, on a 1km grid, although this class is sometimes the only class to occur in a cell, it frequently occurs with other classes as the major or minor component.

As with the earlier WRAP classification, first use of the HOST classification will be via labelling of classes with hydrological indices, e.g. HOST class 1 could be labelled with a BFI of 1.0 and SPR of 0% (NB these are provisional figures only). Clearly the task of estimating a hydrological variable for a catchment based on the proportion of HOST classes will be made easier within the framework found in geographical information systems.

Discussion

From the above account, the HOST project is seen to be making use of many large data sets describing flows, catchments, and soils, to generate a data set describing the hydrological response of soils that can be used to solve practical problems. It would appear that all of the data required for the project are readily available and that progress towards the new soil classification was straightforward. However, this has not been the case and it is well worth looking at the problems that have been encountered.

Perhaps the most basic problem of working with large data sets is that the validity of much of the

basic data has to be accepted, more or less, without question. For example, in a HOST context this meant not reviewing the accuracy of the flow measuring stations (i.e. the validity of the rating equation); if the data were held on the SWA they were considered useable for HOST. As the SWA maintains period of record values of BFI the assembling of a large data set appeared easy. However, HOST was able to draw on station assessments for low flow studies (Gustard *et al.*, 1991) which included viewing an arbitrarily chosen annual hydrograph; this simple check revealed many problems in the data.

The same assessment exercise sought information of artificial influences from gauging authority staff and files, and this too led to many catchments being withdrawn. Finally, many values of BFI had to be recalculated for a restricted period (e.g. only to include pre-impoundment flows at a now-reservoired site). These comments are not intended to reflect badly on the data management policy of the SWA. This archive accepts data and derives flow indices to meet its own objectives and can provide information on the quality and usefulness of the stored data. It is for the user to check that the standards of the archive match those required by the project.

The SPR data were thoroughly checked prior to the review that resulted in the publication of Flood Studies Supplementary Report No. 16 (IH, 1985), but uncertainty remains about the validity of the FSR SPR model at some sites. Boorman *et al.* (1990) present results showing both good and bad estimates of percentage runoff using this model. Thus while both SPR and BFI are seen as the basic hydrological data for HOST, it should not be forgotten that they are in fact the results of applying models to carefully vetted sets of data.

Turning to consider the soil data, different problems emerge. At the start of the project it was not obvious what form the HOST classification would take. A working data set was created that contained just the dominant map unit in each 1km square. Again this appears a simple operation but much is hidden. Any line appearing on a 1:250,000 scale map only gives an approximate location of a feature or boundary.

When the line separates map units (i.e. where one mix of soil series is replaced by a different mix), the line of the transition is even more difficult to map. A

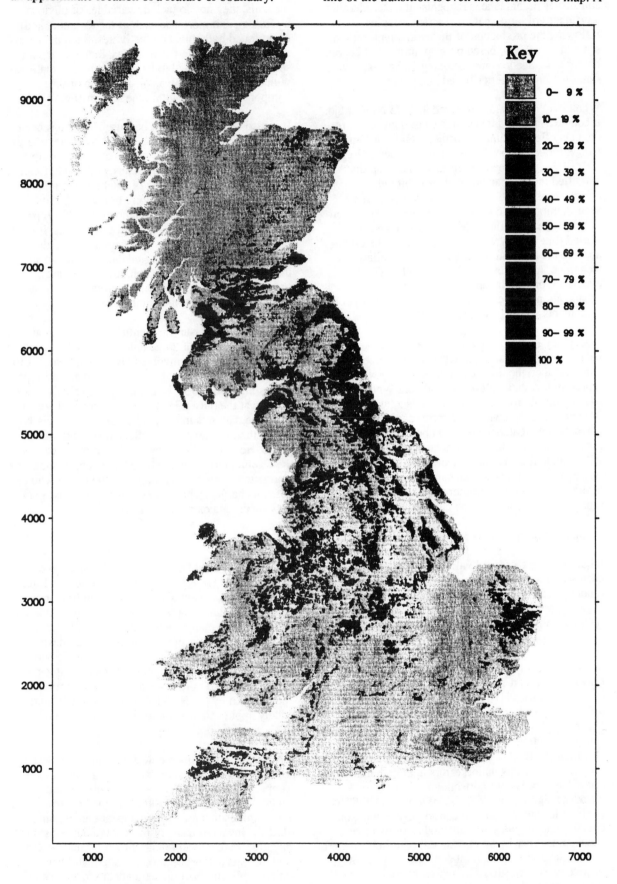

Key

	0– 9 %
	10– 19 %
	20– 29 %
	30– 39 %
	40– 49 %
	50– 59 %
	60– 69 %
	70– 79 %
	80– 89 %
	90– 99 %
	100 %

Figure 4   The distribution of HOST Class 23

better map base for HOST would be one showing the soil units that can be distinguished just using physical properties, i.e. the soil series. However, while both soil survey organizations recognise the considerable advantages of large scale soil series mapping, following the production of the national maps (at a scale of 1:250,000) based on map units it has become harder to persuade commissioning bodies to provide funds to continue series-based mapping.

When the WRAP map appeared in 1975 it left major urban areas unclassified which caused problems for the many flood estimation projects on the urban fringe. Flood Studies Supplementary Report No.7 (IH, 1978) introduced a revised WRAP map that classified these urban areas mainly through correlations between geology and soil type. It was seen as important to provide the same classification of urban areas within HOST and an exercise was started (but is not yet complete) to in-fill the urban areas in the national soil maps using a similar technique. In the development of the HOST classification, catchments with more than 5% urbanization were excluded, reducing the number of catchments with BFI values from 826 to 633.

Inaccuracy in digitising the soil maps is unlikely to be a problem, but, when the data are rasterized on a 1km grid then the dominant map unit may well represent less than half of the grid cell. Where small catchments are overlain on such cells a false impression of the component series can result. So whereas small catchments might be expected to provide good benchmarks for classifying soils as they will include few map units, care must be taken in relying on results from such catchments as the soils abstracted from the computer overlay may poorly represent those found on the catchment.

To make the step from percentages of map units to percentages of soil series found on catchments, required the use of fixed values for the fraction of each series within the map unit. To do this clearly ignores local variations in the map unit composition. Figures describing the map unit composition were only formalised for the HOST project and exclude contributions from very small component series.

The catchment boundaries were digitised from lines drawn by hand on 1:50,000 maps. The construction of the boundaries is easy in upland areas but quite difficult in low lying regions where many ditches exists at right-angles to the expected flow direction. The construction of a hydrologically sound digital elevation model (DEM) at IH has shown many minor, but very few major, errors in these boundaries. The process of digitisation is unlikely to introduce significant error. Future work on HOST is likely to investigate other means of abstracting soil data for catchments. Other methods worthy of consideration are by overlaying either buffers created around the digitized channel network, or areas of flow convergence (that may represent contributing areas) identified using a DEM.

The allocation of soil series to HOST classes uses the six properties described in Table 1. While these variables help to define the hydrological regime of the soils, they not do include variables of obvious hydrological importance such as the saturated and unsaturated hydraulic conductivities. Such data are not readily available for all series. Indeed, for some series values have had to be inferred by correlations with other series, or by a consideration of the component horizons within the soil profile.

It is also worth noting that because HOST has been developed using large data sets and computer analysis, the resulting classification has a greater complexity than the WRAP scheme. Thus while HOST can be applied via manual overlay of catchments on the paper maps and interpretation through a key, this would be tedious on large catchments, or for repeated HOST class abstraction on small catchments. It is imagined that many users will gain access to the HOST system using the digital data sets. To do so they will require access to computer hardware (probably a workstation) with appropriate software for the management of spatial data.

Finally, it is necessary to mention problems of access to, and ownership of, large data sets and their derived products. The issues involved are far too complex to be considered here but those seeking to establish projects similar to HOST would do well to resolve these matters at the outset. Hydrologists may well wish to see large data sets in the public domain, especially where the data have been collected at the public expense. However, the tendency, under guidance from the Cabinet Office, is likely to be the application of a charge to commercial and operational users, who can pass on charges, while access for research use may only incur data extraction charges.

Conclusion

The HOST project is, perhaps, the first endeavour of its kind in the UK's hydrological community. It has used many newly available data sets all held in computer systems to produce a soil classification that can be used in many areas of hydrology. It has, of necessity, had to accept that in order to achieve its objective compromises have had to be made between scientific rigour and the nature of the available data. Despite these compromises and the many problems encountered by the HOST project, a valuable and widely applicable hydrological classification of the UK's soils has been produced.

Hydrology is entering a new era of direct, on-line access to many computer data bases that contain a comprehensive description of our hydrological environment and its variations in time and space. The opportunities that are offered appear endless and fruitful. However, users of these large data sets must take great care to ensure that they fully understand how the data set has been constructed, and hence which applications of the data are appropriate and which are not.

Acknowledgement

Work on the HOST project has been funded by the Ministry of Agriculture, Fisheries and Food, the Scottish Office Agriculture and Fisheries Department, and the Department of Agriculture for Northern Ireland (DANI). Data sets have been made available by SSLRC, MLURI and DANI. The views expressed in this paper are those of the authors and not necessarily the views of IH, SSLRC, MLURI, or funding organizations.

References

Boorman, D.B. 1985. A review of the Flood Studies Report rainfall-runoff model parameter estimation equations. *IH Report No. 94*.

Boorman, D.B., Acreman, M.C. & Packman, J.C. 1990. A review of design flood estimation using the FSR rainfall-runoff method. *IH Report No. 111*.

Boorman, D.B. & Hollis, J.M. 1990. A hydrologically-based classification of the soils of England and Wales, Ministry of Agriculture Fisheries and Food Conference of River and Coastal Engineers, University of Loughborough.

Department of Environment/National Water Council 1981. Design and analysis of urban storm drainage - the Wallingford Procedure. National Water Council (Water Authorities Association)

Farquharson, F.A.K., Mackney, D., Newson, M.D. & Thomasson, A.J. 1978. Estimation of run-off potential for river catchments from soil surveys, Soil Survey Special Survey No.11, Harpenden.

Gustard, A., Roald, L.A., Demuth, S., Lumadjeng, H.S. & Gross R. 1989. *Flow Regimes from Experimental and Network Data (FREND)*, Institute of Hydrology.

Gustard, A., Bullock, A., & Dixon, J.M. 1991. Estimating low river flows in the United Kingdom. *IH Report No. 108* (In press).

Institute of Hydrology 1978. A revised version of the Winter Rain Acceptance Potential (SOIL) map. *Flood Studies Supplementary Report No. 7*.

Institute of Hydrology 1985. The FSR rainfall-runoff model parameter estimation equations updated. *Flood Studies Supplementary Report No. 16*.

Natural Environment Research Council 1975. *Flood Studies Report*.

Development of a new national database for hydrology in Norway

L.A. Roald & S. Beldring

Abstract

The national hydrological databases of Norway are currently stored in a database system based on index sequential files. Changes in the monitoring as well as in computer technology have necessitated a fundamental redesign of the data bases. The ability to handle long time series was examined for three commercially available database management systems, two relational and one object-oriented system. Their performances were compared with the current system. The object-oriented system was chosen as a platform for the new database, and a new data model has been defined.

Introduction

The Hydrology Department of the Norwegian Water Resources and Energy Administration (NVE) is responsible for operating the national monitoring networks of hydrometry, snow and glaciology, sediment transport, and ice and water temperature. Groundwater levels are observed in a network owned jointly by the Norwegian Geological Survey (NGU) and NVE. A small network of soil moisture monitoring stations is now under development.

All historical observations of daily stages were transferred to magnetic tape at the end of the 1960s. The archive was later moved to a database system developed at NVE. The database was also extended to contain data collected in the other networks. NVE is now redesigning the database and is moving it into a commercially available system.

Properties of the current system

Data are currently stored on a database on a Control Data CYBER960 mainframe under the NOS operating system. The system was developed in 1979. It is based on index sequential files, where the indices as well as the records are organised in sorted key order. Any record may be accessed by using its key value. The system is based on a number of Fortran routines and some routines in assembler code. It can be accessed simultaneously by several users reading data, but is a single user system when writing to the database.

The present system assumes a one-to-one relationship between a data series and a station. Each station and series is uniquely identified by a station number and a code. The number of parameters monitored at each station has increased in recent years. Dataloggers are now replacing chart recorders in a considerable part of the network. Parallel monitoring is used for a while during the change-over from one type of instrument to another. The current system handles monitoring of more than one data series at one station by assigning separate codes to each series. The various networks follow different numbering schemes. Each network has separate databases, which are updated independently.

The system was originally developed for handling daily data. Daily series are organised in records containing one year of data. Files were later added to the database for storing data with high time resolution from digitised charts and from data loggers. These data are stored with variable record length. Derived series for locations outside the gauging stations are stored on separate databases with a similar structure to the main database.

The database is usually accessed using one of more than 60 user application programs. These are also available to the water industry, universities and research institutions and to private consultants. The use is mostly interactive and requires fast access to the data. The programs can easily extract data from the different networks. The user applications are used on average 100 times per day.

The system has served NVE well for more than ten years. It was designed to respond quickly and in a flexible way. Data is also packed very efficiently. A major drawback, however, is that the system is strongly dependent on the operating system. The system also requires considerable expertise to maintain, and this is hard to obtain. Some applications also write on certain files within the system. It is necessary to have a fully multi-user system to avoid users being delayed by other users using the same files. Some of the weaknesses of the present system are independent of the choice of dbms. A new numbering system has now been introduced assigning numbers within a common scheme for all the networks. A new data model has also been defined in a general form independent of the dbms to facilitate later migrations to other systems.

Selection of a new database management system (DBMS)

The need for a new database arose when it became clear that the NOS-operating system would be phased out gradually. NVE decided to look for a commercially available dbms with the ability to handle time series.

Requirements of a new dbms

The new dbms must support:

* a flexible data structure with variable record length
* fast retrieval of time series data
* one-to-one, one-to-many and many-to-many relationships
* multiple user system with concurrent read and write operations
* access of several databases concurrently

The system should support:

* portability between computers and operating systems
* adequate facilities for database back-up and recovery
* checkpoint, rollback and database operations logging
* database administration functions, e.g. compression and clean-up
* easy database definition and documentation
* database restructuring possibilities
* Structured Query Language (SQL) interface
* 4th generation language

Performance test of three commercially available dbms

Three commercially available dbms were tested to evaluate their performance in handling long time series. Two of these systems are relational databases, the third is an object-oriented system. A relational database can be considered as a collection of tables with the relations embedded in the tables, while an object-oriented database comprises a collection of objects with a number of attributes.

Mimer is a relational database management system which was developed at Uppsala University Data Centre in Sweden, (Mimer 1984a,b,c, 1985). The dbms is the nucleus in a family of products which access the database. All data are stored in two-dimensional tables. The system can store and traverse hierarchical data structures.

Information Management/Data Management (IM/DM) is a large relational database management system which runs on the NOS/VE operating system. IM/DM and NOS/VE are products of Control Data Corporation (CDC), (CDC 1987a,b,c). An IM/DM database can be structured in many ways using hierarchical or network connections.

Tornado is a hybrid database management system which combines the hierarchical and network database technologies with a semantic capability and functions for handling relational tables. It has some properties typical of object-oriented systems. Tornado was developed at the Centre for Industrial Research, Norway. The system is sold by Metis A/S, Horten, Norway. Tornado consists of a dbms with tools for database administration, a screen handler, a query language and case tools for integrated data modelling and database structuring. The basic entity in the Tornado dbms is the object which identifies the occurrence of a specific abstract or concrete object. Objects are grouped into classes which comprise objects of equal characteristics. The characteristics of objects are described by attributes. Objects can be linked to one another in sets which describe a network structure. Objects may point to relational tables. Tornado dbms offers list structures, tree structures, indexed sequential access methods, networks, relational tables and semantic networks by combination of different database technologies. Tornado dbms may be used as a checked out database on work stations with the original database located on a server computer, (Metis1986a,b,c,1989). BRITOIL applies TORNADO for oil reservoir simulation while Volvo applies it for computer integrated manufacture prototyping (CIM).

Test program

The test consisted in running a Fortran program on databases based on the three systems and on the present dbms. Daily water levels were loaded into each database prior to the test for a time series comprising 70 years of observations. Data was stored in records containing data for a year, each record consisting of a unique key (station number and year), 366 data fields and three additional fields with information about the data.

The database structure in Mimer and IM/DM was chosen equal to the one used in the present system. The Mimer database had to be divided in four tables because of limitations in the record length. Each table contained a key field and data for three months. One of the tables also contained the three fields with general information about the data. IM/DM permits an infinite record length, this means that only one table was necessary in order to store data.

The database structure in Tornado was a collection of objects, each representing a station and having a unique key equal to the station number. Each object pointed to a relational table containing columns with year number, 366 daily values and three fields with information about the data. The year was used as a key field within each table.

The test program reads daily data from the data base for a sequence of years and finds the minimum and maximum values within the series. The program performs no calculations, most of the execution time is used for reading data. The database and program was optimised supported by representatives of the manufacturers of the three systems. Compiling, linking and user dialogue were performed before the response time was measured; this means that only the actual times used for reading data and finding the minimum and maximum values are compared. The response times are presented in Table 1.

Comparison of the systems and results

The test results are not quite comparable as the tests were run on different computers. Mimer and the present system were run on the operating system NOS on a CYBER825, IM/DM was run on the operating system NOS/VE on a CYBER930 while Tornado was run on the operating system EP/IX (Unix) on a CD4360. CD4360 is a Reduced Instruction Set Computer (RISC) while CYBER825 and CYBER930 are Complex Instruction Set Computers (CISC). Tornado was also run on NOS/VE on the CYBER930, this test gave response times twice as long as on the CD4360. Later tests with nine concurrent users reading from the Tornado database gave an average response time of 5.5 seconds. The test was also performed with one user running the program repeatedly, while another user loaded the data to the database.

The results indicate that Tornado dbms is more suited for storing and retrieving time series than the relational dbms. One index sequential search locates the object which points to the relational table with the time series. The data can then be read sequentially. This is more efficient than making a new search for each record in a relational database. Tornado uses clustering techniques when storing data; this will also reduce the retrieval time compared to database systems that do not utilise these techniques. The efficiency of Tornado dbms is also demonstrated by the fact that it is faster than the present database system which uses a very efficient record manager for the operating system NOS.

Tornado also has other advantages compared to the relational databases. The ability to combine different technologies makes Tornado a very flexible system which can handle different data models. Mimer and IM/DM on the other hand pose several problems when trying to implement structures with variable resolution in space and time. Other advantages with Tornado are that the tools for database definition and administration are easy to use, it has a good Fortran interface and the database files are small compared to the database files generated by the relational databases. Since Tornado is written in Fortran and C it should ideally be portable between different operating systems. The disadvantages with Tornado are that the query language does not follow the SQL standard and the fact that the number of installations is small compared to many other commercial database systems.

The test results so far show that Tornado dbms is well suited to handling complex structures and for storing time series data when fast retrieval is considered important. NVE has therefore decided to use Tornado dbms for storing hydrological data. One feature of Tornado is that objects can be connected into sets. Such system specific properties are avoided in order to obtain a general data structure whichcan be utilised later in other systems.

Data model

During the process of designing the database, modelling of data has been performed by the NIAM-method. This is a binary-relationship method which is more detailed than the entity-relationship methods (Verheijen & van Bekkum, 1982). The result of this process is a group of relational tables which are in the fifth normal form, i.e. data base consistency is maintained, no redundant information is stored and no functional dependencies exists between columns in the tables (Date, 1986). Some of the relations in the database given by the tables are represented by objects which point to the relational tables. Usually these objects represent the primary key of the records.

The central concept in the database is the station. A station is always linked to a geographical location. Data are monitored in points such as gauging stations, meteorological stations etc. Some data sampling programs monitor data in many points on well defined geographical objects, such as glaciers, lakes or aquifers and can be stored together with advantage. The system defines two types of stations: point stations which refer to one single geographical

Table 1 *Average response time (seconds) for concurrent database accesses. 70 years of daily values are read by each user.*

No. of users	Present system	Mimer	IM/DM	Tornado
1	6.1	15	7.0	1.5
2	8.5	–	13.5	2.0
3	12.0	–	21.0	2.3
4	13.0	–	27.0	2.4
5	14.0	–	33.0	2.8

location, and area stations which refer to all the data observed for a spatially extended geographical object. Each station may own one or more time series. The series must be representative for the actual point or the upstream catchment in case of flow data. The data can be observed or derived from other series.

Data from observations are stored in observed series. Several observed series can be linked to one station, but in general only one series for each hydrological parameter. All the data in one observed series must represent the same hydrological parameter. If two or more observed series belong to a station for the same parameter, each series will be identified by a version number.

Most of the application programs utilise time series from fixed geographical locations. These data series are in many cases identical to a series of observed data. A data series may comprise two or more series which are adjusted to define one series representative for the point of interest. Such derived series will not normally be stored on the database. The algorithm for deriving the series will be stored instead, and applied whenever the series is read from the database based on the actual observed data. Data series which are used very frequently will, however, be stored on separate archives, one example of this is a database for daily data. Figure 1 shows the relationship between stations, observed series and data series.

The numbering scheme gives the keys to the stations or series in the databases. The numbers follow a hierarchical pattern:

station:
*   main drainage basin number
*   number within drainage basin

*   point number (used for area stations)

observed series:
*   station number
*   hydrological parameter
*   version (in case of more than one observed series with one parameter at one station)

data series:
*   same as observed series

Information describing the stations, observed series, data series and drainage basins is stored in a data base named HYSAR. The observed series are stored permanently in the database HYKVAL with variable time resolution. Most of the application programs operate on daily data. Daily data series will be stored on a database named HYDAG: see Figure 2, which also shows the dataflow to the databases.

Data input and quality control

The system for primary processing and quality control is redesigned in the new system. The drivers which convert data from sensor units to absolute units will produce data in standard formats, regardless of the type of instrument. Data will be loaded to a transaction database, HYTRAN. The transfer into the permanent database, HYKVAL, is done by an interactive program which first makes some initial verification of the data, followed by plotting and interactive correction of errors. Each data value has a flag telling the user if the data has been corrected. A second control program checks the water balance in rivers with several gauging stations and compares floods to synoptic meteorological data. A third program is used interactively to correct for ice jamming, producing a corrected daily flow series on the database, HYDAG.

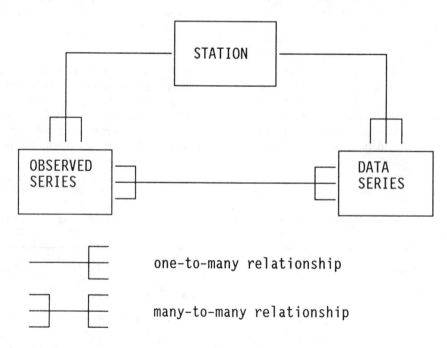

Figure 1   Relationship between stations, observed series and data series

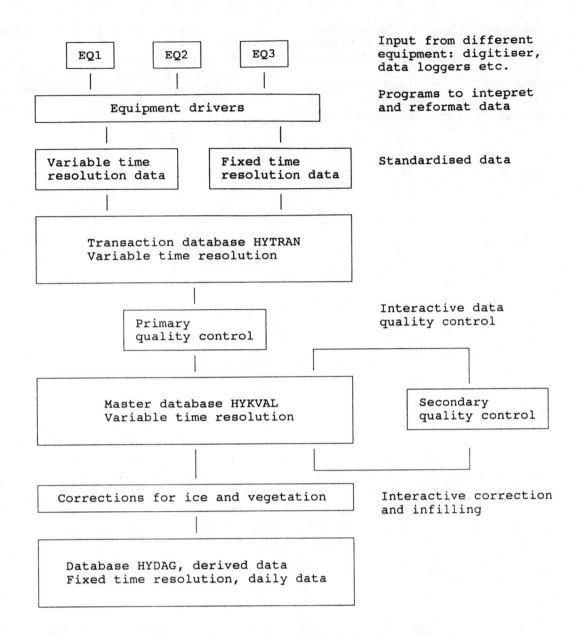

Figure 2   Organisation and dataflow of the Norwegian National Hydrological Database

Progress in the development of the database

The process of designing the databases is nearly complete. The system is implemented on a CD4360 under the EP/IX operating system. Programs and subroutines controlling the objects of the database and performing input and output of data are being developed. Drivers for data collecting equipment currently in use are being rewritten, new drivers will be added when needed. A new interface between the database and the existing application programs is developed.

References

Date, C.J. 1986. *An Introduction to Database Systems*, 4th edn, Addison-Wesley, Reading, Massachusetts, USA.

CDC 1987a. IM/DM Query, report writer and command procedures.Control Data Corporation Publication no. 60489013 F, St Paul, Minnesota.

CDC 1987b. IM/DM Data administration.Control Data Corporation Publication no. 60489014 F, St. Paul, Minnesota.

CDC 1987c. IM/DM Application programming.Control Data Corporation Publication no. 60489015 F, St. Paul, Minnesota.

Metis 1986a. Tornado application-programmer's reference manual. Metis A/S, Horten, Norway.

Metis 1986b. Tornado database administration manual. Metis A/S, Horten, Norway.

Metis 1986c. Tornado database design guide. Metis A/S, Horten, Norway.

Metis 1989. Tornado System and DBMS general information manual.Metis A/S, Horten, Norway.

Mimer 1984a. Mimer data base manager, 3.2.Mimer

Information Systems AB, Uppsala, Sweden.

Mimer 1984b. Mimer query and command language, 3.2.Mimer Information Systems AB, Uppsala, Sweden.

Mimer 1984c. Mimer screen handler, 3.2.Mimer Information Systems AB, Uppsala, Sweden.

Mimer 1985. Mimer report and program generator, 3.2.Mimer Information Systems AB, Uppsala, Sweden.

Verheijen, G.M.A. & van Bekkum, J. 1982. NIAM: An information analysis method. In Olle, Sol & Verrijn-Stuart (eds) *Information System Design Methodologies*, Amsterdam.

Hydrological data transfer into and out of HYDATA

Y.P. Parks & K. Sene

Abstract

Hydrological database and analysis packages have proved invaluable in hydrological studies in recent years, especially with the increased availability and power of personal computers. The availability of professional software has ensured that rapid storage and retrieval of data is now taken for granted.

A limiting factor on the efficient use of a hydrological database management system (DBMS) is the difficulty of data input from data sources, and provision of information to external programs or packages. In recent years the Institute of Hydrology has gained considerable expertise in these areas through the development of its hydrological database system for personal computers (HYDATA). The aim has been to develop a unified system for importing data from telemetry systems, loggers and other databases, and provide flexible methods for exporting data for use in analysis packages and DBMSs. This paper gives a brief description of some of the data transfer methods which have been developed, and discusses some of the lessons learnt when applying these methods.

Introduction

Personal computers are widely used for the storage and analysis of hydrological data. Several hydrological DBMSs are now available commercially, and no doubt many more have been developed in-house for use on specific projects. Although spreadsheet programs can be used for data storage and analysis, and are initially appealing in that they incorporate the facility for graphical output, they suffer from many drawbacks. Typically spreadsheets may not handle a mixture of characters and numerals, they may not provide automatic methods of discriminating between missing and zero values, and the management of large amounts of data can be complex.

Relational databases can also be customised to provide a hydrological database. However the provision of easily understood menus and analysis options requires detailed knowledge of the package, and can be very time-consuming. In addition, relational databases use storage space inefficiently and are slow when accessing data. The default data input and output facilities are limited. Purpose built options can be programmed by the user but again detailed knowledge of the package is required. For the efficient storage and retrieval of hydrological information it is therefore more appropriate to use a purpose-built DBMS.

A major restriction on the efficient use of a hydrological database is the difficulty with which data can be loaded from external sources, such as data loggers, telemetry systems and other database systems. A further restriction is the ease with which data can be output for analysis or display by a user's own software, or by commercially available spreadsheet and analysis packages. Work can be greatly slowed by the constant need to re-arrange data formats or write new computer programs to achieve specific data transfers.

At the Institute of Hydrology, considerable experience has been gained of the problems involved in data transfers, initially through development of the United Kingdom's Surface Water Archive (Lees, 1985) and, latterly, through development of a hydrological database system for personal computers (HYDATA, Institute of Hydrology, 1987) and the workstation based hydrological database WIS (developed in conjunction with ICL). These three systems cover three different applications of hydrological databases, namely the Surface Water Archive for mainframe computers, WIS for workstations linked by a network, and finally HYDATA which is PC based and therefore portable and particularly appropriate for overseas projects. This paper uses HYDATA as an example for the approach adopted in data transfer solutions, but many of the methods have grown out of or are also applicable to the other two databases.

In the case of the HYDATA system, the approach adopted has been to produce an integrated package which can receive and output data in a wide range of formats. Figure 1 describes the components of HYDATA, as well as the external programs written to interface between HYDATA and other packages. Experience has shown that, in the vast majority of cases, data can be loaded and output without any need for writing additional programs or re-formatting data files. This paper describes, in outline, some of the methods used to handle data within the HYDATA system, and some of the problems encountered. It is hoped that this information may be of use to other organisations faced with the task of entering data from a wide range of sources onto a single hydrological database.

The database system

HYDATA is a pc-based hydrological database and analysis package which, at the time of writing, has been used in more than 40 countries. The system has been designed for the processing, storage, management and analysis of most types of hydrological data, including:

(a) water level, rainfall or canal lock counts (at

intervals of 15 min or more);
(b) river gauging data and rating equations;
(c) daily data of several types, namely daily mean flow, daily rainfall, daily storage (for lakes or reservoirs), and a general daily data type for other information of the user's choosing e.g. temperature, evaporation, electrical conductivity. Each of these daily information types can also be converted automatically and stored as monthly information.

HYDATA is menu operated, and provides a complete and robust system for most types of routine hydrological work. For example, results of gauging operations may be entered and used to produce rating equations which are then stored on the database. River levels can also be entered, and transferred using the pre-defined rating equations to derived daily mean flows. Similarly lake and reservoir water levels can be transferred to storages, and lock counts to lockages. The package also includes options for some simple, commonly-used hydrological analysis techniques. These include double mass curve plots, comparison time series plots, flow duration analyses, low-flow frequency analyses and various baseflow analysis routines based on the United Kingdom's Low Flow Study report (Institute of Hydrology, 1977). Thus the complete system provides a database, a comprehensive hydrometric analysis

HYDATA Version 3.1

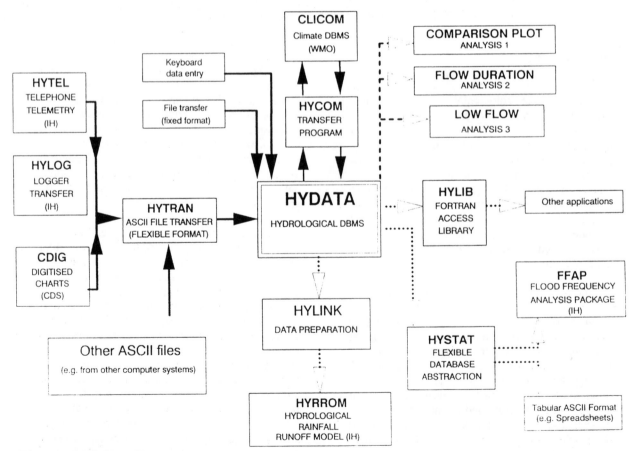

Figure 1 HYDATA and associated software

package, and several additional useful tools for hydrologists and hydraulic departments. The package is also increasingly being used for the storage and processing of meteorological data.

Information transfer

There can be many reasons for transferring data to a hydrological DBMS; routine input of information, for example daily water levels or occasional gauging information; or bulk transfer of information, for example transfer of data from some other computer storage system as part of the initial setting up of the database. If some standard format were in use for the storage of hydrological data it would require little effort to provide a vehicle for transfer into a database. However this is not the case and information is currently available in a wide variety of formats, and also stored in a wide variety of computer systems. This makes the production of a simple routine for the universal transfer of information impossible.

Similarly data is normally required to be exported from the database for reporting purposes, input to modelling and other analysis packages, and bulk transfer of information to other databases. Exactly the same problems exist for exporting information as for importing. Existing information may be arranged in an infinite array of formats to suit local reporting or archiving requirements, but it is not possible to provide a simple routine to produce this wide variety of output.

Ideally a database system needs to incorporate flexible methods to facilitate the transfer of information into and out of the database. At the Institute of Hydrology we have experimented with different methods of data transfer to accompany HYDATA and the following sections describe the strengths and weaknesses of these methods.

Transferring data to the database (Import)

Direct entry via the keyboard

The most obvious, but time-consuming way of entering information is to type it in from the keyboard. In HYDATA values are entered into tables displayed on the screen, much as they would be written in a table on a sheet of paper. Before updating the database, the system checks data for acceptability against user specified limits, and against the preceding value to provide a level of quality control.

Keyboard entry is simplified by the provision of a facility to allow blocks of information to be assigned to the same value, or as missing values. In the latest version, the values entered are displayed simultaneously on a graph and can also be sketched in approximately with a mouse. This method is most appropriate for small quantities of information

provided in variable formats. In general, though, entry from the keyboard is tedious and should only be used if there is no other option. Typically it is only used to load handwritten or typewritten datasets.

Reading an external file

In our experience, the most widely used medium for transferring data is the normal text (i.e. ASCII) datafile on computer disc. The range of possible layouts is limitless; for example, in the last two years, more than 50 layouts have been encountered in the course of our normal hydrological analysis work. In the absence of any industry standard format, the range of file structures used will doubtless continue to increase.

Perhaps the simplest possible file structure is to have one data value per line. Many commercial spreadsheet and statistical analysis packages use this format as a default for exporting numerical data. A chart digitising package, originally developed at the Institute, also outputs data in this format. An option is provided as part of HYDATA to read files directly when in this format. In each operation, a complete year of data is accepted. Multiple years of data can be read by interspersing the data with HYDATA macro commands, which may be entered into the file using a word processor.

General data transfers

Whilst the single value per line format has some use in entering data, most datafiles are more complex than this. In an effort to handle more complex files, an additional package called HYTRAN was produced to interface with HYDATA. HYTRAN is a spreadsheet style program which allows a user to organise a datafile on screen, and then transfer the data values directly to HYDATA or to a datafile with a single value per line format. It is available as part of the main HYDATA system and in future may also be supplied with the WMO's CLICOM meteorological database system. (CLICOM is a widely used meteorological database system supplied by the World Meteorological Organisation (WMO). Many of the data types stored by CLICOM can also be stored on HYDATA, and the two systems are increasingly used together in hydrological and meteorological organisations.)

When using HYTRAN, the input datafile is displayed on the screen and its layout is interpreted interactively by the user. The types of information required are the data interval (e.g. 15-min, daily, monthly), the positions of any text in the file (e.g. comments, station names, dates, times), and the direction in which numbers are to be counted (i.e. across the page, or down the page in yearbook style). Once the layout has been fully specified, the user can order the values and view them with accompanying date and time information. This ensures that the data are correctly defined before transfer to HYDATA. The transfer is then carried out, within the program, after first checking that the station exists on HYDATA and that data values comply with the same quality control checks that apply when entering data within HYDATA. The settings describing the layout can be stored for future use with other files with the same layout. An automatic batch mode of operation is available which allows several files of similar format to be transferred in a single operation. HYTRAN has now been tested on a wide variety of file layouts and it has proved to be a novel and flexible way of loading data without the need for any computer programming or editing of the original datafiles. With practice, the structure of quite complex datafiles can be defined with only a few key strokes. However, the flexibility necessary to provide HYTRAN with the ability to transfer data with a large range of formats has caused some problems when used by untrained operators. As a result we have had to analyse some data formats for outside organisations, and provide them with predefined format files to allow the automatic operation of HYTRAN. Thus increased flexibility can itself sometimes cause problems.

One application of HYTRAN has been to facilitate the transfer of data to HYDATA from loggers and telemetry systems. Two general purpose systems are used within the Institute - called HYLOG and HYTEL - and each is designed to interrogate and download data from a range of hardware types. Both systems write the data to intermediate ASCII datafiles for subsequent transfer by HYTRAN. The advantage of producing intermediate files is that file backups of the data are created automatically, and that the transfer to the database can be performed when required by the user - an important consideration on a single user system, when a large data transfer can tie up the database for long periods.

Retrieving information from the database (Export)

Graphical output and tables

The database provides the facility to plot any of the data stored on a computer screen or on a plotting device. The aim has been to produce good quality graphs for inclusion in reports and to enable rapid checking and verification of data. A wide range of options is provided to allow the user to alter plotting defaults to optimise the appearance of the graph. Figure 2 provides an example of this graphical output and Figure 3 shows the standard tabular output provided as default for daily information. Similar tables are produced for other data types.

Writing to an external file

An option in HYDATA allows any of the data values stored in the database to be exported to a simple ASCII datafile, in which values are written one per line. Although this is a rather limiting format, it is ideally suited for data transfers to spreadsheet packages, which can accept this format with no further modification. The ability to output data to a spreadsheet has proved to be a major advantage, facilitating further analysis and customised plotting of the data to be performed with very little effort.

Access by a user's own software

As part of the database system, two data access libraries are provided for the benefit of users who are able to write programs incorporating FORTRAN subroutines. Two widely-used compilers have been chosen, from the MICROSOFT and PROSPERO companies. These libraries provide the user with

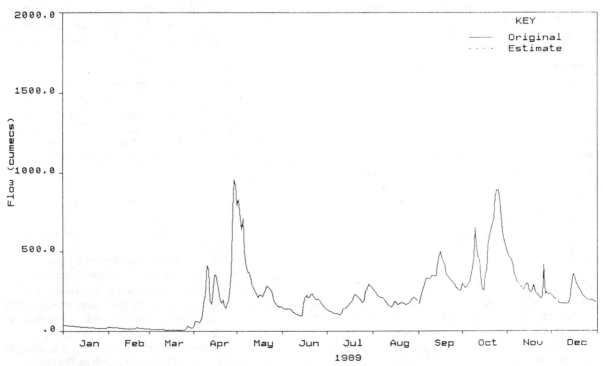

Figure 2 Example of HYDATA graphical output

Station number :   1   Name : Flow station. Demo station   1

Basin no. : 1   Latitude : 10:10:10 N   Longitude : 10:10:10 E   Altitude : 10.0
Area   : 10.0

Year : 1980/1981

	Apr	May	Jun	Jul	Aug	Sep	Oct	Nov	Dec	Jan	Feb	Mar
1	.002e	1.970	.258	.330	.154	.731	-	.179	.097	.057	.027	.007
2	.000e	1.270	.211	.334	.147	1.845	-	.176	.097	.057	.020	-
3	.000e	2.360	.154	.304	.125	12.369	-	.176	.097	.065	.016	-
4	.000e	.726	.137	.304	.096	4.303	.055	.169	.118	.076	.016	-
5	.000e	1.975	.118	.441	.104	2.051	.038	.147	.174	.076	.016	-
6	.000e·	.862	.099	.355	.110	11.091	.038	.147	.176	.076	.016	-
7	.000e	.385	.099	.279	.099	9.281	.038	.147	.176	.085	.016	-
8	.000e	.156	.099	.331	.099	7.614	.024	.147	.176	.085	.011	-
9	.000e	.052	.161	.515	.085	5.715	.024	.147	.176	.071	.007	-
10	.000e	.014	.137	1.739	.075	5.105	.276	.136	.116	.057	.007	-
11	.000e	.022	.125	1.399	.503	2.732	.255	.121	.097	.057	.007	-
12	.000e	1.346	.125	.912	5.669	1.634	.221	.121	.097	.053	.007	-
13	.000e	1.433	.125	.829	5.839	1.089	.207	.121	.085	.041	.043	-
14	.000e	29.936	.110	.661	7.772	.906	.207	.121	.076	.041	.076	-
15	.000e	8.353	.099	.473	2.910	1.165	.327	.121	.076	.041	.110	-
16	.290e	3.940	.099	.353	1.988	.598	.686	.121	.076	.041	.119	-
17	.008e	2.204	.085	.378	1.163	.528	.912	.121	.068	.033	.111	-
18	.000e	1.465	.075	.304	.856	.407	.603	.121	.057	.027	.145	-
19	.000e	1.050	.064	.256	.749	.349	.539	.111	.057	.027	.109	-
20	.000e	.944	.055	.182	.700	.313	.535	.097	.057	.027	.097	-
21	.000	.914	.081	.845	.563	.258	.535	.097	.057	.039	.097	-
22	.000	.709	.268	2.316	1.118	.214	.437	.097	.057	.047	.097	-
23	.000	.754	1.283	.801	1.592	.173	.371	.097	.057	.041	.092	-
24	.002	.737	8.747	.478	4.260	.154	.330	.097	.057	.041	.046	-
25	.009	.660	2.120	.346	4.020	.154	.291	.097	.057	.041	.041	-
26	.000	.572	1.229	.276	5.352	.154	.255	.097	.057	.032	-	-
27	.028	.428	.832	.223	4.876	.147	.240	.097	.057	.016	-	-
28	1.444	.349	.636	.202	2.753	.110	.221	.097	.057	.016	.007	-
29	13.013	.330	.436	.187	2.086	.085	.207	.097	.057	.016		-
30	12.187	.300	.349	.157	1.411	.055	.207	.097	.057	.016		-
31		.283		.154	.973		.207		.057	.022		-
Mean	.89943	2.1451	.61387	.53755	1.8789	2.3777	.29593	.1239	.08955	.04581	.05215	
Maximum	13.013	29.936	8.747	2.316	7.772	12.369	.912	.179	.176	.085	.145	
Minimum	.0	.014	.055	.154	.075	.055	.024	.097	.057	.016	.007	
R/off mm	233.13	574.55	159.11	143.98	503.25	616.29	79.261	32.115	23.985	12.269	12.617	

Flows in cubic metres per second

Insufficient data for annual statistics

Possible data flags

| Missing - flag "-" | Original - no flag set | Estimate - flag "e" |

Figure 3 Example of HYDATA tabular output

FORTRAN 77 subroutines to check the existence of a station, to read its details (e.g. location, parameter limits), and to read data values and rating curves directly from the database. Calls to these routines can be incorporated in a user's own programs, so providing an extremely flexible method of exporting data. Once extracted, the data may then be reformatted and written out in a preferred format, or may be used as input to further analysis routines. Several HYDATA applications have been written in-house which use these subroutines, including a rainfall Geographic Information System (RAINS), a conceptual rainfall runoff model (HYRROM), and a real time flow forecasting model. Data transfer packages have also been written for transferring data to other database systems, such as CLICOM and the UK's Surface Water Archive.

The decision to produce FORTRAN subroutine libraries was made because, in our experience,

FORTRAN is still the most widely-used programming language within the hydrological community. However, in the case of the MICROSOFT compiler, it is possible to combine FORTRAN code with code in other programming languages (e.g. C, Pascal) thus providing a comprehensive route for accessing information from the database.

In our recent experience there is now a general reluctance for hydrological DBMS users to write their own applications either through lack of time or lack of expertise. Although the FORTRAN subroutine library provides a completely flexible export facility for data, the Institute is increasingly being requested to produce purpose built programs to carry out this task.

General purpose access program

Following demand from HYDATA users, it was decided to produce a general purpose program (HYSTAT) for reading data from HYDATA. The types of data which can be accessed include time series data over arbitrary averaging periods (e.g. 10-day, annual) and various types of annual statistics (e.g. peak flows, minima, totals). The program is menu driven, and data can be output either to the screen or to a disc file. Annual peak flows can also be output in a form suitable for transfer to a flood frequency analysis package (FFAP) and to a pc implementation of the United Kingdom's Flood Studies Report (Institute of Hydrology, 1988).

Conclusions

A pc-based hydrological database system can greatly assist with the routine work of a hydrological department and with specific hydrological analyses. However, the efficiency of the system is limited by the ease with which data can be entered or retrieved

for further display or analysis. From our experience, the task of developing links to other software packages and database systems can prove as great as development of the database system itself. With some effort, however, it is possible to devise transfer methods which are simple and intuitive to use, and avoid the need to type in data directly from the keyboard, or to re-format datafiles and write additional software. There is a trade-off, however, between the flexibility of a transfer system and its ease of use. To cover the range of transfer applications that are required it is necessary to provide a range of options including simple inbuilt import and export facilities as well as more flexible systems. Even then there will be requests for customised interfaces from hydrological DBMS users.

For the future, the problems of transferring data between organisations could be greatly simplified if common standards could be adopted for the organisation of datafiles. This is particularly true of the software accompanying automatic recorders, loggers etc. providing the hydrologist with numerous different data file formats to be accessed by their analysis and archiving system. Within the Institute of Hydrology, standard formats have been devised for most of the data types currently handled, and have greatly reducing the time spent in handling data.

References

Lees, M.L. 1985. Inland water surveying in the United Kingdom - A short history. *Hydrological Data UK 1985 Yearbook*, 35-47.

Institute of Hydrology 1980. Low Flow Studies report. IH, Wallingford.

Institute of Hydrology 1987. HYDATA operation manual. IH, Wallingford.

Institute of Hydrology 1988. Micro-FSR operation manual. IH, Wallingford.

Regionalising low flows using an international data base

A. Gustard

Abstract

The paper presents the main results of a regional study of low flows based on an analysis of over 1000 flow records from thirteen European countries. The study was carried out as part of the Flow Regimes from Experimental and Network data (FREND) project which involved research scientists from six European countries working for three years as a major contribution to the Third International Hydrological Programme.

Following a summary of the criteria used for data selection the paper describes four indices of the low flow regime: based on the CV of annual runoff, the flow duration curve, the annual minimum series and a base flow separation procedure. Relationships between one of these measures and basin characteristics illustrate the difficulties in satisfactorily predicting spatial variability, despite the similarities in the range of low flow regimes which occur in different geographical areas.

Introduction

There are a large number of different ways of defining the low flow regime of a river as a result of the need to consider the different definitions of a low flow event, different ways of expressing the frequency of the event and different durations or averaging periods. McMahon & Mein (1986) identified 11 different types of techniques used for both river and reservoir analysis and Beran & Rodier (1985) present a comprehensive survey of the hydrological aspects of drought. This paper summarises the results from deriving four different measures of low flows for European rivers. The techniques are described in detail in the FREND report (Gustard et al., 1989) and are similar to those recommended by the Federal Republic of Germany Small Research Basin Working Group (IHP/OHP 1986) and those reviewed in Lowing (1987).

The primary purpose of regionalising is to develop methods for estimating hydrological parameters at ungauged sites. These techniques have generally been calibrated on a relatively natural data base in one country and their application has therefore been restricted in geographical extent. Furthermore, difficulties are encountered in comparing results between countries because of the use of different definitions of the low flow regime and the use of different catchment characteristics for flow prediction. By using consistent methods of analysis on an international data set of flow and catchment variables from 1350 catchments many of these difficulties were reduced.

The data base contained over 27,000 station years of discharge data, equivalent to 10,000,000 individual values of daily mean flow. In the context of regional hydrology there are two primary advantages of such a large data base. First, long records from individual stations provide more accurate estimates of extreme events. Second, a larger number of catchments increases the diversity of flow regimes and catchment characteristics that are sampled. This enabled differences in low flow regimes over western and northern Europe to be identified together with the primary variables which control the spatial variability of the regime. Furthermore, derived design techniques have a wider applicability over a greater range of catchment types.

Flow and catchment characteristics data

Selection of flow data

Full details of the FREND flow and catchment characteristic data base are presented in Gustard et al. (1989). Data were provided by 13 countries in northern and western Europe, namely: the United Kingdom, Ireland, France, Belgium, Luxembourg, the Netherlands, the Federal Republic of Germany, Switzerland, Austria, Denmark, Norway, Sweden and Finland. The data included time series of river flow data, catchment characteristics and a limited number of daily rainfall series. The criteria used for selecting stations were:

* less than 500 km²
* well-defined low flow rating
* continuous measurement of discharge to provide daily mean flows
* no tidal influences
* limited glacial influence
* direct artificial influences less than 10% of low flows
* availability of derived catchment characteristics or thematic data to calculate them.

The size limitation reduced the need to review the artificial controls on large catchments which in general had a high degree of human influence at low flows and also excluded catchments with a wide range of physical characteristics within the basin. The other criteria followed directly from the objective of regionalisation, where in order to relate flow indices to catchment characteristics it is important to use good quality flow data from relatively natural catchments. The assessments of hydrometric accuracy and artificial influences were based on discussion with national and regional hydrometric agencies who operated the network stations and Universities and Research Institutes who provided data from small research basins. Data were provided on magnetic tape and disc by over 40 organisations in the study area. The distribution by country of the flow series used in the analysis is shown in Table 1 and the location of the 1350 stations in Figure 1. The average record length is just over 20 years with the

Table 1   The number of basins and station years per country for the low flow study.

Country	Number of stations	Number of years	Average number of years per station
United Kingdom	511	9032	17.7
Republic of Ireland	23	490	21.3
France	231	3596	15.6
F.R. Germany	197	5648	28.7
Belgium	41	541	13.2
Denmark	18	817	45.4
Netherlands	13	139	10.7
Switzerland	39	1360	34.9
Austria	78	1682	21.6
Norway	114	2407	21.1
Sweden	48	1098	22.9
Finland	37	907	24.4
Sum	1350	27717	
Average			20.5

Figure 1   Location of the regional low flow stations

average record length being greater in Denmark, Germany and Switzerland. Simple data validation was carried out which included comparing specific low flows with expected regional values and the inspection of hydrographs to identify anomalous peaks and troughs or uniform flows.

Catchment characteristics

The development of relationships between hydrological variables and physical properties of the catchment depends on the availability of suitable indices of basin properties as well as flow data. For the FREND study the selection of basin characteristics to be used was based on hydrological principles, the availability of previously derived characteristics, experience gained from other studies, and the ease of calculation. The characteristics calculated are given in Volume II of the FREND report. Morphometric characteristics for regional studies were calculated from suitable scaled maps by digital cartographic techniques. These included catchment area (km²), annual average rainfall (AAR) in mm, the proportion of urban area, forests and lakes derived from 2.5 km² resolution grids. Catchment averaged values were derived by automatic overlay of digitised catchment boundaries on the thematic data.

In addition to the morphometric and climatic characteristics it was considered important to index the geology or soil type of each catchment. Suitable digital geological data were unavailable for the study, but a five class hydrological soil map available for the majority of the study area was used as an index of catchment response. This was developed from one of the first attempts at using indices of soil in regional studies in Europe which was made by the Institute of Hydrology in the Flood Studies Report (NERC, 1975). The soil index was developed by the Soil Surveys of England and Wales, Scotland, Northern Ireland and the Republic of Ireland to produce national soil maps at a scale of 1:1,000,000 on the base of existing soil surveys. From these the regional surveyors were asked to interpret the soil classification in terms of 'Winter Rainfall Acceptance' (Table 2) and developed a series of Winter Rainfall Acceptance Potential (WRAP) maps for the United Kingdom.

The soil and site properties used to determine the appropriate Winter Rainfall Acceptance Potential class for a given soil association were:
1. Soil water regimes or drainage class
2. Depth to an impermeable layer
3. Permeability above the impermeable layer
4. Slope

Table 2 provides a framework for allocating any given soil association to one of the five WRAP classes from these properties. The winter rain acceptance is basically related to infiltration potential and is the inverse of runoff potential: class 1 soils are permeable with a high acceptance potential, class 5 soils are impermeable with a low acceptance potential.

During the European Flood Study (Beran *et al.*, 1984) the Institute of Hydrology, in cooperation with the national Soil Survey organisations in the European Community, extended the UK WRAP classification to mainland Europe using the five class classification system. The base map for this work was the 1:1,000,000 EC soil map of Europe (CEC Commission, 1985). This WRAP map covering most of the countries in the project area was used to develop a soil index for predicting both flood and low flows (Gustard 1983). In order to transfer the five class WRAP map to the gridded database a digitizing facility was developed using a data capture system linked to a video camera and a microcomputer for image editing (Gross, 1989). The WRAP-class information is stored on a 1.25 x 1.25 km grid and was used to calculated an average soil index for each catchment. A digitised geological data base was not available for the study area and thus it was not possible to derive indices of catchment geology. The five class soil map was thus used to give an index of the hydrological properties of the soil type which at the regional scale is related to the underlying geology.

The FREND database

The FREND data were stored on an IBM 4381 computer at the Institute of Hydrology in Wallingford and can be divided into three categories. First, flow and rainfall time series for individual

Table 2 The classification of soils by winter rainfall acceptance potential from soil survey data (NERC, 1975)

Drainage class	Depth to impermeable layer cm	Slope classes								
		0 - 2°			2 - 8°			> 8°		
		Permeability rates above Impermeable layer								
		Rapid	Medium	Slow	Rapid	Medium	Slow	Rapid	Medium	Slow
1	>80	1	1	1	1	2	2	1	2	3
	40-80	1	1	1	2	2	2	3	3	4
	<40	—	—	—	—	—	—	—	—	—
2	>80	2	2	2	3	3	3	—	—	—
	40-80	2	2	2	4	4	4	4	4	4
	<40	3	3	3	4	4	4	4	4	4
3	>80	5	5	5	5	5	5	—	—	—
	40-80	5	5	5	5	5	5	5	5	5
	<40	5	5	5	5	5	5	5	5	5

Winter rain acceptance indices: 1, very high; 2, high; 3, moderate; 4, low; 5, very low.

stations. Second, gridded topographic, land use and climatic data. Third, numerical indices of catchment and climate characteristics for individual stations derived from the gridded database. All the data types were stored on CACHE-CACHE (French translation of 'hide and seek'), a system developed at the Institute of Hydrology for the storage and retrieval of data using the station number as the key to the data archiving and retrieval. The FREND archive includes the following files:

* MASTER — station directory containing names of stations and streams, location, country codes, flags, catchment characteristics and flow indices
* GDFLOWS — gauged daily mean flows in m^3s^{-1}
* ANNMAX — annual instantaneous flood maxima in m^3s^{-1}
* GDRAIN — daily rainfall in 1/10 mm day^{-1}
* BOUNDER — digitised catchment boundaries

A European station numbering system was developed based on a seven digit number. Northern and western Europe were divided into 23 major geographical regions identified by the first two digits of the number. Thus the Rhine basin was region 16, Sweden region 20, mainland Britain region 00. Each of these regions were subdivided with a maximum of 99 hydrometric areas identified by the next two digits. The last three digits contain the sequential number of the station within the Hydrometric area allowing up to a maximum of 999 stations.

Low flow indices

Annual runoff variability
Although not strictly a low flow index, the annual variability of runoff is a key descriptor of the hydro-logical regime and determines the characteristics of low flow frequency curves, (for long durations) and reservoir storage yield relationships (for high yields). The CV of annual runoff (ARCV) was calculated for 577 stations with more than 15 years of data. In common with other flow indices derived variables were held on the FREND data base for subsequent retrieval and analysis and are published in Volume II of the FREND report (Gustard et al., 1989). The mean ARCV was 0.28 and the spatial distribution over the FREND area indicated consistently low values of less than 0.20 over maritime western areas of the British Isles and south-western Norway with higher values of between 0.4 and 0.6 in parts of eastern France, central parts of the F.R. Germany and in the low-rainfall areas of eastern and central England. Figure 2 compares the CV of annual runoff from the FREND data with that from 126 selected rivers of the world (McMahon & Mein 1986). It can be seen that the annual runoff variability in western and northern Europe is similar to a wide range of world regimes, although very high CVs typical of arid and semi arid regions are of course not represented. The most significant variable for estimating the CV of runoff was found to be the mean annual runoff expressed in mm which explained approximately 50% of the spatial variability of CV.

Flow duration curve, 95 percentile: Q95.

The flow duration curve illustrates the percentage of time during which a specific discharge is equalled or exceeded. The flow exceeded for 95 percent of the time, or on average 18 days per year was used as the key index. Discharge was expressed as a percentage of the mean flow which facilitates comparisons

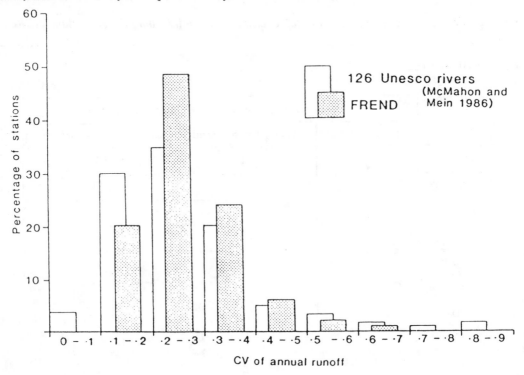

Figure 2   Variability of annual runoff for 126 world rivers (McMahon & Mein, 1986) and FREND rivers.

6.30

Table 3 Summary of low flow measures derived from 1350 European basins

	Mean	Range	Standard deviation
Q95*	16.4	0.1 - 76.7	12.3
MAM(10)*	18.9	0.8 - 87.3	14.0
BFI	0.54	0.14 - 0.99	0.17

* expressed as a percentage of the average flow

between catchments and may also reduce the bias on estimated percentiles caused by above or below average flows during the period of record. Table 3 shows the range in observed values derived from the 1350 flow series, with the highest values found in permeable catchments of the Thames and Paris basins and the lowest values in catchments with impermeable clay or metamorphic geology.

Mean annual ten day minima: MAM(10)

Figure 3 illustrates the 10-day low flow frequency curve derived from six European rivers with discharge standardised by the mean flow plotted against reduced variate (Institute of Hydrology, 1980). The strong influence of catchment geology is clear from the figure and the mean of the 10-day series, MAM(10), was calculated for each station (Table 3). This showed a similar spatial pattern over Europe to Q95.

Base Flow Index: BFI

The index was derived using programmable smoothing and separation rules on the daily mean flow hydrograph and is described in detail in the Low Flow Studies Report (Institute of Hydrology, 1980). By calculating the ratio of separated flow to the mean flow the base flow index is derived which indexes the proportion of runoff derived from stored sources. Values of BFI (Table 3) range from 0.14 for very flashy catchments to near unity for a very stable river with a high base flow proportion.

Relationships between low flow regimes and catchment characteristics

Although most studies have referred to the need to consider the effect of geology of a catchment in any study of low flows, geological data were not available in digital form for this study, so soil data were used as geological surrogates. The CEC soil types (Commission of the European Communities, 1985) were allocated to one of five WRAP classes according to their hydrological properties and soil class proportions were derived for each catchment.

The proportion of these five classes, denoted by S1, S2, S3, S4 and S5 (S1 indicating the most permeable soils), were related to the Base Flow Index (BFI). The regression equation derived from all the catchments in the study area where soil data was available provided a method for weighting the relative permeability of each soil type.

$$BFI=0.44+0.28S1+0.13S2+0.05S3-0.09S5 \quad (1)$$
$$R = 41.9\% \quad \text{standard error} = 0.132$$

By studying individual regions of the study area it was apparent that this relationship varied across Europe, and was more successful in some areas than others. For example the proportion of the variance of BFI explained ranged from 64% (UK) and 61% (Denmark) through 29% (Belgium and Ireland) to less than 11% in most other countries. In particular, the F.R. Germany showed a very poor relationship between BFI and soils. Part of the cause of this was attributed to the classification of the CEC soil types into WRAP classes. To investigate this further the F.R. Germany was studied in greater detail, using the individual CEC soil types for each catchment derived manually from the CEC map. Of the 43 different soil types present in the country only eight proved significant at the 95% level in regression with BFI, with 33% of the variance explained, and a standard error (s.e.) of 0.11. This represents an improvement on the equivalent equation using the five WRAP classes for the F.R. Germany. The recent availability of the CEC soil map in digital form means that further study could now be carried out using these soil types directly, in order to characterise in more detail the hydrological response of European soils.

Regression analysis was used to predict the 95 percentile discharge Q95, expressed in m^3s^{-1}, from catchment characteristics. Included in the data set of characteristics was a single value index of soil type, 'SOIL', derived from weighting individual soil classes using the coefficients in the regression of WRAP class with BFI (Equation 1). Preliminary inspection of the residuals of regression of the Q95 regression equation showed that a logarithmic transformation of the variables was appropriate.

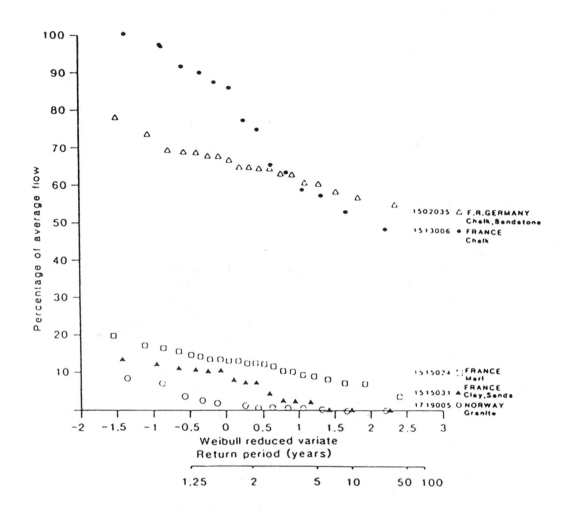

Figure 3   Ten-day annual minimum series for catchments of contrasting geology

Although the significant catchment characteristics (at the 95% level) varied in the different regions, AREA (in km²) was significant everywhere, with a value approximating to unity, and annual average rainfall (AAR, in mm) and SOIL were significant in all regions but one. Low flows increase with SOIL: a greater SOIL value indicates a more permeable soil and therefore more storage available to sustain flow during dry periods. Proportion of urban area (URBAN), proportion of forest cover, stream density and distance to the sea were also significant variables in some regions. The regression equation for the whole of the study area for which soil data were available is

$$Q95 = 7.62 \times 10^9 \, AREA^{1.02} \, AAR^{1.85} \, SOIL^{0.73} (URBAN+1)^{5.57}$$
$$R^2 = 72.2\% \quad \text{factorial standard error} = 2.10 \qquad (2)$$

Improvements in this relationship resulted from considering smaller subsets of data within the region, for example, factorial standard errors were 1.86 (UK and Republic of Ireland), 1.60 (F.R. Germany) and 1.46 (Austria and Switzerland). Smaller errors were

found using the 10-day mean annual minimum as the dependent variable.

Preliminary investigation showed that the pooled curves of stations with similar mean annual minimum values (expressed as a percentage of their average flow) in different hydrometric regions were similar in slope. Figure 4 shows examples of the ten-day flow frequency curves for different hydrometric regions for stations with mean annual 10 day minima MAM(10) of 10-20% average flow and 30-40% average flow. The figure indicates that the variability in the low flow regime itself is closely related to the magnitude of low flows, and that this relationship is consistent between regions. It was thus possible to treat the entire data set as a whole, and produce pooled annual minimum series so that the annual minimum flow of a given return period can be estimated for any location in the study area.

The consistency of the frequency relationship between hydrometric regions was also found when analysing flow duration curves and also when investigating the relationship between mean annual minimum values of different durations. For example, it was found that using the full European data set, that the 60-day duration mean annual minimum MAM(60) expressed as a percentage of the mean flow was related to the 10-day duration minimum MAM(10) by

$$MAM(60) = 6.37 + 1.09MAM(10) \qquad (3)$$
$$R = 92.2\% \qquad s.e. = 4.71$$

However the regional variation of the constant and coefficient in equation 3 were very small (Table 4) with the coefficient ranging from 0.97 to 1.20 and the constant term from 4.1 to 10.5. These results demonstrate that there is a consistent relationship between minimum flows of different durations across the study area.

Conclusions

The low flow investigation in the FREND project has sought to describe the spatial and temporal variability of the frequency of low flows and to apply existing techniques for estimating extreme events at ungauged

sites. Four methods of indexing the characteristics of the flow regime have been described and some of them have been used to evaluate the spatial and temporal variability of low flows in northern and western Europe.

Low flow indices were related to a number of catchment characteristics, one of the most important being soil type, although its success in predicting low flow behaviour was found to vary considerably over the study area. Improvements in flow estimation were made by subdividing the FREND data into regional subgroups and by using the EC soil types for developing relationships with the Base Flow Index (BFI). Further work on the hydrological classification of soil and geology would be valuable for providing a consistently reliable index for use in future estima-tion of low flows at an ungauged site. One important conclusion was that both the duration and frequency relationships for the flow frequency and flow dura-tion curve were found to be remarkably consistent over the study area.

The low flow investigations were contingent upon the international archive of flow and catchment

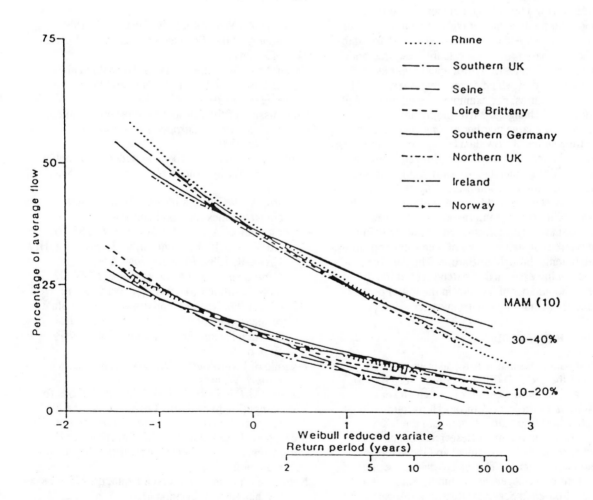

Figure 4   Pooled flow frequency curves for stations grouped by hydrometric region and 10 day duration mean annual minimum value

6.33

Table 4   Regional variations in the regression model for estimating MAM(60) from MAM(10)

Region	Constant	Coefficient	$R^2\%$	s.e.
FREND study area	6.37	1.09	92.2	4.71
England, Scotland, Wales	8.47	0.97	90.5	3.68
Northern Ireland, Republic of Ireland	7.59	1.01	74.6	3.59
Denmark, Northern F.R. Germany	10.27	1.01	86.5	6.32
Danube	10.46	1.05	88.2	5.22
Rhone	6.51	1.11	88.5	4.34
Loire, Britanny	4.17	1.14	93.5	2.92
Seine	4.37	1.08	98.1	3.13
Rhine	5.63	1.20	87.2	6.18
Southern Norway	5.78	1.13	74.7	5.84
Northern Norway	6.45	1.04	49.3	5.40
Sweden	4.56	1.08	92.0	2.05
Finland	4.73	1.01	93.9	1.87

characteristic data. Developing such an archive requires liaising with a large number of hydrometric agencies and reading data provided in a multitude of different formats. Although time-consuming to establish, the data base provides a valuable resource both for large scale studies of hydrological regimes and for regional studies which are no longer restricted by national boundaries. For example, in studying global environmental change, the hydrologist must have easy access to a large number of long (in excess of 50 years) time series of flow data before confident statements can be made concerning regime changes. In developing design methods for estimating extreme events in, for example, south-east England, data have traditionally been pooled from the entire UK. With the availability of large international data bases, a more systematic data selection can be made using a larger number of station years of data from appropriate catchments throughout Europe. The data base is currently being expanded to extend record length, to increase the number of stations in the initial project area and to include stations from eastern Europe.

Acknowledgements

The research presented in this paper was carried out as part of the FREND (Flow Regimes from Experimental and Network Data) project, which was a contribution to Project 6.1 of the Third International Hydrological Programme. Funding in the UK was from Natural Environment Research Council, the Department of the Environment and the Overseas Development Agency. Thanks are due to the staff of over 40 European Agencies including National and State Hydrological Services, Research Institutes and University Departments who have contributed data to the project.

References

Beran, M.A., Wiltshire, S. & Gustard, A. 1984. *Report of the European Flood Study*. Institute of Hydrology.

Beran, M.A. & Rodier, J. 1985. Hydrological aspects of drought *UNESCO Studies and Reports in Hydrology 39*. Paris.

Commission of the European Communities 1985. *Soil map of the European Communities 1:1,000,000*.

Gross, R. 1989. An inexpensive video data capture system for hydrological maps. *Hydrol. Sci. J.* 34 (2).

Gustard, A. 1983. Regional variability of soil characteristics for flood and low flow estimation. *Agric. Wat. Manage.* 6, 255-268.

Gustard, A., Roald, L., Demuth, S., Lumadjeng, H. & Gross, R. 1989. *Flow Regimes from Experimental and Network Data (FREND)..* 2 Vols. Institute of Hydrology, Wallingford, UK.

IHP/OHP 1986. Recommendations for the evaluation of measurement data of small hydrological research basins. English translation of IHP/OHP Report No. 5, 1985.

Institute of Hydrology 1980. *Low Flow Studies Report*. Wallingford, UK.

Lowing, M.J. (ed.) 1987. Casebook of methods for computing hydrological parameters for water projects. *Studies and Reports in Hydrology*, 48.

McMahon, T.A. & Mein, R.G. 1986. *River and Reservoir Yield*. Water Resources Publications. Colorado.

Natural Environment Research Council 1975. Flood Studies Report. London.

A national archive of flood event data for the UK

H. Houghton-Carr & D.B. Boorman

Abstract

A major archive of flood event data from UK catchments is described, both in terms of the data held and the systems used for their storage. Reference is made to major projects that have benefited from the archive. The continued collection of data, especially from a representative basin set, is considered.

Introduction

Many large data sets are available to hydrologists. Most users of these data sets require access to small subsets of the stored information but benefit from the coordinated and well structured approach to data management that is necessary if large volumes of data are to be handled efficiently. Other projects, however, are only possible if large data sets are available. In a UK context two outstanding examples of this type of project are the Flood Studies Report (NERC, 1975) and the Low Flow Studies (Institute of Hydrology, 1980). The latter of these was able to draw on the data base of daily mean flows established at the Water Data Unit, although many extra data were also collected. For the Flood Studies Report (FSR) data describing flood peaks and flood events had to be collected. While the abstraction and archiving of flood peak data (i.e. annual maxima and POT series) was straightforward, this was not the case for the flood event data.

The analysis and modelling of flood events requires data not commonly archived in a suitable form. Firstly, the requirement is for different data types to be available in a collated and easily accessible form, and secondly, the data must be at a sufficiently fine time interval to reveal the detailed structure of the event. The two primary data types are flow and rainfall, both of which are generally available in the UK as daily or monthly totals or averages. This paper describes the development of a flood event archive at the Institute of Hydrology (IH). The following sections give details of the data held in the archive, the history of the archive (including data base management systems), and examples of how the archive has aided hydrological studies.

Flood event data

The main function of the archive is to provide flood event data for hydrological studies. However, as the data come from a large number of sites and are collected by many different organisations, an important secondary function is to hold descriptive information that gives users of the data a greater knowledge of their study site and any problems that may have arisen during data processing. Some of this information relates to drainage basins and may, as in the case of catchment area, also be essential for data analysis.

Time-series data

Flow data are stored on the archive as instantaneous values, generally at hourly or 15-minute intervals. These data are most usually obtained from the measuring authority in the form of stage data that must be converted to flows using a rating equation. In many cases this requires stage charts to be digitised, but sometimes they can be obtained from stage levels on a computer archive (the data often being abstracted in monthly blocks).

Rainfall data are required at daily and sub-daily (normally hourly) durations. Daily rainfalls are easily obtained from the Meteorological Office (MO) archive for all of their approved gauges; additional data may be added from other gauges when necessary. Recording rainfall data are obtained from the relevant measuring authority as charts (to be digitised), or as tabulations showing hourly totals (often using software provided by raingauge logger manufacturers), or as listings of bucket tip times (to be converted to hourly totals).

Soil moisture deficit (SMD) data are available in many forms for different periods. Basically they are obtained from the MO either as daily Estimated SMDs for SMD stations using a modified Penman model (Grindley, 1967) held on micro-fiche, as tabulations, or as month-end areal averages for MORECS squares (MO Rainfall and Evaporation Calculation System, MO, 1981).

It will be appreciated that gathering data together from many different data suppliers, abstracting the particular periods of interest and collating the various data types, is a time-consuming process. Great care is needed when establishing the true timing of the data, especially in the use of BST and GMT, and local variations in ascribing data to the start or end of the observation period.

Descriptive and derived data

The archive contains descriptive data that relate to sites at which data are observed, catchments upstream of flow gauging stations, and the results of event analysis.

Information about sites includes their grid reference, operator's name, and dates for which data are available. Catchment data include the catchment characteristics, such as basin area and annual average rainfall, which are used in event analysis, and descriptive indices, such as stream frequency and mainstream slope, that may be used to compare catchments or in empirical studies of catchment response. In addition to these single-valued specific items of data, text entries are held to describe flow gauging stations and (separately) their catchment areas.

Derived data are the results of analysing the event data using standard models, for example, the time-to-peak and percentage runoff from applying the FSR unit hydrograph and losses model. These results may be held both against the event from which they are derived, and as an average for all events on a catchment.

Development of the flood event archive

The requirement for an archive of flood event data first came from the Flood Studies Project which began in 1969 and required data from many catchments throughout the UK. Before that time studies had been more limited in scope and used less formal methods of storing the data.

The history of the archive directly reflects developments in data base management systems in the computer industry. At first the archive was based on a system of files with each file containing one data type for one event. This allowed the information to be prepared separately for each data type as it arrived, and to be combined into a processed file (a PFILE) once all the data were available for the event. The great disadvantage of the system was the large number of files required for all the data strings and hence the need for an efficient (manual) method of keeping track of the files. It was a natural development therefore to automate this collation process using in-house developed software, that wrote to and read from random-access files from FORTRAN programs. This stored the individual portions of event data (using catchment number, event number, and data type code as the key) and allowed the PFILE to be produced on request. The data base had the very limited ability to store input data and produce collated output files. Existing analysis programs could be used without the need for modification.

As time went by the software was developed to hold other data types (e.g. named items like catchment area, which had previously been held as part of a header block for every event) and became of more general applicability. It acquired the name Cache-Cache (Sekulin, 1980) and was used in many different sections of IH. This was the state of the archive in 1985 when the analyses for FSSR16 (NERC, 1985) were performed.

However, there were many limiting features of the archive:
1) An event had a very strict definition that was only useful for rainfall-runoff modelling.
2) Where events overlapped, the data would be stored twice leading both to inefficient use of disc space and problems of updating should errors be found.
3) When events were shortened, data had to be removed from the archive.
4) The data could only be accessed through FORTRAN programs, which was especially frustrating for one-off accesses to the data and for less technically proficient users of the data.
5) Including extensions to existing data strings was difficult (e.g. adding a flow rating equation number).
6) Accessing the data on any basis other than the catchment number and event number key was very tedious.
7) It was difficult to access data simultaneously in more than one Cache-Cache archive.

Many of these problems were solved when the archive was transferred to a commercial relational data base management system (RDBMS), namely ORACLE, in 1987. This transfer required a radical rethink of how the data should be stored to fit the table-based RDBMS structure.

Relational data base tables have a predefined set of "columns" (with specified names and data type definitions) into which many "rows" of data may be inserted. So, for example, the table FLOW has columns headed GAUGE, TIME, and FLOW into which some 674,576 rows of data have been entered. This very simple structure makes it possible to prevent duplicate entries for any gauge and time, but is slightly wasteful in storing many time values. In an archive in which the data were more regular an alternative structure would be more appropriate, but for relatively sparse flow data without a constant data interval this form is quite acceptable. To link the flow data back to the event-based structure requires additional data now held in a separate table (named COMPONENT) with columns specifying the event number, gauge, start time and end time. To retrieve the flow data for a particular event requires joining the two tables together so that data at the specified gauge between the start and end times are selected. In fact the actual statement needed to return the data is very similar to the syntax of the last sentence. Since frequent requests are made to return the flows for an event, a view (EVENT_FLOW) of the data has been created that allows the user to ask for the flows for the event. A view is a RDBMS device to allow the user to see the data in a different form to the way they are actually stored; this can be through a join in which data from a number of tables are combined, as above, or by restricting the view of the data to a subset of rows or columns of the tables.

Provided careful thought has been given to the design of the data base, it is possible to store most types of data efficiently and flexibly using a RDBMS. The flood event data fit very comfortably within this framework, but it would not be appropriate to describe data structures in greater detail in this paper. (The archive is fully described in Boorman and Houghton-Carr, 1991). The next section gives a general impression of the archive and its contents. It is worth noting here the many advantages and small number of disadvantages that have accrued from the move to ORACLE.

The main advantages are:
1) Very versatile access to data, often in ways not envisaged even when the data base was designed.
2) Easy links to other data stored within ORACLE.
3) Access to data via a query language (SQL), forms, and FORTRAN programs.
4) Good facilities for manipulating dates and text.
5) Ability to add extra tables as the need arises.
6) Possible to add columns to existing data.
7) Good housekeeping facilities.
8) Time series data can be held independently of event definitions (makes loading of data and adjusting of event times very easy).
9) Very complex data requests can be formulated.

The disadvantages are:
1) Slow response times using shared existing

hardware (on IBM 4381).
2) Date/times often have to be given in rather tedious fashion.
3) Time spent on data base design.

While the authors are very pleased with the structure of the data and the performance and facilities offered by the archive, it is well worth noting two alternative ways of handling some of these data.

Rainfall data must be stored within the data base against a particular duration (e.g. 15 minutes, hourly or daily). A better solution for the storage of continuous rainfall data is to store just sufficient data to allow the reconstruction of the continuous record, i.e. very sparse data when rainfall is low and denser information when rainfall rates are high. This scheme which is used in RAINARK (Hydro-Logic Ltd software) allows very good packing of data at the expense of processing the data to the required format on access.

The same method of data packing can be used for flow data again saving on storage space. However, as flows are usually processed from stage data, some data bases prefer to archive stages and rating equations as they see the stage values as the true data and the flows as an interpretation of them. TIDEDA (Thompson and Rodgers, 1985), developed by the New Zealand Ministry of Works and Development, adopts this approach.

Data in the flood event archive

The archive currently contains data describing 4316 UK flood events; most (4261) of these are 'FSR-type'

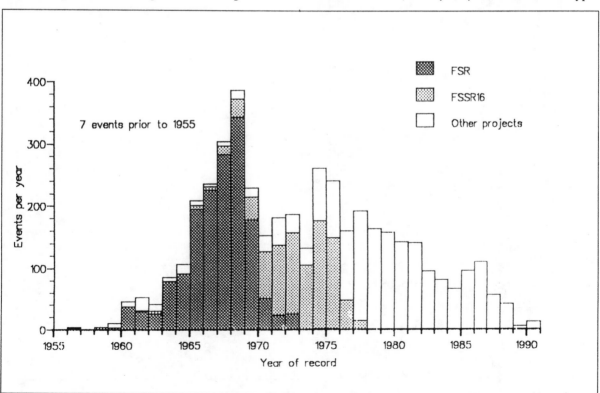

Figure 1   Distribution of flood events by date and project

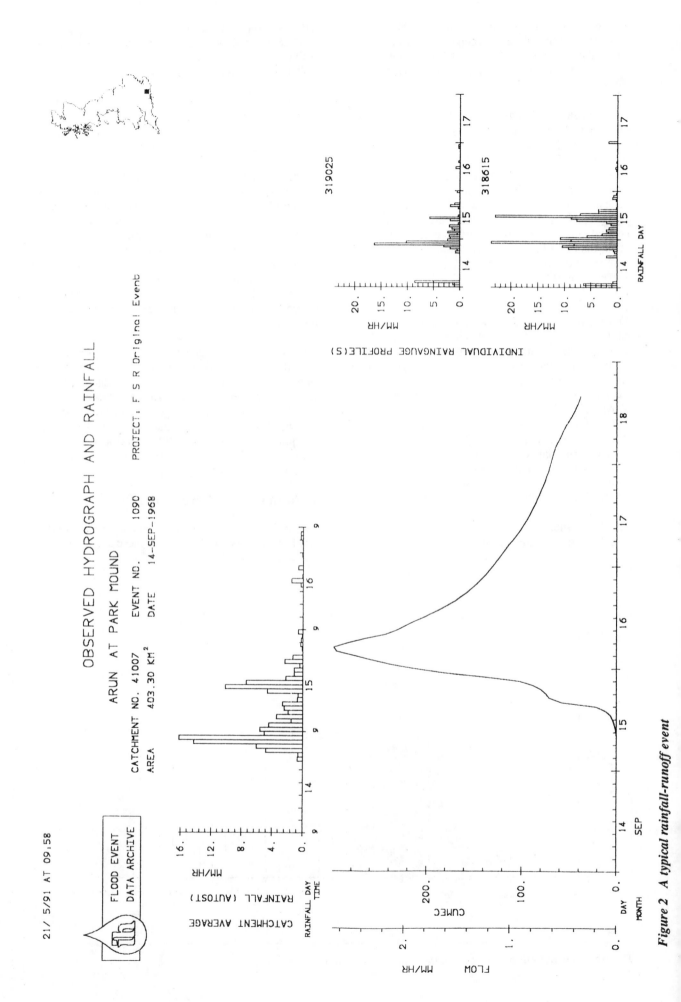

Figure 2 A typical rainfall-runoff event

6.38

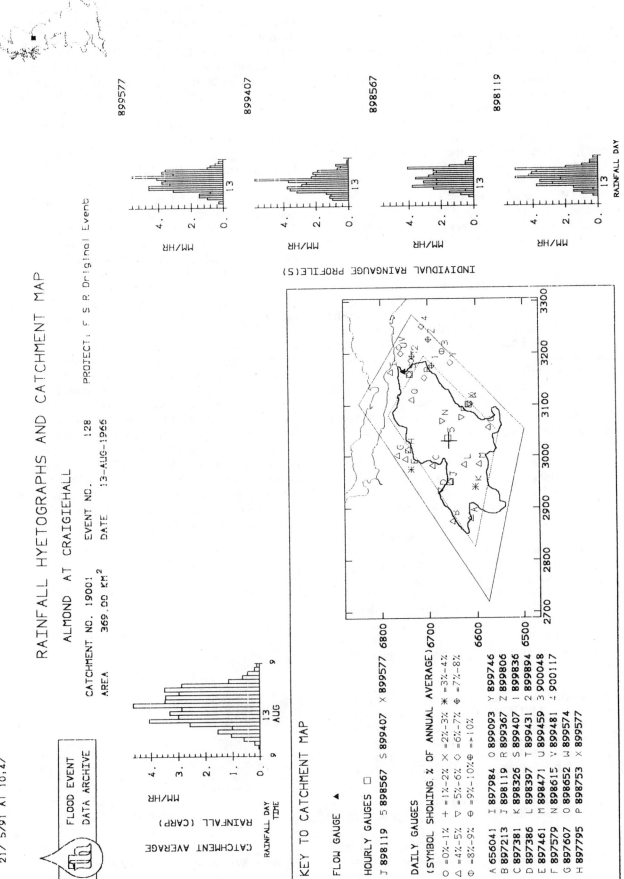

Figure 3   Example of a plot from the rainfall-averaging program

6.39

events, i.e. fairly simple, short-duration rainfall-runoff events. Figure 1 shows the distribution of the event dates with a breakdown according to project for which they were collected. Of course, once entered on the archive events may be used for many different projects.

Figure 2 is a standard retrieval illustrating a typical rainfall-runoff event. It has already been explained how the flow data for the event are retrieved from the FLOW table for the dates specified in COMPONENT table; a very similar retrieval returns observed and catchment average rainfall hyetographs, from tables RAIN and CARAIN3 respectively. The average rainfall is used for lumped modelling, e.g. using the unit hydrograph and losses model of the FSR. The catchment average rainfall profile shown in Figure 2 uses a slight modification of the method described in Jones (1983) based on all hourly and daily rainfall data available for the event. The catchment average rainfalls derived by different averaging techniques are stored in different tables (hence the '3' in CARAIN3).

Figure 3 is a plot produced by the rainfall averaging program. The map shows the catchment boundary and a quadrilateral (a simplified representation of the catchment) that is expanded to define a search area for raingauges. Locations of gauges are plotted, and the hyetographs from recording gauges are shown together with the derived catchment average rainfall profile. All the information for the catchment map is obtained from ORACLE tables, some maintained as part of the flood event archive and others established by associated projects.

When events are analysed using a standard method, as for example in the FSR analyses, many problems can arise. Often the problems lead to a rechecking of the data (as using the data often provides excellent validation) but frequently the problem is caused by the analysis method. If it can be established that data are incorrect then they are deleted. Where it appears to be an analysis problem then the event is coded as to its usefulness for the project. Using FSSR16 as an example, of a total of 2564 events available to that project only 1306 could be used fully. The others were coded as rejected (i.e. the combination of event and FSR model was rejected) and where possible this was attributed to a particular cause (e.g. snowmelt or inadequate raingauge coverage).

It has already been noted that results from analyses, such as for FSSR16, are stored in the archive. It is very easy, using SQL, to access these data in any number of ways and to select them according to many different criteria (e.g. type and location of catchment; event magnitude). Reviewing the number of events on the 210 catchments used in FSSR16 shows that only 17 catchments have more than 20 events and that 30 catchments have 5 or less events.

To enable the selection of events across catchments according to the rarity of the event, return periods

values have been ascribed to the flow peaks and rainfall depths. The flow return periods were calculated from flood frequency curves based on annual maxima data; rainfall return periods were calculated using an inversion of the methods used to calculate design storm depths from FSR Volume 2. Figure 4 shows a histogram of the return periods of the flow peaks for 1002 events from 87 of those catchments used in FSSR16. The majority (89%) of these events have return periods of less than 5 years. While this has been a straightforward exercise to perform, it has raised questions about the selection of events for inclusion in the archive and about the suitability of the data for developing methods of estimating extreme flood magnitudes.

Enhancement of the data archive

As can be seen from Figure 1, IH has continued to make it a major priority to collect flood event data. This has two main objectives; firstly to extend the number of catchments for which large numbers of events are available (essential for the understanding of the variability of hydrological processes), and secondly to incorporate more data describing extreme events. This latter aim will only be met with the necessary passage of time.

Data collection is being concentrated on a set of basins that form a representative sample of UK catchments. Wherever possible these are catchments for which some event data are already available but many additional catchments have been included. At present about 100 catchments have been identified in consultation with staff from local hydrometric agencies, but more will be added to fill gaps. For each of these catchments a very full description is being prepared and will be included in a Representative Basin Catalogue to be available in draft form towards the end of 1991. A problem in the collection of these data in the past has been to maintain the

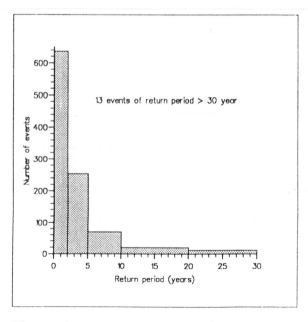

Figure 4 Return periods of rainfall events

continuity of data collected by a number of operators. It is hoped that the value of long-term data from these representative sites will be recognised and that this problem can be overcome. With the current uncertainty over how the UK's climate may be changing it is essential that these strategic data sets are established and maintained efficiently.

In addition to the data from representative basins, data from extreme flood events are also being added to the archive. These data are often of lower quality (e.g. poorer raingauge coverage) but can be accommodated easily within the archive framework outlined above.

Conclusion

As a result of nearly 20 years' work an extensive archive of flood event data has been assembled and is available in a versatile, easy to use management system. The data have been used for many major hydrological studies, most notably the FSR and the revisions contained in FSSR16. Collated and processed data are, and have been, made available to hydrologists working in the UK water industry and universities. The collection of flood data is continuing with the effort being concentrated on a representative set of catchments plus data from extreme events occurring elsewhere.

Acknowledgements

The development of the Flood Event Archive described in this paper has been supported by the Ministry of Agriculture, Fisheries and Food. The authors are grateful for the cooperation of the various hydrometric agencies in the UK (especially the National Rivers Authority divisions and River Purification Boards) in providing data.

References

Boorman, D.B. & Houghton-Carr, H.A. 1991. UK representative basin and flood event data. Institute of Hydrology Report to MAFF (draft).

Grindley, J. 1967. The estimation of soil moisture deficits. *The Meteorological Magazine* 96, 97-108.

Institute of Hydrology 1980. *Low Flow Studies*.Institute of Hydrology.

Jones, S.B. 1983. The estimation of catchment average point rainfall profiles.*IH Report No. 87.*

Meteorological Office 1981. The Meteorological Office Rainfall and Evaporation Calculation System MORECS. Meteorological Office Hydrological Memorandum No. 45.

NERC 1975. *Flood Studies Report.* Natural Environment Research Council.

NERC 1985. *Flood Studies Supplementary Report No. 16.*Natural Environment Research Council.

Sekulin, A.E. 1980. CACHE-CACHE: A library system for storage and retrieval of data. Institute of Hydrology Software Guide (unpublished).

Thompson, S.M. & Rodgers, M.W. 1985. Micro-TIDEDA user's manual. Hydrology Centre, Ministry of Works and Development, Christchurch, Publication No. 4.

The application of a continental scale radar database to hydrological process parametrization within atmospheric general circulation models

C. G. Collier

Abstract

Atmospheric General Circulation Models (GCMs) used for climate research operate on a resolution of about 250 km and provide outputs averaged on a daily and monthly basis. Variations of soil properties and of infiltration are not adequately defined at these scales, and therefore it is necessary to parametrize these processes. Unfortunately the relationship between rainfall and runoff is highly non-linear, and the rate of infiltration will vary throughout a catchment area making parametrization very difficult. Since 1986 the Commission of the European Communities (CEC) COST-73 Weather Radar Networking Project has encouraged the exchange of weather radar data between the countries of Europe. As part of the work undertaken in this project, instantaneous radar composite images over North West Europe were generated every hour with a grid resolution of about 5 km. Data from radars located in the UK, Ireland , France, the Netherlands, Switzerland, and Belgium have been used.

In the paper we discuss the nature of this database, and consider its reliability for estimating sub-daily and monthly precipitation. We explore how this database might be used to develop a more effective parametrization scheme for surface hydrological processes within GCMs. Finally the adequacy of such a database for continental scale hydrological studies is assessed. It is noted that there is considerable scope for further studies of this type using radar data from most countries in both western and eastern Europe.

Introduction

The global and regional climates simulated by Atmospheric General Circulation Models (GCMs) are demonstrably sensitive to the parametrization of the surface hydrological processes. Consequently, an adequate surface climate may only be achieved by explicit incorporation of such processes in a physically realistic framework (Thomas, 1990).

Unfortunately the GCMs used for climate research have time and space resolutions coarser than used in global numerical weather prediction models, typically 250 km x 250 km as opposed to better than 150 km x 150 km. Furthermore, climate models are integrated over much longer periods, and therefore the interactions between the land surface and the atmosphere and the hydrological cycle are especially important. Although future advances in computer systems will undoubtedly enable the spatial and temporal resolutions of GCMs to be improved, it is unlikely that hydrological processes will ever be resolved adequately, and parametrization will remain essential.

Most GCMs in current use have rather simplistic, one-dimensional empirical runoff ratio and evapotranspiration efficiency functions. However, recently it has been demonstrated that it is possible to improve the parametrization of the land surface, and new schemes have been shown to perform better than the simpler versions (see, for example, Henderson-Sellers et al., 1990). Nevertheless, there is still no consensus as to the appropriate complexity of surface hydrological parametrization required in climate models (Thomas, 1990). Indeed, there remains the problem of aggregating or disaggregating spatially heterogeneous surface processes without distorting what is actually happening.

Since runoff reflects variations in precipitation, it is especially necessary to investigate how best to describe regional precipitation patterns, such that their temporal distribution and spatial statistics are adequately represented. This is essential if the impact of climate change on a continental scale is to be estimated reliably. For example, Russell & Miller (1990) were able to estimate the runoff for the world's major rivers from mean annual model precipitation without any disaggregation of the precipitation field. However, they concluded that, although the results were useful, the precipitation field over continents is one of the major deficiencies of the model. Runoff for medium and small rivers cannot be estimated in this way.

How then can disaggregation of the models' precipitation field be achieved? One approach to the determination of the hydrologic response to climate change involves the use of a climate model to provide suitable boundary conditions for a limited area model which can represent mesometeorological processes (Giorgi & Bates, 1989). Precipitation can be represented much better using the higher resolution model, and therefore surface processes are likely to be more realistic. However there are difficulties in coupling such models having quite different resolutions as pointed out by Thomas (1990), and it is necessary to develop a sampling strategy whereby individual weather events evident in the GCM simulations are selected for simulation with the limited area model. In this way it may be possible to provide climate information at a scale appropriate to the river basin scale.

The use of a high resolution model coupled to a GCM would seem to replace the statistical-dynamical approach to parametrization of hydrologic processes on the grid scale of the GCM. However, the two approaches are not in conflict, but are complementary. In the former case it is necessary to adequately represent the hydrological cycle in the simulation of individual weather events by the GCM. Otherwise the climatic boundary conditions for the high resolution model will be inappropriate.

In this paper we explore the details of the temporal distribution and spatial statistics of continental scale precipitation patterns derived using data from European weather radars. This study is carried out using a disaggregation procedure developed initially by Eagleson (1984). The aim is to provide a more detailed description of continental scale precipitation patterns in mid-latitudes for use in GCMs. In the first part of this study reported here we describe statistically the variation of precipitation over a typical GCM grid square, and how this changes during particular weather events. Later work will examine the frequency of precipitation events and their statistical structure.

The precipitation database

The COST programme (Co-Operation in Science and Technology) is a programme for European States which see advantage in pursuing joint research or development projects. It is organised under the aegis of the European Commission who supply the Secretariat, although it is funded from within existing national programmes. A recommendation for a research project to be known as COST-73, explicitly on weather radar networking, was made in early 1986 following an earlier project, COST-72, on the measurement of precipitation (Collier et al., 1988). By the end of 1986 eight countries (Belgium, Federal Republic of Germany, Finland, France, Italy, Switzerland, The Netherlands, United Kingdom) had signed a Memorandum of Understanding (MOU) bringing the project into being with a secretariat supplied by the CEC. The funding arrangements were as for COST-72, funded that is from within existing national programmes. These countries were joined in 1987 by Austria, Denmark, Ireland, Portugal and Sweden, during 1988 by Spain and Yugoslavia, in 1989 by Norway and in 1990 by the Commission of the European Communities as a full participant, bringing the total number of countries participating to sixteen.

The MOU contained a research programme divided into five main areas (1) radar systems: performance characteristics of different radar techniques, display requirements, equipment standardization and investigation of new techniques; (2) radar site and national network centre data processing: computer requirements, meteorological calibration and data correction algorithms, software specification and compositing different data types and data from different radars; (3) data transmission: standardization of formats and protocols and testing different transmission media; (4) bilateral radar data exchanges: coordination of installations and operations across national boundaries and studies of the properties of radar data; and (5) European network investigations: operational requirements for European radar composite data, archiving, real-time trials, commercial exploitation and proposals for a modus operandi for a coordinated European weather radar network based upon national plans.

The Management Committee felt that this work could best be tackled within a framework of activities divided into work which could be undertaken via desk top studies using archive data and existing experience, and work which required the production and distribution of wide area radar data in real-time. The latter work involved the investigation of the logistics of exchanging data internationally and the production of composite images over a very wide area. Until recently this area covered only that part of north west Europe shown by the small frame in Figure 1.

However, products have recently been produced for the large frame in Figure 1, namely covering most of

Europe. As in the COST-72 Project, the United Kingdom offered to undertake the collection of data and its composition into wide area products which were returned on an experimental basis to other European countries.

Instantaneous composite images for the area of the small frame in Figure 1, generated from radar and Meteosat infrared data, have been produced in real time and archived every hour since the start of the COST-73 Project in late 1986. An example of the

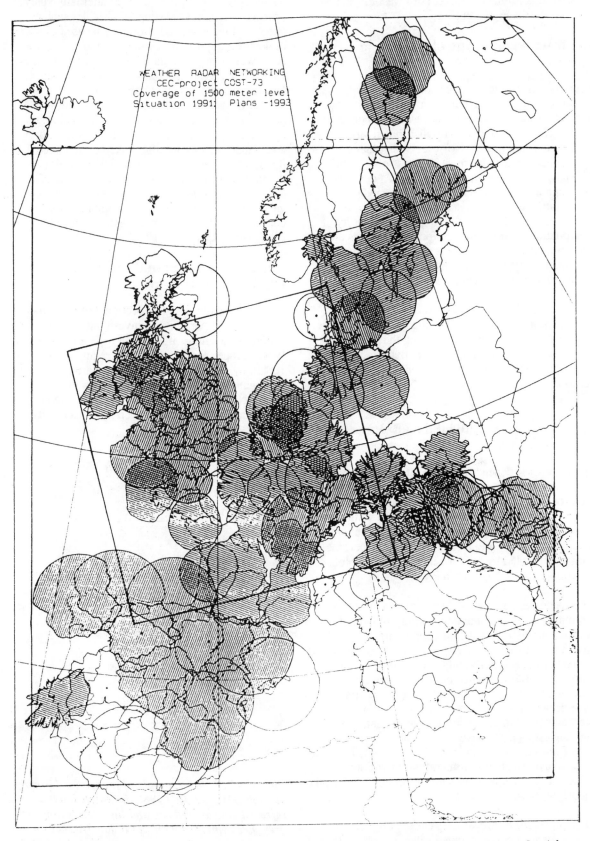

Figure 1   Radar coverage (shading shows coverage of lowest beam below 1500m above the surface) in Europe , September 1991. The small frame shows the extent of COST-73 composite images archived since late 1986.

image data is shown in Figure 2a. The radar data may be integrated to provide estimates of daily precipitation amounts as shown in Figure 2b, given that inaccuracies caused by sampling errors will result, particularly for convective rainfall. Figure 2c shows the rainfall accumulations over northwest Europe on the same day as Figure 2b.

The fractional wetting of GCM grid squares

Precipitation over the grid area of a GCM is produced by linking the output from the moist-convective and large-scale condensation schemes of the model. This precipitation is distributed uniformly over the entire grid area. However, individual grid squares have, typically, areas in excess of 10^4 km^2 with the model integrations being carried out over long time increments, and therefore the model precipitation intensities reaching the surface are usually too low. In addition the spatial variability of precipitation is large and therefore grid squares are not wetted uniformly. There is a need to parametrize fractional wetting in order to achieve realistic estimates of runoff and evapotranspiration.

Eagleson (1984) and Eagleson et al. (1987) have reported studies of the fraction of a GCM grid square, K, affected by precipitation reaching the surface. Warrilow et al (1986) assumed that over fraction K of an entire grid square, the point precipitation intensity, P, is exponentially distributed with mean E(P)/K as in

$$fp(P) = \frac{K}{E(P)} \exp\{-KP/E(P)\} \text{ for } P>0 \qquad (1)$$

The value of K depends upon the GCM spatial and temporal resolution ranging from zero to one. E(P) is the expectation of precipitation over the entire grid area, which is taken as the GCM resultant simulation of all precipitation reaching the land surface at any time step over any grid area or as, in this paper, the rainfall estimated by a radar network. Hence, plots of equation 1 give K/E(P) when P=0.

As K becomes larger as the precipitation becomes more intense, or the saturated hydraulic conductivity becomes smaller, then the unsaturated fraction will have a higher runoff ratio. The excess of precipitation intensity over soil infiltrability at a point (Horton runoff) and the occurrence of precipitation over saturated and impermeable surfaces (Dunne runoff) have been identified (Freeze, 1974) as two major mechanisms of inducing surface runoff. Entekhabi and Eagleson (1989) have reported how surface runoff ratio function varies as a function of grid mean surface layer relative soil saturation for various values of K. As K decreases the proportion of Horton runoff increases.

This method of disaggregating GCM grid precipitation depends upon selecting a value, or values, for K which are representative of the type of storms which

most influence the hydrological cycle. Entekhabi and Eagleson (1989) suggest that K may be related to the relative size of the air mass parcels that have moist convective parametrizations with variable plume fractions (known as Kuo-type, see for example Krishnamurti et al., 1988). As an alternative they propose that remote sensing of variables such as outgoing long wave radiation may be used as a way of determining the climatology of convectively active areas within larger fields. They suggest that, for most GCMs in current use, typical storms, for example large thunderstorms, cover about half of the grid area. It is assumed that large-scale condensation occurs over the entire storm area, but small scale convective precipitation covers 60% of the storm area. Hence values are often taken in the range 0.3 to 0.5. Eagleson et al. (1987) found that for air mass thunderstorms in Arizona the average value of K is 0.66. In the next section we examine whether typical values for K in mid-latitude precipitation systems are consistent with the recommendations made by Entekhabi & Eagleson (1989).

Variations of K in mid-latitude precipitation systems

The database discussed in Section 2 of this paper provides an opportunity to investigate the spatial and temporal variations of K over a wide area of North West Europe. A grid square of size approximately 100km by 100km was moved over particular precipitation fields such as that shown in Figure 2. The fractions of the grid square area covered by precipitation of greater than a range of intensity values were calculated.

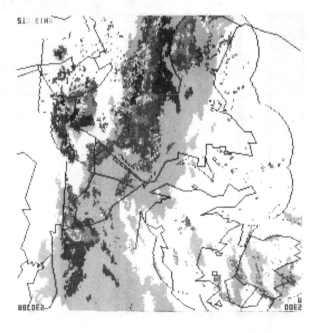

Figure 2 (a)* An example of the COST-73 image at 2300 GMT, 23 July 1988, in which satellite infrared data at medium and high levels (appear grey) are combined with radar data (darker and lighter shades). The coloured original shows the radar intensity levels (see Collier et al., 1988).

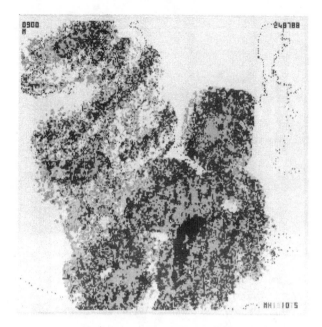

Figure 2(b)* A daily integration of the COST images for 0600 GMT, 23 July 1988 to 0600 GMT 24 July 1988. The largest black area represents rainfall greater than 30mm

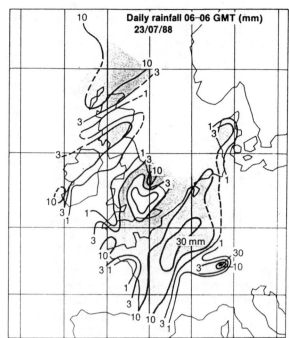

Figure 2(c) A raingauge-derived rainfall field for the same period

The individual precipitation images were assumed to approximate to the hourly precipitation accumulations. This procedure will have introduced errors, and further errors arising from radar measurement deficiencies are also ignored in this analysis. Whilst radar measurements over periods of an hour or less are known to be accurate only to within a factor of two, the area of rainfall estimated by radar is regarded as reliable in most cases. As radar data are integrated over longer time periods the accuracy over areas improves. For a general review of radar measurements of precipitation see Collier (1989). Figure 3 shows how the fraction of grid area rainfall to a depth greater than the given value varies.

Curves for line convection, an isolated thunderstorm and a mature depression are compared with the curve given by Eagleson *et al.* (1987) (also in Entekhabi & Eagleson, 1989) for thunderstorms in Arizona. The Arizona curve corresponds to a value of K of 0.66, and closely follows the thunderstorm curve for the European data. The curves for the mature depression have been obtained by moving the grid square across the occluding cold front, curve A being in front of the surface front, but astride an upper level front, and curve E being in the area of scattered showers behind the surface front. These curves correspond to low values of K with increasingly low runoff as one moves from A to E for fixed E(P). However in moving from A to E the value of E(P) decreases and therefore K decreases quite rapidly. Curve E has a value of K much smaller than 0.1.

---

*Figures 2(a) and 2(b) cannot show the detail of the original high-quality colour plots.

Figure 4, similar to Figure 3, gives an indication of the spatial variations of K/E(P), and hence K. Values of E(P), the mean rainfall rate observed over a grid square, were evaluated for each case, giving the following values for K:

Curve (Fig 3-4)	E(P)	K
A	0.6	0.30
B	0.3	0.16
C	0.1	0.07

D-E are comparable to C.

From the limited data, it would appear that K values are comparable to values associated with thunderstorms in regions of frontal development, but decrease markedly elsewhere in frontal systems. Curves A to C are for grid squares located as follows: A to the north west of the centre of a developing depression, B to the north east astride an occluding cold front and C to the south of the depression centre in an area of scattered convection. For the same synoptic case, Figure 5 shows the variations just south of the centre of the depression as it develops rapidly (2000-2300), then begins to decay with an associated cold front undergoing the occlusion process (0500-0800). These curves suggest that for frontal precipitation excluding line convection (for example B in Figure 4 and 2000 in Figure 5) the exponential relationship of equation 1 may not be appropriate. In these locations, and at these times, a log-normal relationship, might be more appropriate:

$$f_p(P) = \frac{K}{E(P)} \exp\left[-\frac{K}{E(P)}(\ln(1+P))/2\right] \qquad (2)$$

Figure 6 gives a comparison of fp(P) curves derived

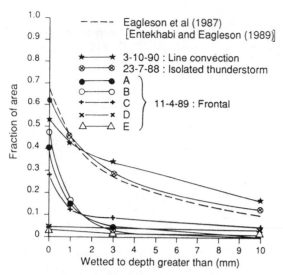

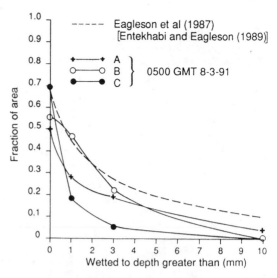

Figure 3 *Observed distribution of precipitation for northwest Europe over a GCM grid square for different types of precipitation. The ordinate is the fraction of an entire grid square having rainfall greater than a given value P. The analysis of Eagleson et al. (1987) for air mass thunderstorms in Arizona is shown for comparison (-----).*

Figure 4 *As for Figure 3 illustrating the spatial variation of precipitation distribution for a developing depression over northwest Europe (see text for details).*

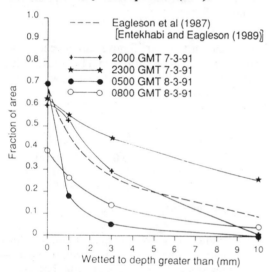

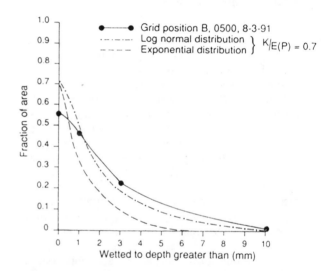

Figure 5 *As for Figure 3 illustrating the temporal changes in precipitation distribution through the development of the same depression analysed in Figure 4.*

Figure 6 *A comparison with observations at 0500 GMT, 8 March 1991 of the representation of fraction precipitation (cf Figure 3) using both a log-normal and exponential distribution functions.*

from equations 1 and 2 with observations from 0500 GMT on 8 March 1991. From the observations, E(P) is taken as approximately 0.3mm h^{-1}, giving for this case a value of K of 0.2 for the broken curves. The value of K for the measured data (solid line) is 0.16. Use of equation 1 rather than equation 2 to disaggregate GCM grid rainfall during rapid frontal development may result in an underestimation of the fraction of the grid area having heavier rainfall for fixed values of K and E(P). The associated runoff would therefore be decreased using equation 1. In addition use of fixed K values in the range 0.3 to 0.5 would result in an overestimation of the fraction of the grid area having heavier rainfall in decaying frontal situations and small scale scattered convec-

tion. Since present GCMs use time steps of around 30 minutes, this difference should have a significant effect on the spatial variability of soil moisture and hence on the model climate (Rowntree & Bolton, 1983, Rowell & Blondin, 1990). We might expect use of equation 2, at least in mid-latitudes in winter when frontal precipitation is common, to result in increased soil moisture and evapotranspiration, and hence rainfall, although the actual effect will depend upon the frequency of occurrence of frontal systems over particular areas. In addition, use of K values which are too large will cause frontal rainfall to be distributed too widely over a grid square, reducing evapotranspiration and humidity locally and perhaps precipitation. Hence use of equation 2 with more appropriate values of K in frontal rainfall may go some way to improving the present observed performance of most GCMs which underestimate the precipitation between 45%°N and 60%°N in winter (Gates *et al.*, 1990).

Conclusion

In this paper we have discussed one application of a continental scale weather radar database to the study of the representation of hydrological processes in GCMs. Although this work is preliminary, it seems likely that an improved method of disaggregating model precipitation may be needed. Further analysis of the database is clearly necessary. However such a parametrization should be incorporated into a GCM only if it promises to improve the model climate. Further consideration and validation of this is necessary.

The COST-73 weather radar database offers hydrometeorologists the opportunity to study continental scale precipitation fields over a wide range of timescales. Efforts are being made to ensure that these data continue to be archived after the end of the Project in September 1991.

References

Brooks, C.E.P. & Carruthers, N. 1953. *Handbook of Statistical Methods in Meteorology*. Meteorological Office, HMSO, London, MO 538.

Collier, C.G. 1989. *Applications of Weather Radar Systems. A guide to uses of radar data in meteorology*. Ellis Horwood Ltd., 294 pp.

Collier, C.G., Fair, C.A. and Newsome, D.H. 1988. International weather-radar networking in western Europe, *Bull. Amer. Met. Soc.*, 69, 16-21.

Eagleson, P.S. 1984. The distribution of catchment coverage by stationary rainstorms, *Wat. Resour. Res.*, 20., 581-590.

Eagleson, P.S., Fennessey, N.M., Wang, Q. and Rodriguez-Iturbe, I. 1987. Application of spatial Poisson models to air mass thunderstorm rainfall, *J. Geophys. Res.*, 92, 9661-9678.

Entekhabi, D. and Eagleson, P.S. 1989. Land surface hydrology parametrization for atmospheric general circulation models, *J. Climate*, 2, 816-831.

Freeze, R.A. 1974. Streamflow generation, *Wat. Resour. Res.*, 12, 627-647.

Gates, W.L., Rowntree, P.R. and Zeng, Q.C. 1990. Validation of Climate Change, The IPCC Scientific Assessment, 94-130, Cambridge University Press.

Giorgi, F. & BATES, G.T. 1989. On the climatological skill of a regional model over complex terrain, *Monthly Weath. Rev.*, 117, 2325-2347.

Henderson-Sellers, A., Pitman, A.J. & Dickinson, R.E. 1990. Sensitivity of the surface hydrology to the complexity of the land-surface parametrization scheme employed, *Atmosfera*, 3, 183-201.

Krishnamurti, T.N., Bedi, H.S., Heckley, W. & Ingles, K. 1988. Reduction of the spin up time for evaporation and precipitation in a spectral model, *Monthly Weath. Rev.*, 116, 907-920.

Rowell, D.P. & Blondin, C. 1990. The influence of soil wetness distribution on short-range rainfall forecasting in the West African Sahel, *Q. J. Roy. Met. Soc.*, 116, 1471-1485.

Rowntree, P.R. & Bolton, J.A. 1983. Simulation of the atmospheric response to soil moisture anomalies over Europe. *Q. J. Roy. Met. Soc.*, 109, 501-526.

Russell, G.L. & Miller, J.R. 1990. Global river runoff calculated from a global atmospheric general circulation model, *J. Hydrol.*, 117, 241-254.

Thomas, G. 1990. The regional hydrologic impacts of global climate change: the role of climate models. *Palaeogeog., Palaeoclimatology*, (Global & Planetary Change Section), 82, 343-368, Elsevier Science Publishers, Amsterdam.

Warrilow, D.A., Sangster, A.B. & Slingo, A. 1986. Modelling of land surface processes and their influence on European climate. UK Meteorological Office, DCTN 38, 94 pp [Available from the UK Meteorological Office].

A temporal look at hydrological extremes

A. J. Coyle, B. E. Kelbe, D. W. Reed & E. J. Stewart

Abstract

Hydrology has long been a fertile area for the application and development of extreme value methods. The paper reports preliminary results from a study which, for once, is concerned less with estimating the magnitude or frequency of extremes than with indexing their temporal character. In particular, the project is examining the effect that data discretization has on the estimation of extremes.

It is rare for a hydrological analysis to use "continuous" data. Often it suffices to consider daily or monthly totals rather than attempt to treat data recorded with very great temporal detail. In many cases there is little choice; higher resolution values were either never available, have been lost, or would now be too costly to extract from the medium on which they are held. Whereas daily or monthly totals provide no obstacle to the estimation of **long-term average** values, it is known that the estimation of **extremes** is biased by discretization. For example, it is common to apply a multiplier of 1.11 or 1.14 to convert statistics of 1-day maximum rainfall to their 24-hour counterparts.

Improved logging and storage systems, and the passage of time, have led to a greater number of high resolution datasets becoming available and it is now possible to examine discretization effects more thoroughly. The paper presents analyses of a range of hydrological and meteorological variables. While one product of the research will be more comprehensive correction procedures, a greater outcome may be a better understanding of inter-relationships **between** variables through appraisal of their temporal character. For once, statistics may complement rather than displace a more physical approach. Some preliminary results are presented.

The large data sets now available to hydrologists should be valuable in resolving a number of the scaling problems which face environmental research in the 1990s.

Background to the study

Time series data form the basis of most hydrological investigations, particularly those which seek to quantify the magnitude of extremes. Although specially sampled datasets can be useful in certain applications, those most generally useful are sampled at a regular time interval.

Following Hershfield and Wilson (1958) and Weiss (1964), it is well known that some allowance for "data interval effects" is warranted in the estimation of extreme rainfalls. Correction factors are commonly applied to convert estimates of maximum rainfall accumulated over fixed 24-hour periods (corresponding to the observational "day") to estimates of maximum rainfall expected in any 24-hour period. For example, Volume II of the Flood Studies Report (Natural Environment Research Council, 1975) includes the correction formula:

$$M5\text{-}24\text{hour} = 1.11 \ M5\text{-}1\text{day} \qquad (1)$$

where M5 denotes the rainfall depth with an annual exceedance probability of 1/5.

Whereas the requirement to correct for *discretization* is well-recognized in maximum rainfall estimation, this does not seem to be the case for other variables. In the late 1970s, the North West Water Authority looked at the correction of water resource assessments based on monthly data, particularly for Pennine reservoir systems sensitive to short, sharp droughts (Pearson, 1979). Beran and Rodier (1985) cite the Low Flow Studies Report finding that low flow quantile estimates by calendar month analysis can be converted to those by daily analysis by adding 15 days to the implied duration (Institute of Hydrology, 1980). However, the premier textbook in British practice (Twort et al., 1985) makes no reference to the bias introduced by the use of monthly data to estimate drought flows of a given rarity. Moallemi-Pour and Michel (1989) apply Weiss's correction formula to maximum runoff accumulations without comment; this assumes that the temporal characteristics of runoff extremes are comparable to those of rainfall extremes.

Allowances for discretization appear to have received little attention in studies of extreme winds. Mapped estimates of maximum hourly mean wind speed are pivotal in the assessment of wind loads in building design (Building Research Establishment, 1989), and these statistics will inevitably suffer discretization effects. There are several complications for this variable, not least variations due to local exposure and to the directional characteristics of the regional wind climate (Cook and Prior, 1987). The maximum hourly mean wind speed is often a stepping stone to the estimation of a design load corresponding to a maximum gust. In this context, bias due to discretization may seem a minor issue; yet estimating very short duration maxima from hourly mean data is ultimately a discretization problem.

With the exception of recent work by van Montfort (1990), studies of discretization appear to have been rather specific. The paper reports preliminary results from a general study of Allowances for Discretization in Hydrological and Environmental Risk Estimation (ADHERE).

Objectives

The ADHERE project has four main aims: to index discretization effects on environmental extremes, to develop correction formulae, to build models of the variation of quantile estimates with duration, and to examine whether discretization effects can reveal links and contrasts between variables.

Terminology and conventions

Words like "duration", "period" and "interval" are sometimes used synonymously and sometimes not. It is hoped that the terminology adopted below avoids ambiguity without upsetting too many traditional usages.

The long-term time series being analysed is called the *total data record*. In the ADHERE project it generally comprises 2^{14} consecutive data. Each datum is a *basic data value* observed (or available) at a *basic data interval*. For *cumulative* data, such as rain-

fall, the value relates to the whole interval. This contrasts with *sampled* data, such as tide observations at hourly intervals, in which the value is associated with the beginning of the data interval. A variable such as mean hourly wind speed will be treated like rainfall: the averaging can be considered equivalent to scaling of an accumulation by a fixed constant. However, it is recognized that some basic data have a *mixed origin*. For example, hourly mean temperature data derived from an automatic weather station may originate from data sampled at 5-minute intervals but not retained; similarly, daily mean flow data often come from water levels sampled at 15-minute intervals.

The main reason for choosing to standardize on a total data record of 2^{14} values is to facilitate analyses that split the record into a number of *data sampling periods* that are equal in length. A further convention has been to adopt 32 (2^5) data sampling periods, each comprising 512 (2^9) values. The resultant standard record lengths are summarized in Table 1.

Table 1 Standard record lengths in ADHERE project

Basic data interval	Total data record length (2^{14} intervals)	Data sampling period (2^9 intervals)
15 min	170 days 16 h	5 days 8 h
20 min	227 days $13^1/_3$ h	7 days $2^2/_3$ h
1 hour	682 days 16 h	21 days 8 h
1 day	44 years 313 days	1 year 147 days

As a consequence of these conventions, analyses have differed only in terms of four factors: the variable, the site, the basic data interval, and the start date of the total data record. While estimates of extremes are likely to be at least moderately sensitive to the chronology, it is thought that the discretization effects themselves will be relatively insensitive to the particular period of record, except of course where there has been some change in the sensing or data processing techniques. The assumption will be tested in a later phase of the project.

In flood frequency applications, the target variable is often the instantaneous peak flow of T-year return period. However, in most other applications the requirement is to estimate the extreme accumulation (or average) that is surpassed over a given *duration*.

For example one might wish to estimate a 50-year, maximum 6-hour rainfall accumulation or a 10-year, minimum 7-day mean air temperature (perhaps to trigger social security supplements). If the duration is many times greater than the basic data interval, it is likely that the discretization represents a sensible economy that leads to little bias in the estimates.

However, if the duration is little greater than the basic data interval, the discretization effects may be severe.

Methods of analysis

Three categories of methods are being used to analyse discretization effects in the ADHERE project: descriptive, fractal, and extreme value. The present paper deals primarily with the last type.

Descriptive

Plots of the data in time and frequency domains provide an initial appreciation of each data series. The ADHERE project is using only records of the highest quality - at least in terms of data continuity - but a visual check for possible rogue values is nevertheless advisable. Figure 1a shows 20-minute air temperature data from an experimental site at Aston Rowant, Oxfordshire.

The standard record length of 2^{14} values is not especially convenient for 15 or 20-minute data, since it spans only part of the annual cycle; thus the results presented are for illustration only. The underlying trend in Figure 1a might be expected to cause difficulty in a frequency analysis but, as Figure 1b shows, the spectrum is reasonably well defined apart from a trough at a period of about 33 days. The perceptible transition at about eight to 16 days is in broad agreement with the period of synoptic changes in atmospheric circulation.

Table 2 identifies the data series discussed in the paper and provides some descriptive statistics.

Fractal

The development of methods of analysis that seek to characterize the fractal structure of geophysical phenomena is a burgeoning area of research. It is evident that fractal methods are relevant to tackling a number of important problems associated with scale, one of the most topical being to bridge between hydrological modelling (at catchment scale) and climate modelling (at global scale). However, there appears to be little agreement on which methods should be applied to what problems, many of the advances being made by mathematicians and physicists with strong theoretical interests.

Many environmental variables are held to be "scaling", a loose definition of which is that they exhibit similar variability at different time-scales. Ladoy *et al.* (1991) present two methods of characterizing scale dependence in geophysical time series, one based on energy spectra, the other on plots of non-exceedance probability. Both seek to relate differences at small time-scale to differences at large scale. The latter analysis yields an index of intermittency, while the former highlights the temporal range over which there is scale invariance.

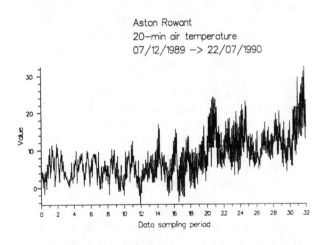

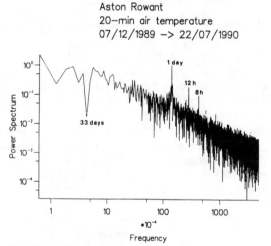

Figure 1   Example of ADHERE data series: (a) time series plot (b) spectral analysis

Table 2 Examples of series analysed

Type[1]	Variable	Basic data interval	Start date	Site	Unit	Min[m]	Max[m]	Mean	St[d] Dev[n]	Skew-ness
S	Air temperature	20-min	7/12/89	Aston Rowant, Oxon.	$^{\circ}K$	-4.6	32.5	7.7	5.3	0.9
S	Residual tide	hourly	1/ 1/69	Walton-on-the-Naze, Essex	mm	-416	514	-7	69	0.5
M	Air temperature	hourly	31/12/87	Carreg Wen, Powys	$^{\circ}K$	-5.9	25.6	6.4	4.9	0.4
C	Wind speed	hourly	18/ 7/87	Carreg Wen, Powys	$m\ s^{-1}$	0.0	15.8	4.3	2.9	0.7
C	Rainfall	hourly	18/ 7/87	Carreg Wen, Powys	mm	0.0	12.5	0.32	0.95	4.6
C	Catchment rainfall	hourly	1/ 7/72	R. Dee to Manley Hall, Clwyd	mm	0.0	3.4	0.06	0.02	6.1
C	Rainfall	15-min	1/ 7/72	Site in Dee catch[t], SH890283	mm	0.0	2.3	0.03	0.10	6.9
C	Rainfall	daily	1/ 1/25	Alwen Reservoir, Clwyd	mm	0.0	70.9	3.6	5.9	2.9
C	Rainfall	daily	1/ 1/30	Creech Grange, Dorset	mm	0.0	78.7	2.6	5.4	3.8
C	Rainfall	daily	1/11/04	Cape Town, RSA	mm	0.0	96.5	1.6	4.7	5.6
C	Rainfall	daily	1/12/39	Upington, RSA	mm	0.0	75.0	0.4	2.8	11.2

[1]Key to variable type:
C   cumulative (or average)
S   sampled
M   mixed origin

In a study of Sahelian rainfall series, Hubert and Carbonnel (1988) apply a fractal method based on "box-counting". However, it is difficult to define "wet" and "dry" in a consistent manner and the resulting estimates of fractal dimension seem difficult to interpret.

A more transparent technique is structure function analysis (e.g. Stull, 1988), which is analogous to variogram analysis (e.g. Delhomme, 1978). The structure function summarizes how the variance in neighbouring values is typically related to their separation in time. The linear segment in Figure 2 suggests that air temperature is, at least, "scaling" for time-scales between one and six hours; the structure function follows a power law with an exponent of about 1.6. Interpretation of the temporal structure of air temperature at shorter time-scales is inevitably limited by the 20-minute resolution of the data; whereas, for lag times greater than six hours, the diurnal cycle has a marked effect.

More advanced multi-fractal techniques, such as the Probability Distribution Multiple Scaling method (Lavallee *et al.*, 1991), may lead to a more comprehensive characterization of scaling properties of environmental variables.

Extreme value

"Fixed" and "variable" extractions

Assessing the effect of discretization on the extraction and analysis of extreme values is central to the objectives of the ADHERE project. The extraction process used is akin to the annual maximum method, the difference being that maxima are drawn from the data sampling periods rather than from years. Thus for the series considered in this paper, there are always 32 maxima, each drawn from a data sampling period of 512 basic data values. In some applications, shortfalls rather than exceedances may be of interest. A simple device is to change the sign of all data values, so that the minima become maxima.

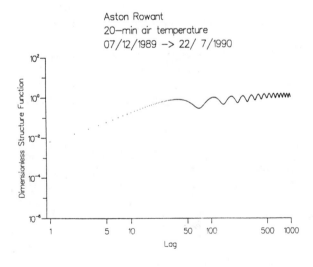

Aston Rowant
20-min air temperature
07/12/1989 -> 22/ 7/1990

Figure 2   Example of structure function

In many applications it is the extraction of maxima over a duration of D basic data intervals that is of interest. There are two ways in which this can be done for cumulative data, and we consider as an example the extraction of 4-day maxima from daily rainfall data.

The first way is to aggregate the data so that the 512 daily values in each data sampling period provide 128 4-day ones. We call analyses based on this approach *fixed* in the sense that the selection of the 4-day maximum is not free to search out the largest accumulation over any consecutive 4-day period. In effect the data series has been degraded to one in which the basic data interval is four days.

The second way is to consider all 512 4-day aggregations that the daily data permit. (Because only the largest value is used in the "period maximum" analysis, problems of dependence do not arise explicitly.) Analyses based on this approach will be termed *variable* in the sense that the 4-day duration is permitted to span any four days. In executing these extractions, a convention is followed whereby maxima that span adjacent data sampling periods are neither overlooked nor replicated.

Modelling the effect of discretization

Where the duration is very many times greater than the basic data interval, the variable analysis can be expected to provide a good representation of "truth". In contrast, the fixed analysis will misrepresent many of the extreme events. Misrepresentation takes two forms. In many cases, the extracted maximum corresponds to the true maximum event but, through discretization, part of the event is "lost" and the maximum thereby under-represented. In other cases, a second (or lower) ranking event is better synchronized with the fixed analysis and, as a result, *displaces* the true maximum event. The relative frequency with which the latter phenomenon occurs is one measure of the incidence of discretization, if not its impact.

The effect of discretization is always to under-appreciate extremes. This is because the fixed maxima are never greater than, and are often appreciably less than, the variable ones. An obvious measure of the discretization effect is to compare the magnitudes of the abstracted period maxima. Figure 3 shows the ratio of the mean of the period maxima in the variable analysis to that in the fixed analysis, for the Aston Rowant air temperature data. It is convenient to present the ratio as variable:fixed because the practical requirement is usually to correct a coarse (fixed) analysis to a refined (variable) analysis. The graph shows how the ratio varies with duration. The variable and fixed results coincide for a duration of one data interval, for which the analyses are equally degraded by discretization.

Also shown is the least-squares fit of a simple model:

$$r = 1 + a \, (1 - e^{-b(D-1)}) \qquad (2)$$

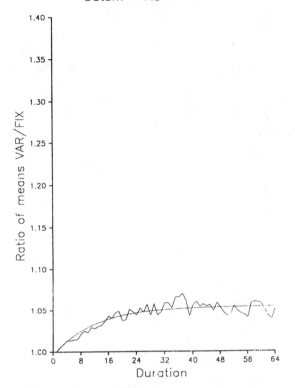

Aston Rowant
20—min air temperature
07/12/1989 — 22/07/1990
Datum −4.6

Figure 3   Example of ratio of mean of period maxima in the variable analysis to that in the fixed analysis: smooth curve denotes model fit by equation (2)

where r denotes the variable:fixed ratio, 1+a is the asymptotic value to which the ratio tends for large durations, and b indexes the rate at which the limit is approached. The root mean square error (RMSE) summarizes the scatter about the synthetic relationship. While this provides some measure of goodness of fit, a small/large RMSE may indicate that the variable is highly regular/intermittent rather than that the model is necessarily appropriate/ inappropriate. In the Figure 3 example, the scatter is somewhat less for durations up to 30 data intervals (i.e. 10h) than for longer durations.

Results

Within the remit of a first paper on the ADHERE project, it is practical only to show sample results. Attention is therefore focussed on the discretization effect on the period maxima.

Discretization effect on the mean of the period maxima

Further results from fitting the Equation 2 model are illustrated in Figs. 4 and 5. The series considered in Figure 4 are all hourly, and three of them pertain to automatic weather station data from Carreg Wen, Powys.

Looking first at the results for rainfall, it is seen that the asymptotic value of 1.146 is in broad agreement with the widespread use of a correction factor of 1.13 (Hershfield and Wilson, 1958) or 1.14 (Weiss, 1964), and with recent detailed investigations by Demaree (1985) and van Montfort (1990). Too much should not be read into this one result; analyses for five other hourly rainfall series (one "point", and four "catchment") yielded somewhat higher values. It would seem that the value of 1.11 used in UK practice (NERC, 1975) may be something of an underestimate. (That Equation 1 refers to the ratio of 5-year quantiles, rather than to the ratio of mean period maxima, does not adequately explain the discrepancy.)

The idea that a universal factor might apply, for converting statistics of 1-day rainfall maxima to those of 24-hour maxima, can be expected to have limitations. In some regimes, heavy rainfall has marked diurnal traits and, where heavy rainfall tends to occur towards the middle of the measurement day (Stewart, 1986), one might expect a correction factor closer to unity. The influence of climatic regime is to be investigated by reference to hourly rainfall data for diverse sites in Australia, kindly supplied by the Bureau of Meteorology, Melbourne.

Comparisons **between** variables are impeded by the lack of a consistent datum. While zero provides an obvious datum for rainfall and wind run measure- ments, it is less suitable for variables such as air temperature or residual tide. A convention was therefore adopted of using a datum equal to the minimum of the series of 2^{14} values (see Table 2).

It is seen from Figure 4 that the discretization effects in estimating wind speed and air temperature extremes are much smaller than for rainfall. This is thought to reflect their less intermittent nature, in comparison to the more chaotic extremes of rainfall. The contrast is, of course, evident in the very much greater skewness of the rainfall variable (Table 2).

From Figure 4 it is seen that the time at which the ratio of means begins to stabilize is longest for air temperature and shortest for rainfall. The fourth series shown in Figure 4 refers to the residual tide (i.e. the actual tide *minus* the astronomical component) at Walton-on-the-Naze, Essex. Given that the primary factors influencing the residual tide are air pressure and wind velocity, it is to be expected that the temporal character of the residual tide will reflect those of the main forcing functions. Some similarity is evident in the residual tide and wind speed results; air pressure data have yet to be acquired for the ADHERE project.

Figure 5 considers daily rainfall data from four sites: two in Britain and two in the Republic of South

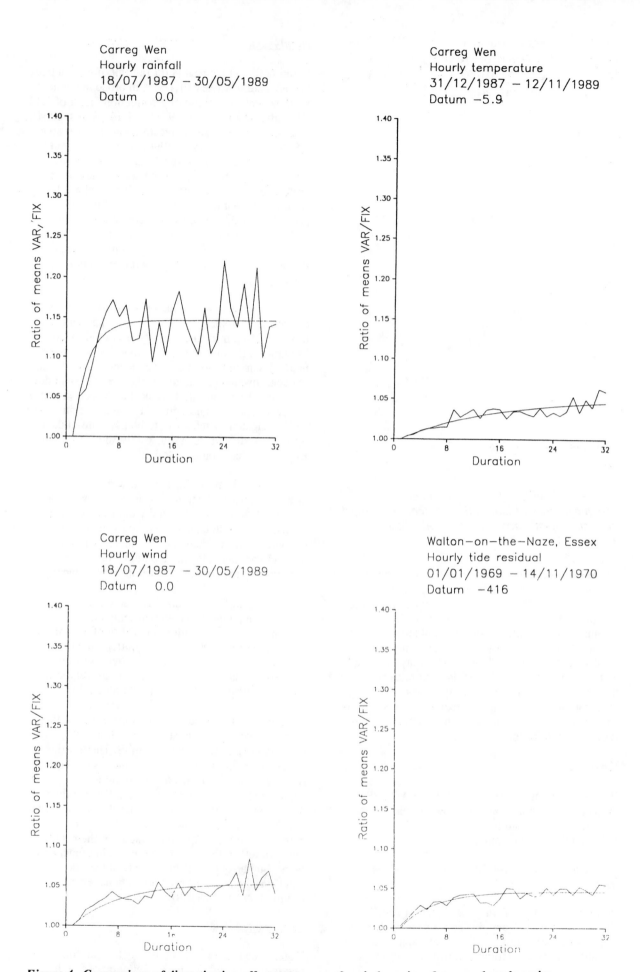

Figure 4 *Comparison of discretization effects on mean of period maxima for some hourly series*

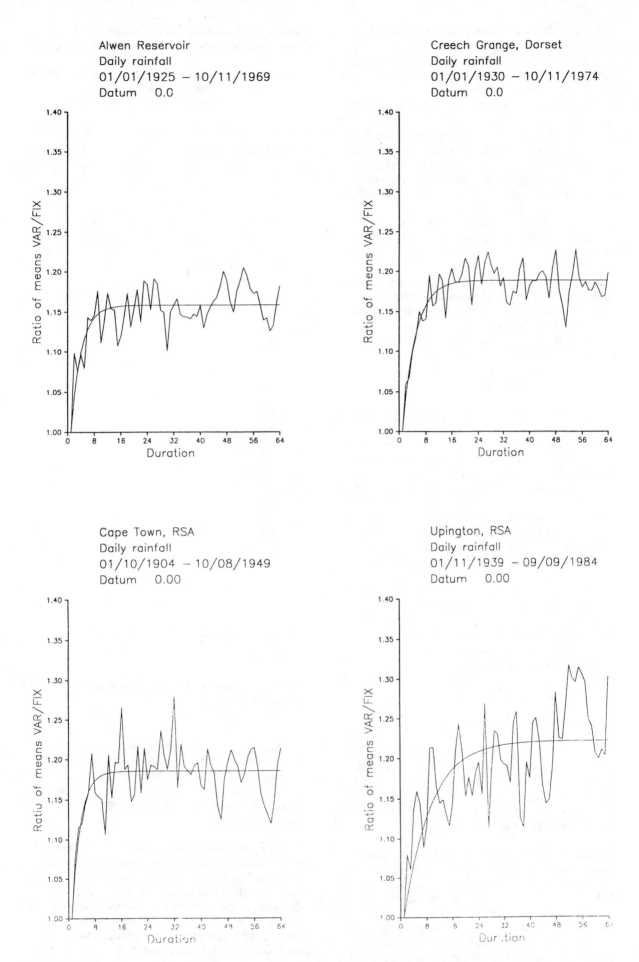

Figure 5   Comparison of discretization effects on mean of period maxima for some daily rainfall series

Africa. Rainfall accumulations at Alwen Reservoir (average annual rainfall of 1282 mm) are typically greater than at Creech Grange (947 mm), the latter having a rather more continental climate. Cape Town has a Mediterranean climate (625 mm), while Upington has a sub-arid climate (151 mm). Looking at results for a duration of 30 days, it can be seen that the mean annual maximum 30-day rainfall depth is about 1.2 times greater in the variable analysis than in the fixed analysis. There is a hint that temperate climates (e.g. Alwen Reservoir) require a lower factor and harsher climates (e.g. Upington) a higher factor. However, the broad conclusion is that it is necessary to increase values by about 20% when seeking to estimate 30-day rainfall extremes from monthly data.

To date, the ADHERE project has considered only a modest range of temporal scales. However, for rainfall at least, there is evidence of self-similarity, i.e. similar behaviour at a range of time-scales, as indicated in Table 3. Rather than quoting values of parameter b, the rate of approach to the limit is conveniently indexed by the duration at which a value of 1+0.99a is reached.

Discretization effect on the CV of the period maxima

Having examined the effect of discretization on the mean of the period maxima, it is natural to consider also the effect on their variability. This is conveniently summarized by comparing values of the coefficient of variation (CV), i.e. the ratio of the standard deviation to the mean. Figure 6 shows that, for the Aston Rowant air temperature data, the "fixed" and "variable" analyses lead to broadly similar estimates of CV at all durations.

It is instructive to note the extent to which statistics, such as the CV, vary smoothly in the variable analysis but irregularly in the fixed analysis. The variability of the fixed analysis from duration to duration highlights the desirability of methods of frequency analysis that synthesize extremes of different durations in an internally consistent fashion (e.g. Polarski, 1989).

Displacement of true maxima

It was suggested earlier that a useful index of discretization may be the relative frequency with which "true" period maximum events (ie. as seen in the variable analysis) are displaced in the fixed analysis. Figure 7 provides an illustration for the Aston Rowant air temperature data.

The area *below* the lower line indicates the proportion of the annual maxima in the fixed analysis that are entirely different to those in the variable analysis ("distinct"). There is a hint that, for durations greater than about 36 data intervals (ie. 12 h), some 40% of the annual maximum events are consistently "missed". The area *between* the lines represents the proportion of annual maximum events that partially

Table 3 Parameters of Equation 2 model for some Clwyd rainfall series of various basic data intervals

Site	Basic data interval	Asymptotic value 1+a	Duration (in BDIs) at 1+0.99a	RMSE
Grid ref. SH890283	15 min	1.171	20	0.032
Manley Hall catchm't	1 h	1.175	12	0.032
Alwen Reservoir	1 day	1.153	13	0.025

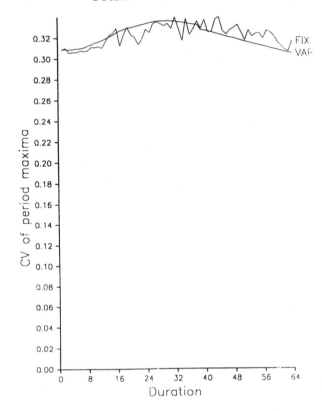

Figure 6 Example of discretization effect on CV of period maxima

overlap. The area *above* the upper line indicates the proportion of annual maxima that are correctly matched in the fixed analysis ("identical"). This rapidly reduces from 100% at a duration of one data interval (i.e. 20 min) to 13% at a duration of six data intervals (i.e. 2 h).

The disparate time-scales, over which the "identical" events decay and the "distinct" events grow, can be interpreted as follows. For durations up to about six data intervals (i.e. 2 h), the *variable* analysis itself suffers from the coarseness of the basic data interval. Whereas, for durations beyond about 36 data intervals (i.e. 12 h), the effect of discretization on the *fixed* analysis is fully developed.

Conclusions

Some analytical methods, and preliminary results, have been presented from a study of discretization effects on the estimation of hydrological and environmental extremes. The intermittent character of extreme rainfall gives rise to significant discretization effects and the need for correction is confirmed. Correction factors required for other variables, such as wind speed and air temperature, appear to be more modest.

Although a factor of 1.14 is typically about right for converting estimates of 1-day maximum rainfall to 24-hour maximum values, the supporting argument put forward by Weiss (1964) is simplistic. It is perhaps fortuitous that an unrealistic assumption that storms typically have a uniform temporal profile is counterbalanced by neglect of the "displacement" effect.

While a principal objective of the ADHERE project is to provide correction factors, it is possible that the study of discretization effects will contribute to a wider understanding of the fractal structure of geophysical time series. Essex (1991) has shown that the ability to observe scaling behaviour is intimately linked to the size of data sets. Variation in time is often indication of variation in space. The large data sets now available to hydrologists, many of them of high quality, should be valuable in resolving a number of the scaling problems that face environmental research in the 1990s. One goal is to bridge the gap between hydrological modelling (at catchment scale) and climate modelling (at global scale), so that land surface and atmosphere interaction can be represented more fully.

Acknowledgements

The ADHERE project is funded by the Terrestrial and Freshwater Sciences Directorate of the Natural Environment Research Council. Some of the analyses were programmed by Christine Simmonds, a mathematics student on placement from Brunel University.

We gratefully acknowledge the cooperation of many organizations in making high quality data series available to the discretization study. With regard to those series cited in the paper, specific thanks go to Graham Alcock (Proudman Oceanographic Laboratory) and to David Marshall, Howard Oliver, and Anne Roberts (all of the Institute of Hydrology). The Computing Centre for Water Research at the University of Natal supplied daily rainfall series without charge. Acknowledgements are due also to the Ministry of Agriculture, Fisheries and Food, the Department of the Environment, and the Department of Education and Science, for funding specific projects during which data series were gathered. Finally, we are pleased to record that the UK Meteorological Office gave permission to include analyses from two long-term daily rainfall records.

References

Beran, M.A. & Rodier, J., 1985. *Hydrological Aspects of Drought*. Studies and Reports in Hydrology, UNESCO, Paris, 149pp.

Building Research Establishment, 1989. The assessment of wind loads, Part 3: Wind climate in the United Kingdom. Digest 346, BRE, Watford, 4pp.

Cook, N.J. & Prior, M.J., 1987. Extreme wind climate of the United Kingdom. *J. Wind Eng. & Indust. Aerodyn.*, 26: 371-389.

Delhomme, J.P., 1978. Kriging in the hydrosciences. *Advances in Wat. Resour.*, 1, 5:251-266.

Demaree, G., 1985. Intensity-duration-frequency relationship of point precipitation at Uccle. Publ. Series A, Report No. 116, Inst. R. Meteorol., Belgium.

Essex, C., 1991. Correlation dimension and data sample size. In Schertzer, D. & Lovejoy, S. (eds), *Non-linear Variability in Geophysics*, Kluwer Academic Publishers, 93-98.

Hershfield, D.M. & Wilson, W.T., 1958. Generalizing of rainfall-intensity-frequency data. IUGG/IAHS publ. no. 43: 499-506.

Hubert, P. & Carbonnel, J.P., 1989. Dimensions fractales de l'occurrence de pluie en climat soudano-sahélien. *Hydrol. Continent.*, 4, 3-10.

Institute of Hydrology, 1980. *Low Flow Studies Report No. 1*, IH, Wallingford.

Aston Rowant
20-min air temperature
07/12/1989 – 22/07/1990

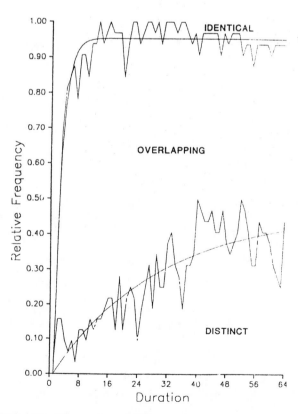

Figure 7 Illustration of "displacement" effect

Ladoy, P., Lovejoy, S. & Schertzer, D., 1991. Extreme variability of climatological data: scaling and intermittency. In Schertzer, D. & Lovejoy, S. (eds) *Non-linear Variability in Geophysics*, Kluwer Academic Publishers, 241-250.

Lavallée, D., Schertzer, D. & Lovejoy, S., 1991. On the determination of the codimension function. In Schertzer, D. & Lovejoy, S. (eds), *Non-linear Variability in Geophysics*, Kluwer Academic Publishers, 99-109.

Moallemi-Pour, A. & Michel, C., 1989. Contribution a une meilleure estimation des parametres d'une crue decennale: la methode "DELTAQIX". *Hydrol. Continent.*, 4, 113-122.

Natural Environment Research Council, 1975. *Flood Studies Report*, Volume II: Meteorological Studies. NERC, London.

Pearson, D., 1979. Derivation of reservoir operating rules. Presentation to Pennines Hydrological Group, Leeds, 17 January 1979.

Polarski, M., 1989. *Fitting Distributions to Annual Minimum Flows of Different Durations.* IAHS Publ. No. 187: 97-104.

Stewart, E.J. 1986. A modelling study of the spatial and temporal variability of rainfall in south-west Saudi Arabia. M.Sc. Thesis, Imperial College, London.

Stull, R.B., 1988. *An Introduction to Boundary Layer Meteorology.* Kluwer Academic Publishers, 666pp.

Twort, A.C., Law, F.M. & Crowley, F.W., 1985. *Water Supply.* 3rd edition, Edward Arnold, London, 548pp.

van Montfort, M.A.J., 1990. Sliding maxima. *J. Hydrol.*, 118: 77-85.

Weiss, L.L., 1964. Ratio of true to fixed-interval maximum rainfall. *Proc. Am. Soc. Civil Engrs.*, 90, HY1: 77-82.

Authors' affiliations

Mike Acreman	Institute of Hydrology
Alastair Adamson	formerly University of Newcastle-upon-Tyne
David Archer	NRA Northumbrian
Stein Beldring	Water Resources and Energy Administration, Norway
Keith Beven	University of Lancaster
John Bircumshaw	Southern Water Services Ltd
David Boorman	Institute of Hydrology
Giles Brown	University of Southampton
Rob Brown	W S Atkins
Sue Bryant	Institute of Hydrology
Andy Bullock	Institute of Hydrology
Mike Clark	Southampton University
Chris Collier	Meteorological Office
Vin Collinge	University of Lancaster
Andrew Coyle	Institute of Hydrology
Richard Cross	NRA Severn-Trent
Cliff Dobson	NRA Severn-Trent
Ann Dixon	NRA South West
Nigel Fawthrop	NRA Anglian
Colin Fenn	Southern Science Ltd
Mark Futter	Kingston Polytechnic
Cathy Glenny	NRA Thames
Hugh Goldsmith	Howard Humphreys
Angela Gurnell	Southampton University
Alan Gustard	Institute of Hydrology
Mike Hall	Middlesex Polytechnic
Ed Henderson	University of Lancaster
Peter Herbertson	NRA Southern
Chris Hill	University of Southampton
Brian Hodgson	NRA Welsh
John Hollis	Soil Survey and Land Research Centre
Helen Houghton-Carr	Institute of Hydrology

Nigel Ironside	W S Atkins
Tony Jakeman	CRES, Canberra, Australia
Ian Johnson	Institute of Hydrology
Sally Johnson	Cobham Resource Consultants
Charles Jones	Mott MacDonald
Bruce Kelbe	University of Zululand (visiting Institute of Hydrology)
Jane Kinniburgh	NRA Thames
Allan Lambert	Welsh Water plc
Allan Lilly	Macaulay Land Use Research Institute
Ian Littlewood	Institute of Hydrology
Terry Marsh	Institute of Hydrology
John Mawdsley	NRA Northumbria
Peter Midgley	NRA Southern
Colin Neal	Institute of Hydrology
Terry Newman	NRA Wessex
Yvonne Parks	Institute of Hydrology
Elfyn Parry	NRA Severn-Trent
Rob Raiswell	University of Leeds
Duncan Reed	Institute of Hydrology
Alison Reeves	University of Lancaster
Nick Reynard	Institute of Hydrology
Lars Roald	Water Resources and Energy Administration, Norway
Alice Robson	Institute of Hydrology
Paul Rosier	Institute of Hydrology
Kevin Sene	Institute of Hydrology
Martin Sharp	University of Cambridge
Peter Shaw	NRA Southern
Hilary Smithers	North West Water Ltd
Lisa Stewart	Institute of Hydrology
Richard Symonds	NRA Wessex
Antony Tollow	University of Durban-Westville, South Africa
Martyn Tranter	University of Southampton
Alan Weston	Welsh Water plc
Dennis Wheeler	Sunderland Polytechnic